AN INTRODUCTION TO
PLANT DISEASES

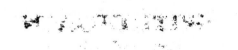

AN INTRODUCTION TO

PLANT DISEASES

B. E. J. WHEELER

Reader in Plant Pathology,
Imperial College, London.

JOHN WILEY & SONS LTD.
London . New York . Sydney . Toronto

Library of Congress Catalog Card No. 70–94877

SBN 471 93751 7

Printed in Great Britain by
Dawson & Goodall Ltd.,
The Mendip Press, Bath.

Preface

This would be a very long preface if I were to set down in detail the reasons why I wrote this book in its present form. Suffice it to say that it is based on a course which I give to beginners in plant pathology and it is an approach to the subject which I have found useful. I hope it may prove to be so for others. The fact that there are few introductory texts in plant pathology is also a ready excuse for writing this one.

As the title suggests, the greater part of the book is concerned with plant diseases. Each chapter deals with a particular type of disease and is very largely self-contained, so these chapters can be read in any order, but they do divide into several groups. Thus Chapters 2–4 deal with diseases of the root and vascular systems, covering mainly what is elsewhere described as soil-borne diseases or more correctly, soil-borne pathogens; Chapters 5–15 deal with diseases of the shoot system—first those that are recognized by the fructifications of the fungal pathogens (Chapters 5–8), followed by those in which death of the host tissues (Chapters 9–11), excessive growth of tissues (Chapters 12–14), and colour changes in the leaf (Chapter 15) are striking features. Chapter 16 concludes the review of plant diseases and deals specifically with storage diseases of fruits, seeds and perennating organs.

I have tried to standardize certain aspects of the text: references are abbreviated as in the *World List of Scientific Periodicals* (4th Edn), the names of pathogens are those used in the *Review of Applied Mycology*, and all temperatures are given in centigrade unless stated otherwise. Most measurements have also been converted to metric units; there are a few exceptions, mostly in tables which I have reproduced directly from other publications.

To a certain extent any course (and so any book based on it) is a reflexion of the teacher's own training and of his special interests. My own interests in fungi and fungal pathogens owe much to the training I received at Bristol from Lillian E. Hawker and later, at the Commonwealth Mycological Institute, and it is a pleasure to acknowledge this. My first formal training in plant pathology was at Cornell and those who have studied in the plant pathology department there will at once recognize the influence of this teaching in the last four chapters of this book. Although I have tried I have found no better approach to the principles of plant disease control. Similarly, I have tried within chapters to select specific diseases which illustrate points of general interest but inevitably one's own training and interests again make this choice mainly a personal one and this accounts for the comparatively large number of tropical diseases.

Many people helped me in different ways during the preparation of this book. Friends and colleagues gave me photographs or allowed me to reproduce figures from their published papers. I am grateful both to them and to the publishers concerned. Formal acknowledgement is made under the figures but I would like also to acknowledge the help I received in this connexion from R. T. Burchill, R. T. A. Cook, J. E. Crosse, S. D. Garrett, D. H. Lapwood, F. Joan Moore, D. H. Phillips, P. W. Talboys and D. B. Slope. Special thanks are due to A. Ironside formerly of the Department of Botany and Plant Technology, Imperial College, who not only supplied some original photographs but also undertook most of the photographic work involved in reproducing figures from other sources. I am grateful too for the help I received from the Commonwealth Mycological Institute: Dr. G. C. Ainsworth, formerly its Director, kindly allowed me to use the library and the Librarian, Miss S. Daniels, greatly helped me in searching the now extensive literature of plant pathology. Above all, I am especially grateful to my wife who not only typed two successive drafts of this book but also gave me every help and encouragement throughout.

Imperial College Field Station   B. E. J. WHEELER
Silwood Park
Sunninghill
Berks
May 1969

Contents

vii

fungi, non-pathogenic diseases; Factors influencing postharvest diseases—field conditions, harvesting and handling, conditions during transit and storage; Control.

CHAPTER I

Introduction:
concepts of plant pathology

This book is about plant diseases—the various forms in which they appear, the agents which cause them, the factors which influence their development and the principles of controlling them. Its aim is to introduce the reader to plant pathology which is the study of disease in plants. It is not unreasonable then at the outset to ask 'What is disease?'. Many people have attempted a definition but this is not easy, simply because there is no clear demarcation between the healthy and diseased state. Most definitions imply that disease involves a change from the normal or healthy state, particularly in respect of the plant's physiological processes and that this change does harm or causes injury to the plant. An example is: 'a harmful deviation from the normal functioning of physiological processes' (British Mycological Society, 1950). No attempt is made to define normal or healthy, but as far as a plant is concerned this implies the growth, appearance and behaviour that we expect when the plant is grown under the conditions which we consider are favourable for it. In these definitions disease is envisaged as abnormal, injurious and physiological in nature. It is also a process (Horsfall and Dimond, 1959). Disease results not from a single change in a plant but from a succession of changes, though these may be initiated either by a single event or by the continuous action of some agent.

Symptoms

Fortunately disease is more readily recognized than defined. It is associated with various visible changes in the plant which we call symptoms. Where one particular causal agent is involved there is often a number of symptoms which together form a characteristic symptom-picture or syndrome to which a specific disease name is given. The recognition of a disease by its symptoms comes largely with experience but symptoms in general fall into groups depending on the processes by which they develop, viz:

1. Death of the tissues or necrosis (British Mycological Society, 1953). Various terms describe the extent and shape of necrotic lesions, particularly on leaves: stripe for narrow, elongated lesions; scorch, scald, fire and blotch for indefinite areas which often become blanched and then brittle; and leaf spot for well-defined lesions of limited extent. Occasionally the dead tissue of a leaf spot falls away and the symptom is then called shot-hole.

2. An abnormal increase in the tissues. This can result from both an increase in size (hypertrophy) and an increase in number (hyperplasia) of cells. The more common symptoms of this type are witches' brooms, galls, cankers and scab (Chapters 12, 13, 14).

3. A failure to attain normal size or development (hypoplasia). An overall dwarfing or stunting of the plant is common in many diseases. In some the leaves are specially affected, the leaf blade either failing to develop at all (alaminate leaves) or developing abnormally (see Bos, 1963: Figure 24).

4. Change in colour. Yellowing or chlorosis is a common symptom of disease and one often associated with tissues surrounding a necrotic area. The chlorophyll may be degraded or fail to develop: in the latter instance the symptom could be considered to fall in the previous group. There may be other colour changes such as development of red pigments (sometimes called anthocyanescence), and silvering of leaves due to an increase in the air spaces.

5. Wilting, caused by an interference with the normal movement of water within the plant.

6. Unusual development or transformation of organs. For example, in certain Caryophyllaceae the pistillate flowers normally have only rudimentary stamens, but in plants infected with the smut fungus *Ustilago violacea* these develop although at maturity they contain not pollen but smut spores. Similarly in maize infected with *Ustilago maydis* the staminate inflorescences may bear pistillate

flowers. A transformation of a different type occurs in certain fungal diseases of fruit. The fruit dries out, becomes hard or mummified and is then, virtually, a fungal sclerotium.

7. Disintegration of tissues. This is termed a rot. It may be accompanied by a release of cell fluids (wet rot), so much so that there is an exudate from partially disintegrated tissue (leak). Alternatively, the cells may crumble to a powdery mass (dry rot).

8. Excessive gum formation. This is particularly associated with diseases of trees and is known as gummosis or gumming.

The emphasis here is on symptoms visible to the naked eye but there may be other host responses which are visible either with the light microscope or with the electron microscope and these too can be regarded as symptoms, though the time required to find them limits their diagnostic value.

Causes of disease

Disease as interpreted on p. 1 can be caused by various agents either acting singly or in combination one with another, and the study of these agents is termed the etiology of the disease (Orlob, 1964). The agents themselves fall into seven groups. There are the bacteria, fungi and viruses which together probably account for the greatest number of diseases, nematodes, some insects (excluding those that only serve as vectors for other disease agents), a few flowering plants such as broomrape (*Orobanche*), dodder (*Cuscuta*) and witchweed (*Striga*), and finally a heterogenous group which includes mineral deficiencies and excesses, and unfavourable environmental conditions. Disease-inciting agents that are themselves living organisms are called pathogens: there is no generally accepted term for the remainder. Nor is there general agreement on the range of causal organisms with which plant pathology should deal. The above groups follow the concept of Moore (1952) that 'plant pathology is concerned with all pathological conditions in plants and plant produce, whatever causal agent is involved', though in this book emphasis is on diseases caused by fungi, bacteria and viruses.

Sometimes the presence of the causal agent is more obvious than any change in the plant. This is so in some fungal diseases, for instance in the Rusts the fungal fructifications are a sure guide to the nature of the disease. Visible growths of the causal agents such as these are often called the signs of the disease, to distinguish them from symptoms which arise predominantly through host reactions.

Disease relationships

Disease in many instances involves a relationship between plants and other living organisms which is to a large extent a nutritional one. The fungus, bacterium, or nematode, etc., derives from the plant an essential part of the material necessary for its existence but confers no benefit in return and, in this sense, it is a parasite and the plant harbouring it is its host. For some organisms the association with a plant is obligatory; as far as we know they grow only within the living plant and otherwise exist in nature only in some dormant form such as a spore. These are often called obligate parasites and most have not yet been grown on artificial media. It is perhaps safer, if one is searching for an easy definition, to limit the term obligate strictly to the latter. In this sense many Smut fungi are not obligate parasites since they can be cultured on agar media, although in the field they apparently grow only on or within their appropriate hosts. There are other organisms that live on the remains of dead plants and animals and are thus essentially saprophytes but given the right conditions are able to parasitize plants: they are called facultative parasites. Not all parasites, however, can be classified so neatly for in nature there are many which vary in their parasitism between these two extremes.

The terms parasite and host describe a nutritional relationship between two organisms, but the growth of a parasite in its host usually results in changes which are detrimental to the plant, and considered on its ability to induce disease, a parasite can also be a pathogen. There is no generally accepted, equivalent term for the diseased plant and this is usually called a host even in this context. The term suscept has been suggested (American Phytopathological Society, 1940) but is not much used, yet it has some merit, for the degree to which a plant responds to the activities of a given pathogen, as judged by symptoms, is called its susceptibility. This is a variable property. At one end of the scale there is the plant that reacts with severe symptoms to a particular pathogen: this is highly susceptible or sensitive. At the other extreme is the plant that a given organism is unable to enter and on which it cannot establish a pathogenic relationship: this is immune. In between are plants with features that hinder the development of a pathogenic relationship. These features thus result in various degrees of susceptibility; equally they confer on the plant possessing them a certain degree of disease resistance, this term being the antithesis of susceptibility.

In some pathogen–host combinations visible symptoms are difficult to detect because they consist of nothing more than minute, necrotic flecks. These result from the rapid death of the host cells when invaded by the pathogen. Although this implies extreme sensitivity at the cellular level and the phenomenon is called hyper-sensitivity, a plant which reacts in this way to a particular pathogen is highly resistant because spread of the pathogen is prevented and virtually no disease develops. In other pathogen–host combinations involving certain viruses, no symptoms are visible, yet tests show that the virus is widely distributed throughout the plant; in this instance the host is called a symptomless carrier.

It must be emphasized that terms relating to susceptibility and resistance have meaning only for the interaction of a specific pathogen and host under defined conditions. Under unusual experimental regimes it is often possible to produce disease in plants with organisms not known to affect them adversely in nature (Johnson, 1932). Environment can also modify the degree to which the relationship between a recognised pathogen and its host is expressed in disease symptoms. Some conditions favour disease largely through their action on the host, for example excess nitrogen frequently leads to lush growth which particular parasites readily colonize. These conditions, therefore, predispose the plant to a specific disease (Yarwood, 1959). In contrast, varieties of a plant which all appear susceptible in laboratory and greenhouse tests often show marked differences in disease under field conditions. Some are considerably less affected than others and are said to show field resistance. This is considered further in Chapter 21.

Disease establishment
There is a basic sequence of events by which the pathogen–host relationship is established. The pathogen must first arrive at the host surface. Artificially, we take a spore suspension of a fungus and spray leaves with it: we inoculate the plant. Under natural conditions this phase, the inoculation stage, involves three things—the inoculum, e.g. fungal spores, the source of inoculum, e.g. plant debris on which the fungus has overwintered, and an agent to disseminate the inoculum, e.g. wind, rain, insect vector. Then follows a period in which the pathogen enters the tissue (penetration) or is placed within it, e.g. by an insect vector; depending on the type of inoculum this may in the former instance be preceded by germination and growth on the host surface. Often during this phase there are no visible symptoms and the period is called the incubation stage. With some diseases this may extend to several months. The first symptom visibly indicates the establishment of a

pathogenic relationship and is considered by some to mark the beginning of the infection stage, i.e. the plant is then infected. This is only a convenient method of distinguishing the incubation and infection periods, for there may be internal host changes long before this but it can become an academic exercise to distinguish the two phases more precisely. Indeed, in particular diseases, e.g. see p. 290, the growth of the parasite is arrested shortly after penetration and then recommences when the host tissues mature. There are no symptoms visible to the naked eye during the first phase but this is frequently called latent infection.

These terms relate mainly to an individual pathogen and host. Much of plant pathology is concerned with disease within crops and their occurrence within particular areas. When many plants are infected in a crop the disease is said to have reached an epidemic or epiphytotic level and the study of the factors which lead to and influence such outbreaks is called epidemiology. Some diseases also occur regularly in certain areas; these are said to be endemic.

Principles of plant disease control

One of the chief aims of plant pathology is to devise methods for controlling diseases economically. The methods themselves vary widely and how one classifies them is largely a matter of personal choice, but in effect they are based on four general principles. Two are concerned chiefly with the pathogen. If this is not already present in an area then methods are devised to exclude it (exclusion); if it does get in then attempts are made to eradicate it (eradication). Even if this latter operation is not completely successful it may serve to contain the disease outbreaks. The other two concern the host. By applying a chemical to the plant surface or by modifying the conditions under which the plant is growing it is often possible to protect it from attack (protection). Also, by breeding, it is sometimes possible to obtain varieties of the particular plant which resist attack. This has been called immunization but, because for animals this implies certain features which apparently plants do not possess, it is better left as breeding for disease resistance.

Approach to plant pathology

Plant pathology can be studied in several ways. One approach is through the pathogen. This is the classical method which developed from the studies of Koch, de Bary, Erwin F. Smith and others who showed that fungi and bacteria could cause disease (Keitt, 1959). Many textbooks, for example those by Heald (1943), Brooks (1953), and Walker (1957), deal with diseases on an etiological basis and this is convenient because the groups are well defined—diseases caused by fungi, diseases caused by bacteria and diseases caused by viruses. To the plant pathologist, however, the diseased plant is of primary importance if for no other reason than that he is first confronted with it. Division of diseases based on pathogens takes little account of this situation. In this context, an approach based on symptoms seems desirable, but there are usually several symptoms which characterize a given disease and pursued logically this system becomes unmanageable. A physiological approach is a third possibility. Since disease involves harmful changes in physiological processes, it can be considered in relation to the process most affected—photosynthesis, growth and reproduction. This is the method of the *Advanced Treatise* (Horsfall and Dimond, 1959, 1960), but is suitable only for the advanced student because it requires a fairly wide, general knowledge of individual plant diseases.

This book is in effect a compromise between these methods. Some diseases can be grouped readily on a pathogen basis and moreover the presence of the pathogen calls attention to the type of disease. These are the Downy and Powdery mildews, the Rusts and the Smuts. In others the pathogens are confined to particular types of plant or to particular areas of plants and this often determines the way in which they are controlled, e.g. damping-off and seedling blights, root diseases and foot rots. The division of the remainder is somewhat arbitrary but there is usually one outstanding symptom which is of special interest or diagnostic value, e.g. canker, gall, leaf curl. Overall, attention is focussed on the diseased plant.

REFERENCES

American Phytopathological Society (1940). Report of the committee on technical words. *Phytopathology*, **30**, 361–8
Bos, L. (1963). *Symptoms of Virus Diseases in Plants*, 142 pp. Centre for Agricultural Publications and Documentation, Wageningen.
British Mycological Society (1950). Definitions of some terms used in plant pathology. *Trans. Br. mycol. Soc.*, **33**, 154–60
British Mycological Society (1953). Some further definitions of terms used in plant pathology. *Trans. Br. mycol. Soc.*, **36**, 267
Brooks, F. T. (1953). *Plant Diseases*, 386 pp. Oxford University Press.
Heald, F. D. (1943). *Introduction to Plant Pathology*, 580 pp. McGraw-Hill, New York.

Horsfall, J. G. and Dimond, A. E. (Ed.) *Plant Pathology: an advanced treatise*, Vol. I (1959), Vol. II, III (1960). Academic Press, New York.

Horsfall, J. G. and Dimond, A. E. (1959). The diseased plant. In *Plant Pathology: an advanced treatise*, **1**, 1–17. Academic Press, New York.

Johnson, B. (1932). Specificity to penetration of the epidermis of a plant by the hyphae of a pathogenic fungus. *Am. J. Bot.*, **19**, 12–31

Keitt, G. W. (1959). History of plant pathology. In *Plant Pathology: an advanced treatise* (Ed. J. G. Horsfall and A. E. Dimond), **1**, 61–97. Academic Press, New York.

Moore, W. C. (1952). Introduction. *Pl. Path.*, **1**, 1

Orlob, G. B. (1964). The concepts of etiology in the history of plant pathology. *Pflanzenschutz–Nachrichten "Bayer"*, **17**, 185–268

Walker, J. C. (1957). *Plant Pathology*, 707 pp. McGraw-Hill, New York.

Yarwood, C. E. (1959). Predisposition. In *Plant Pathology: an advanced treatise* (Ed. J. G. Horsfall and A. E. Dimond), **1**, 521–62. Academic Press, New York.

CHAPTER 2

Damping-off and seedling blights

The diseases of germinating seeds and of seedlings, collectively known as damping-off and seedling blights provide a convenient starting point in plant pathology since they affect the initial establishment of a crop. The main features are familiar to most people who have tried to grow plants from seed. Emergence is poor even with seeds of high germinative capacity: there are patches with no seedlings at all. Seedlings that have emerged often show water-soaking, browning or shrivelling of the stem tissues at soil level and they keel over and die as a result (Figure 2.1). These two stages are known, respectively, as pre-emergence and post-emergence damping-off. The latter may also be called seedling blight in the sense that the young plant dies suddenly but this term is perhaps better reserved for the decline and subsequent death of seedlings that are apparently well established. In this instance a check in growth is often the first indication that all is not well and this is followed by yellowing and even some wilting of the foliage. When the plants are pulled up they are found to have extensive browning and rotting of the smaller roots, or stem lesions at soil level. These diseases can occur when soil conditions are unfavourable for plant growth, particularly with regard to their nutritional status but are more commonly caused by certain fungi.

THE FUNGI INVOLVED

Many individual fungi are associated with damping-off and seedling blights but they are distributed in relatively few genera and can be conveniently dealt with on this basis.

9

FIGURE 2.1 Post-emergence damping-off of tomato seedlings. From R. McKay, 1949, *Tomato Diseases*, by permission of Mrs. R. McKay and The Three Candles Limited.

Pythium

The species most often encountered are *Pythium debaryanum*, *Pythium ultimum*, *Pythium aphanidermatum*, *Pythium arrhenomanes* and *Pythium graminicola*. A further five species amongst those described by Middleton (1943) may also be involved: *Pythium irregulare*, *Pythium vexans*, *Pythium splendens*, *Pythium mammilatum* and *Pythium spinosum*. Most of them have a wide host range; Middleton for example, lists 226 hosts for *P. debaryanum* and more have been recorded since his publication. Some are associated particularly with certain host families, such as *P. arrhenomanes* and *P. graminicola* with the Graminae. The publications by Waterhouse (1967, 1968) provide useful additional guides to the identification of *Pythium* species. All species have a mycelium without cross-walls, (i.e. coenocytic), though septa may be formed in old hyphae, and they reproduce by sporangia and oospores. The latter are of special interest since they enable the fungus to survive during conditions adverse to mycelial growth.

Phytophthora

Two species, *Phytophthora parasitica* and *Phytophthora cryptogea*, can at times be very troublesome on tomato. In addition to damping-off, they attack young plants about 120–150 mm high and cause a brown to black discoloration of the external stem tissues at or just above soil level, a feature to which the term foot rot is sometimes applied (Figure 2.2). When affected plants are pulled up the primary root system is found to be badly decayed or rotten. Essentially the disease is a progressive rot of the root system in which the base of the stem also becomes involved.

Under moist conditions, sporangiophores are produced on the host tissues, or they can be induced to form by incubating portions of diseased plants in a damp chamber. The two species can be differentiated on several morphological features; in particular, *P. cryptogea* has sympodially branched sporangiophores bearing pear-shaped sporangia while *P. parasitica* has unbranched sporangiophores with ovoid and papillate sporangia (see Waterhouse, 1956). Normally in both species the sporangia function as such and produce zoospores within an extruded vesicle. Both species produce oospores and also thickened resting bodies or chlamydospores, which retain their germinative capacity for many months.

FIGURE 2.2 Foot rot of young tomato plant caused by *Phytophthora cryptogea*. From R. McKay, 1949, *Tomato Diseases*, by permission of Mrs. R. McKay and The Three Candles Limited.

Recently two other species, *Phytophthora arecae* and *Phytophthora richardiae* have been reported to cause a foot rot of tomatoes in Holland (Verhoeff and Weber, 1966).

Rhizoctonia

Many damping-off diseases are caused by a fungus which on agar media produces a mycelium of hyphae 6–12μ diameter with a characteristic mode of branching. Branches arise almost at right angles and are constricted at the point of attachment to the parent hypha; there are septa within the parent hypha on either side of this and the base of the side-branch is swollen and also septate (Figure 2.3*a*). At first the mycelium is hyaline or light brown but later darkens and produces irregular, dark brown, and often aggregated sclerotia. Isolates with these general characteristics are referred to the form-genus *Rhizoctonia* and most to one species, *Rhizoctonia solani*. Some isolates can be induced to form a *Corticium* perfect state in which basidia arise directly from a greyish web of hyphae: there is no enclosed fruiting structure (Figure 2.3*b*). On the morphological characters of this state two species have been distinguished, *Corticium solani* and *Corticium praticola*. However, the situation is not so simple as this would suggest. The *Corticium* state is only sporadically found in nature and is not formed at all by some isolates. On certain agar media (Flentje, 1956), the cultural appearance of some isolates may be sufficiently distinct to refer them to

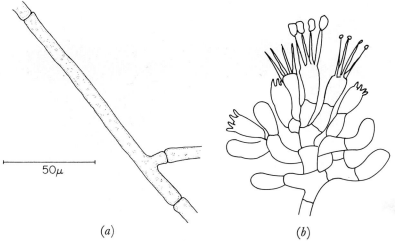

50μ

(*a*)   (*b*)

FIGURE 2.3 *Rhizoctonia solani* (*a*) mode of branching (*b*) *Corticium* (basidial) state. (*b*) from Flentje, 1956, *Trans. Br. mycol. Soc.,* **39,** 343–56

C. praticola in the absence of the perfect state, but generally isolates of *R. solani* vary widely in their cultural characters and physiology. More important, they vary in their pathogenicity: some attack a wide range of plants, others show considerable host specificity and some are non-pathogenic (Flentje and Saskena, 1957; Flcntje, 1957). These differences suggest that there may be several species within the range of isolates referred to *R. solani*, but attempts to relate cultural and physiological characters with pathogenicity, or to devise a reliable method for producing the perfect state so that these species can be defined, have not been successful. In addition, there is some confusion regarding nomenclature. The mycelial state is *R. solani* but *Pellicularia filamentosa* is often considered to be the valid name for *C. solani*, and *C. praticola* has correspondingly been reclassified as *Pellicularia praticola*. Donk (1956), however, has also reclassified *C. solani* as *Thanetophorus cucumeris* and this name is used in recent Australian and American publications.

Strains of *R. solani* cause damping-off on a wide range of cultivated plants—cereals, potato, root and fodder crops, legumes, vegetables and ornamentals (Moore, 1959). On lettuce the fungus is often associated with *Pythium* spp. and later with *Botrytis cinerea* (Ellis and Cox, 1951). On beet it is implicated in the disease known as black-leg which leads to an uneven seedling stand (Hull, 1960). Sclerotia of *R. solani* are frequently found on potato tubers and the name black scurf is commonly applied to this condition (Dana, 1925). The fungus attacks the developing sprouts and often kills them before they emerge; young shoots may also be killed after emergence when lesions completely encircle the stem bases. The *Corticium* (basidial) state is sometimes formed on these stem lesions and appears as a white collar.

Fusarium

Various species are specially important in seedling diseases of cereals and often more than one species is involved. Their identification is a major problem for the pathologist because there is as yet no general agreement on species determination within the genus. There is a useful but provisional key to the fusaria by Booth (1966).

At present there are two main systems of classification, the detailed one of Wollenweber and Reinking (1935) and the simplified version of Snyder and Hansen (1940, 1941, 1945). In the Wollenweber system the genus is divided into 16 named sections within which a total of 65 species, 55 varieties and 22 forms of *Fusarium* are differentiated. In Snyder and Hansen's system this has been reduced

F. *avanaceum* (*F.*
roseum f.sp. *cerealis*)
barley, wheat, oats.
C.M.I. description 25

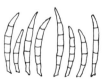

F. *graminearum* (*F.*
roseum f.sp. *cerealis*)
Perfect state:
Gibberella zeae
maize, barley, wheat, oats

F. *nivale* (*F. nivale*
f.sp. *graminicola*)
Perfect state:
Calonectria nivalis
oats, barley, wheat

⊢ ⊣
10μ

F. *culmorum* (*F.*
roseum f.sp. *cerealis*)
wheat, oats, barley.
C.M.I. description 26

F. *moniliforme* (*F.*
roseum f.sp. *cerealis*)
Perfect state:
Gibberella fujikuroi
rice, maize, sorghum
C.M.I. description 22

FIGURE 2.4 Species of *Fusarium* commonly involved
in damping-off diseases. Snyder and Hansen name in
parentheses; description published by Commonwealth
Mycological Institute, Kew. Spores reproduced from
Gordon, 1952, *Can. J. Bot.* **30**, 209–51 by permission
of the National Research Council of Canada.

to 9 species and 34 forms. Undoubtedly parts of Snyder and Hansen's revision have gained more general approval than others but both systems have their adherents. Much of our knowledge of the fusaria associated with cereals stems from the work of Gordon (1952), and his nomenclature is used here. Five species most often involved are shown in Figure 2.4; three of them have an ascomycete (perfect) state.

The pathogenic activities of these fungi are not always confined to seedlings. *Fusarium culmorum* also causes a foot rot and a blight of the ears; so does *Gibberella zeae*, and is best known as the causal agent of wheat scab in which the heads and grain become infected. In many instances a progressive invasion of the plant from the seedling stage produces symptoms which have been given various disease names, e.g. spring yellows, foot rot, deaf ear and head blight. Infection of the ears can lead to contamination or infection of seed, and within this group infection of young plants may arise either from this seed-borne inoculum or from mycelium present in the soil.

Seed infection by *Fusarium nivale* occurs on oats in Scotland (Noble and Montgomerie, 1956). This fungus has long been known as the causal agent of snow mould of turf and grasses. The name of the disease is derived from the epithet *nivalis* given to the fungus by Fries in 1825, partly because of its abundant white mycelium and partly because it attacks grasses when they are covered with snow. It was only later that its importance in damping-off of cereals was recognized. Seedlings fail to emerge from seeds heavily infected with *F. nivale* particularly when sown in heavy soils. Less severely infected seed gives rise to seedlings which penetrate the soil but often show browning at soil level, and the first leaf blade may be attacked so that it lies flat on the ground. The degree of seed infection depends on the stage of flower development at the time of penetration by germinating conidia. Penetration between anthesis and the beginning of grain development gives rise to a deep-seated infection of the seed; if infection occurs after this the fungus tends to remain superficial.

Helminthosporium

This is another group which is chiefly associated with seedling diseases of cereals (Sprague, 1950) and, like *Fusarium*, one in which species determination is by no means easy. Four species are of special interest, each of them with an ascomycete (perfect) state (Figure 2.5). *Helminthosporium avenae* (perfect state *Pyrenophora avenae*)

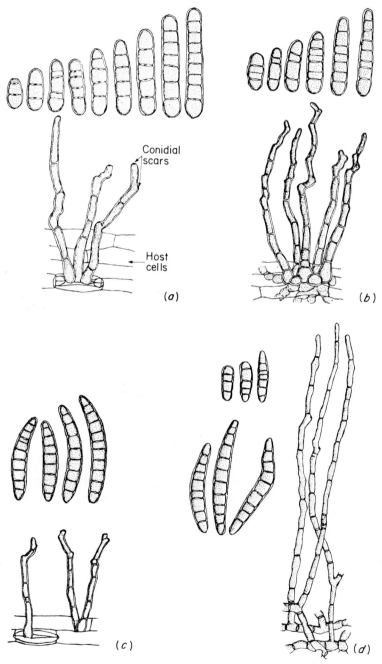

FIGURE 2.5 Species of *Helminthosporium* commonly involved in damping-off and seedling blights. (*a*) *H. avenae* on oats (*b*) *H. gramineum* on barley (*c*) *H. sativum* on barley (*d*) *H. oryzae* on rice. ×250. Redrawn from Drechsler, 1923, *J. agric. Res.*, **24**, 641–740

causes a seedling blight of oats and also a leaf stripe of older plants. This is common in north and west Britain and in Northern Europe. The fungus is carried mainly as mycelium on the seed (Dennis, 1933). *Helminthosporium gramineum* (perfect state *Pyrenophora graminea*) causes a similar seedling disease and leaf stripe of barley. It is also mainly seed-borne. *Helminthosporium sativum* (perfect state *Cochliobolus sativus*) causes a seedling blight of barley and wheat. This is an important disease in North America but is relatively unimportant in Europe. The fungus is carried on the seed either as mycelium or spores, and may also persist in crop residues. *Helminthosporium oryzae* (perfect state *Cochliobolus miyabeanus*) causes a seedling blight and a leaf spot of rice, and is also both seed-borne and soil-borne (Watts-Padwick, 1950).

Colletotrichum

Fungi of this genus are much less common as causes of damping-off and seedling blights. In the U.S.A. *Colletotrichum truncatum* sometimes kills lima bean seedlings (Cox, 1950) and *Colletotrichum glycines*, perfect state *Glomerella glycines*, causes a seedling blight of soybean (Lehman and Wolf, 1926; Ling, 1940). The mycelium of these fungi is seed-borne, and also persists for relatively long periods in crop residues. Another species, *Colletotrichum lini*, causes a seedling blight of flax which can be destructive and occurs wherever the crop is grown. The fungus is mainly seed-borne either as spores on the seedcoat or as mycelium within the outer layers (Muskett and Colhoun, 1947).

Other species

There remain two species worthy of note, *Botrytis cinerea* and *Pleospora bjoerlingii*. As previously indicated, *B. cinerea* often causes damping-off of lettuce in association with *Pythium* and *Rhizoctonia*. It is most destructive when some damage has already been caused by these fungi for it first colonizes the moribund material and then rapidly advances into the healthy tissues that remain. *P. bjoerlingii* is better known in its pycnidial state as *Phoma betae*. As the specific epithet indicates it is a pathogen of beet, and it is carried on the fruit ball as mycelium and pycnidia. It may also colonize beet debris in soil. Generally it is not such a rapid invader as the *Pythium* spp. which attack this host and a higher proportion of seedlings survive.

FACTORS AFFECTING DISEASE SEVERITY

Although some of these fungi, e.g. *Fusarium culmorum* and *Helminthosporium avenae*, can infect more mature plants the majority are limited in their parasitism to the seedling stage, and the plants become progressively more resistant to attack. Some examples are alfalfa and clover to *Pythium debaryanum* (Chi and Hansen, 1962), cotton to *Pythium ultimum* (Arndt, 1943), and lettuce and cauliflower to *Rhizoctonia solani* (Shephard and Wood, 1963). This feature of damping-off and seedling blights is in many respects the key to understanding how environmental conditions influence disease incidence. Growth of these fungi and growth and maturation of the seedlings are mutually exclusive and disease severity largely depends on the relative effects which the environment has on these processes. Leach (1947) demonstrated this in his studies of the effects of temperature on pre-emergence damping-off. He showed that the ratio, velocity of seedling emergence to growth rate of pathogen, was inversely related to pre-emergence kill. Put simply, damping-off is most severe when conditions favour growth of the pathogen but not the host.

There have been many investigations of factors affecting these diseases but with such a heterogeneous collection of fungi and of plants attacked it is hardly surprising that different results have been obtained with different host–parasite combinations. Moreover, some experiments have been conducted by artificially inoculating sterile or non-sterile soil with one fungus, others with field soil in which damping-off results from the activities of two or three fungi. A third difficulty is that the various factors involved seldom operate singly but interact with one another. None the less if the results are considered in relation to the general concept of these diseases suggested by Leach's work then a certain coherence is obtained.

The effects of soil moisture illustrate this. Damping-off by species of *Pythium* and *Phytophthora* is most severe at high moisture levels, and these are conditions well known to favour growth and indeed are essential for zoospore production by these fungi. Beach (1949) found, for example, that severity of attack by *P. ultimum* on peas continued to increase with percentage soil moisture to the saturation point. A similar result was obtained by Roth and Riker (1943) for *Pythium irregulare* and red pine (*Pinus resinosa*). High soil moisture levels were also reported to favour damping-off by *Pythium* spp. on lettuce (Abdel-Salaam, 1933), clover (Graham and others, 1957) and certain tree seedlings (Wright, 1957); and by *Phytophthora parasitica* on tomato (Richardson, 1941).

The position with *R. solani* is slightly different. On both tomato and red pine damping-off was found to increase with soil moisture to approximately two-thirds saturation but to decline at moisture levels above this. Significantly, Blair (1943) found that growth of *R. solani* in soil was poor at high moisture levels and Sandford (1938) found that the ability of potatoes to recover from *Rhizoctonia* attack by secondary sprouts was better in a wet soil than a dry one.

In contrast Colhoun and Park (1964) found that damping-off of wheat by *Fusarium culmorum* and *F. graminearum* was most severe in dry soil, and in a study of damping-off of tree seedlings Wright (1957) found that *Fusarium* spp. were most abundant in dry soil.

Leach's work on soil temperature was done with *P. ultimum* and *R. solani* on spinach, sugar beet and watermelon, and *Phoma betae* on beet. Beach (1949) obtained similar results with *P. ultimum* and *R. solani* on tomato, cucumber, spinach and peas. In each instance the effects of temperature were related to the ratio of growth rates, host to pathogen.

With *F. graminearum* (*G. zeae*) on maize and wheat the influence of temperature appears to be primarily through the host (Dickson and others, 1923). The fungus grows over a range $3°-32°$ with an optimum $24°-28°$. Wheat germination is more uniform and stronger plants are produced at temperatures between $8°-16°$, while corn seedlings develop best at soil temperatures $24°-28°$. In contrast seedling blight is more severe at high soil temperatures ($24°-28°$) with wheat, at low soil temperatures with corn.

Similar trends can be distinguished for soil pH in relation to damping-off. Buchholtz (1938) found that damping-off by *P. debaryanum* was favoured by acidity and that, for Iowa soils, there was a significant correlation between seedling stand and soil pH. Griffin (1958) obtained similar results from experiments in which seedlings were grown in soil inoculated with *P. ultimum*: damping-off increased markedly below pH 5.2. There was also a negative correlation between disease incidence and host growth rate. He concluded that the vigour of the host was the main factor affecting damping-off with change of soil pH. The rate of growth of the pathogen appeared to be of little importance but the thorough mixing of inoculum with the soil and the wide pH range ($4-8$) of this fungus probably explain this.

In contrast, damping-off of red pine by *P. irregulare* is greatest between pH $5.2-8.5$; below pH 5.2 losses are small (Roth and

Riker, 1943). This could well be attributed to the low pH optimum of this host which grows poorly above pH 7. On the other hand, damping-off by *R. solani* increased rapidly below pH 5·2 suggesting that the growth of the pathogen may also be an important factor, at least in relation to host growth.

Seeding rate and depth of planting are factors which may also be important in particular instances where they adversely affect plant growth. Damping-off of flax by *Colletotrichum lini*, for example, is favoured by thick sowings (Muskett and Colhoun, 1947), and seedling blight of oats by both *Fusarium nivale* and *F. culmorum* is increased by deep planting (Noble and Montgomerie, 1956; Simmonds, 1928), probably because the susceptible coleoptile becomes attenuated under these conditions.

Host Factors Influencing Infection

Seedling vigour is undoubtedly an important factor in damping-off but there are other host factors which influence infection in more subtle ways, for instance exudates from germinating seeds and from seedling roots affect the behaviour of fungi involved in damping-off (Schroth and Hildebrand, 1964; Rovira, 1965). These may be important initially in stimulating germination of resting spores. Barton (1957) found that oospores of *Pythium mamillatum* germinated in soil near 2–5 day old turnip seedlings but not in soil without them. Oospores also germinated in distilled water in the presence of germinating turnip seed.

Exudates may also attract motile spores to roots (Carlile, 1967). There is some evidence for this from the experiments of Bywater and Hickman (1959) with zoospores of *Phytophthora erythroseptica* var. *pisi* and pea roots. When washed roots were placed in a zoospore suspension overnight the pattern of zoospores encysted on the roots suggested that they were attracted to a region some 1–3 mm behind the root tip. Royle and Hickman (1964) obtained more convincing evidence with zoospores of *Pythium aphanidermatum* and roots of the pea variety Alaska, for they produced both plant roots and zoospores aseptically and thus avoided the objection that bacteria might influence the process. They showed that the *Pythium* zoospores were attracted not only to roots, particularly to the zone of elongation behind the root tip, but also to capillary tubes containing sterile root exudates incorporated in agar. Roots of other hosts influenced the zoospores in a similar way, among them beet, onion, maize and strawberry.

Growth of fungi at the root surface may also be influenced by exudates. There were indications of this from the experiments with *P. aphanidermatum* for once zoospores had encysted, they produced germ-tubes which grew towards the roots. Evidence for a stimulation in growth of *Rhizoctonia solani* near roots was obtained by Kerr (1956). He partly buried cellophane bags containing seeds of radish, lettuce or tomato in soil infested with this fungus and examined them after three days. He found aggregations of hyphae on the outside of the bag, and directly opposite roots of radish and lettuce but none near roots of tomato. In an extension of this work, Kerr and Flentje (1957) soaked filter paper disks in root exudates and placed them on the surface of an agar plate which was then covered with cellophane and inoculated with *R. solani*. They found that exudates from lettuce and radish stimulated branching of the fungus, and aggregations of hyphae were formed over disks containing them, like the 'infection cushions' produced on the host (Figure 2.6). Similar results were obtained by Ullah and Preece (1966) with *Helminthosporium sativum* and root exudates of the wheat variety, Nord Desprez. Spores germinating on cellophane over root exudate, produced a much branched mycelium as they do on the intact wheat coleoptile; spores germinating over distilled water did not.

These and other observations clearly indicate that in some instances root exudates stimulate fungal growth; what is disputed is that they do so in a way related to specificity of parasitism. It is tempting to suggest from Kerr's results that tomatoes are less susceptible to *R. solani* because the roots do not stimulate the formation of the infection cushions, and this idea that differing responses to exudates may be an important feature of pathogenic specialisation in *R. solani* has been developed by Flentje and his associates (Flentje, 1965). De Silva and Wood (1964), however, found no indication of this with two strains of *R. solani* pathogenic to cabbage and lettuce respectively and an isolate of *Corticium praticola* of less specialised pathogenicity. Exudates from the roots of both cabbage and lettuce seedlings stimulated the growth of these fungi to the same extent.

On the other hand, work by Schroth and Cook (1964), with three bean (*Phaseolus*) varieties suggested that exudation of different quantities of certain substances could account for differences in their susceptibility to pre-emergence damping-off by *R. solani* and *Pythium* spp. The influence of the amount of exudate produced on disease severity has been further emphasised by Flentje (1964), Flentje and Saskena (1964), and Kerr (1964) in their studies of

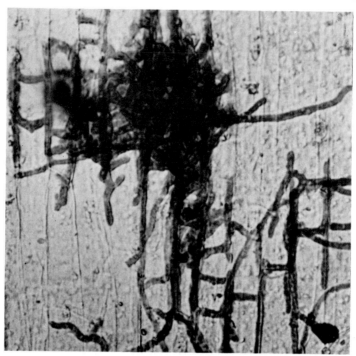

FIGURE 2.6 Infection cushion produced by *Corticium praticola* on surface of a lettuce hypocotyl. From de Silva, 1963, A comparative study of the pathogenicity of three strains of *Rhizoctonia solani* Kuhn, Ph.D. Thesis, University of London.

pre-emergence rotting of peas. This occurs some 2–4 days after sowing and is usually associated with *P. ultimum* and secondary invasion by species of *Fusarium*. These workers consider that exudation of sugars from the germinating seeds is the major factor governing fungal attack and that high soil moisture levels favour the disease because of their effect on the production of these diffusable substances by the seed.

CONTROL

Enough has been said to emphasize the importance of seedling vigour in relation to these diseases. The first line of approach in their control must therefore be good seedbed management, whereby conditions ideal for the development of the particular crop are maintained. This sounds simple but in practice it often requires a good deal of experience and experimentation.

One feature which many of the fungi concerned have in common is their ability to survive for relatively long periods in soils. There are several forms in which they do so: (1) as mycelium in the soil, e.g. *Rhizoctonia solani*, or colonizing crop residues, e.g. *Phoma betae;* (2) as resting spores, e.g. oospores of *Pythium* and *Phytophthora*, chlamydospores of *Fusarium* spp.; (3) as sclerotia, e.g. *R. solani, Botrytis cinerea*. Indeed those in the first category do not merely survive, they have an active saprophytic stage. Once damping-off becomes troublesome on a site, therefore, steps must be taken to reduce the inoculum level of these fungi. This is achieved by partial soil sterilization. By doing this we hope that either the seedlings will grow and mature before any introduced pathogen has a chance to recolonize the site, or the soil will become colonized with sapro-phytic microorganisms which will exclude or suppress the pathogens. There are a variety of individual methods for sterilizing soil, most involving treatment with heat or chemicals, and these are discussed in Chapter 19.

Treatment of seed with a chemical is another method of con-trolling damping-off and seedling blights. It is essential where the fungus is at least partially seed-borne as is so with *Fusarium nivale* on oats and *Helminthosporium sativum* on wheat. It may also be effective in avoiding severe damping-off where the inoculum is soil-borne by preventing penetration by the pathogen during the earliest stages of growth when the seedling is most susceptible. Organomercurials such as methylmercury dicyandiamide (panogen) and the com-pound tetramethylthiuram disulphide (thiram) are amongst those commonly used.

A further possible method of controlling damping-off fungi is to make use of microorganisms which are antagonistic to them, i.e. biological control (Garrett, 1965). This is an attractive idea in view of the increasing concern about the widespread application of toxic chemicals. There is little difficulty in obtaining from soil several microorganisms which inhibit the growth of damping-off fungi but there has been little success in maintaining a practical degree of inhibition by inoculating soil with them. A much more promising line of approach is to add to soil organic materials such as chitin and grass meal, which will stimulate the development of a wide range of saprophytic microorganisms, some of which are antagonistic to the pathogen.

B

REFERENCES

Abdel-Salaam, M. N. (1933). Damping-off and other allied diseases of lettuce. *J. Pomol.*, **11**, 259–79

Arndt, C. H. (1943). *Pythium ultimum* and the damping-off of cotton seedlings. *Phytopathology*, **33**, 608–11

Barton, R. (1957). Germination of oospores of *Pythium mamillatum* in response to exudates from living seedlings. *Nature, Lond.*, **180**, 613–4

Beach, W. S. (1949). The effects of excess solutes, temperature and moisture upon damping-off. *Bull. Pa agric. Exp. Stn.*, No. 509, 29 pp.

Blair, I. D. (1943). Behaviour of the fungus *Rhizoctonia solani* Kühn in the soil. *Ann. appl. Biol.*, **30**, 118–27

Booth, C. (1966). *Provisional Key to Fusaria*, 11 pp. Commonwealth Mycological Institute, Kew.

Buchholtz, W. F. (1938). Factors influencing the pathogenicity of *Pythium debaryanum* on sugar beet seedlings. *Phytopathology*, **28**, 448–75

Bywater, J. and Hickman, C. J. (1959). A new variety of *Phytophthora erythroseptica*, which causes a soft rot of pea roots. *Trans. Br. mycol. Soc.*, **42**, 513–24

Carlile, M. J. (1967). The orientation of zoospores and germ-tubes. In *The Fungus Spore* (Ed. M. Madelin), pp. 175–86. Butterworths, London.

Chi, C. C. and Hansen, E. W. (1962). Interrelated effects of environment and age of alfalfa and red clover seedlings on susceptibility to *Pythium debaryanum*. *Phytopathology*, **52**, 985–9

Colhoun, J. and Park, D. (1964). *Fusarium* diseases of cereals. I. Infection of wheat plants, with particular reference to the effects of soil moisture and temperature on seedling infection. *Trans. Br. mycol. Soc.*, **47**, 559–72

Cox, R. S. (1950). Stem anthracnose of lima beans. *Tech. Bull. N. C. agric. Exp. Stn.*, No. 90, 28 pp.

Dana, B. F. (1925). The *Rhizoctonia* disease of potatoes. *Bull. Wash. agric. Exp. Stn.*, No. 191, 78 pp.

Dennis, R. W. G. (1933). The *Helminthosporium* disease of oats. *Res. Bull. W. Scotl. Coll. Agric.*, No. 3, 74 pp.

Dickson, J. G., Eckerson, S. H. and Link, K. P. (1923). The nature of resistance to seedling blight of cereals. *Proc. natn. Acad. Sci. U.S.A.*, **9**, 434–9

Donk, M. A. (1956). Notes on resupinate Hymenomycetes II. The tulasnelloid fungi. *Reinwardtia*, **3**, 376

Ellis, D. E. and Cox, R. S. (1951). The etiology and control of lettuce damping-off. *Tech. Bull. N. C. agric. Exp. Stn.*, No. 94, 33 pp.

Flentje, N. T. (1956). Studies on *Pellicularia filamentosa* (Pat.) Rogers. I. Formation of the perfect stage. *Trans. Br. mycol. Soc.*, **39**, 343–56; (1957) III. Host penetration and resistance, and strain specialization. *Trans. Br. mycol. Soc.*, **40**, 322–36

Flentje, N. T. (1964). Pre-emergence rotting of peas in South Australia. II. Factors associated with the soil. *Aust. J. biol. Sci.*, **17**, 651–64

Flentje, N. T. (1965). Pathogenesis by soil fungi. In *Ecology of Soil-borne Plant Pathogens* (Ed. K. F. Baker and W. C. Snyder), pp. 255–66. John Murray, London.

Flentje, N. T. and Saskena, N. K. (1957). Studies on *Pellicularia filamentosa* (Pat.) Rogers. II. Occurrence and distribution of pathogenic strains. *Trans. Br. mycol. Soc.*, **40**, 95–108

Flentje, N. T. and Saskena, H. K. (1964). Pre-emergence rotting of peas in South Australia. III. Host–parasite interaction. *Aust. J. biol. Sci.*, **17**, 665–75

Garrett, S. D. (1965). Toward biological control of soil-borne plant pathogens. In *Ecology of Soil-borne Plant Pathogens* (Ed. K. F. Baker and W. C. Snyder), pp. 4–16. John Murray, London.

Gordon, W. L. (1952). The occurrence of *Fusarium* species in Canada. II. Prevalence and taxonomy of *Fusarium* species in cereal seed. *Can. J. Bot.*, **30**, 209–51

Graham, J. H., Sprague, V. G. and Robinson, R. R. (1957). Damping-off of Ladino clover and Lespedeza as affected by soil moisture and temperature. *Phytopathology*, **47**, 182–5

Griffin, D. M. (1958). Influence of pH on the incidence of damping-off. *Trans. Br. mycol. Soc.*, **41**, 483–90

Hull, R. (1960). Sugar beet diseases. *Bull. Minist. Agric. Fish Fd., Lond.*, No. 142, 1–2

Kerr, A. (1956). Some interactions between plant roots and pathogenic soil fungi. *Aust. J. biol. Sci.*, **9**, 45–52

Kerr, A. (1964). The influence of soil moisture on infection of peas by *Pythium ultimum*. *Aust. J. biol. Sci.*, **17**, 676–85

Kerr, A. and Flentje, N. T. (1957). Host infection in *Pellicularia filamentosa* controlled by chemical stimuli. *Nature, Lond.*, **179**, 204–5

Leach, L. D. (1947). Growth rates of host and pathogen as factors determining the severity of pre-emergence damping-off. *J. agric. Res.*, **75**, 161–79

Lehman, S. G. and Wolf, F. A. (1926). Soybean anthracnose. *J. agric. Res.*, **33**, 381–90

Ling, L. (1940). Seedling stem blight of soybean caused by *Glomerella glycines*. *Phytopathology*, **30**, 345–7

Middleton, J. T. (1943). The taxonomy, host range and geographic distribution of the genus *Pythium*. *Mem. Torrey bot. Club*, No. 20, 1–171

Moore, W. C. (1959). *British Parasitic Fungi*, 430 pp. Cambridge University Press.

Muskett, A. E. and Colhoun, J. (1947). *The Diseases of the Flax Plant*, 112 pp. W. and G. Baird, Belfast.

Noble, M. and Montgomerie, I. S. (1956). *Griphosphaeria nivalis* (Schaffnit) Müller and von Arx and *Leptosphaeria avenaria* Weber on oats. *Trans. Br. mycol. Soc.*, **39**, 449–59

Richardson, L. T. (1941). A *Phytophthora* tomato disease new to Ontario. *Can. J. Res.*, C **19**, 446–83

Roth, L. F. and Riker, A. J. (1943). Influence of temperature, moisture and soil reaction on the damping-off of red pine seedlings by *Pythium* and *Rhizoctonia*. *J. agric. Res.*, **67**, 273–93

Rovira, A. D. (1965). Plant root exudates and their influence on soil microorganisms. In *Ecology of Soil-borne Plant Pathogens* (Ed. K. F. Baker and W. C. Snyder), pp. 170–84. John Murray, London.

Royle, D. J. and Hickman, C. J. (1964). Analysis of factors governing *in vitro* accumulation of zoospores of *Pythium aphanidermatum* on roots. I. Behaviour of zoospores. *Can. J. Microbiol.*, **10**, 151–62

Sanford, G. B. (1938). Studies on *Rhizoctonia solani* Kühn. IV. Effect of soil temperature and moisture on virulence. *Can. J. Res.*, C **16**, 203–13

Schroth, M. N. and Cook, R. J. (1964). Seed exudation and its influence on pre-emergence damping-off of bean. *Phytopathology*, **54**, 670–3

Schroth, M. N. and Hildebrand, D. C. (1964). Influence of plant exudates on root-infecting fungi. *A. Rev. Phytopathol.*, **2**, 101–32

Shephard, M. C. and Wood, R. K. S. (1963). The effect of environment, and nutrition of pathogen and host, in the damping-off of seedlings by *Rhizoctonia solani*. *Ann. appl. Biol.*, **51**, 389–402

Silva, R. L. de and Wood, R. K. S. (1964). Infection of plants by *Corticium solani* and *C. praticola*—effect of plant exudates. *Trans. Br. mycol. Soc.*, **47**, 15–24

Simmonds, P. M. (1928). Studies in cereal diseases. III. Seedling blight and foot-rots of oats caused by *Fusarium culmorum* (W.G.Sm.) Sacc. *Bull. Dep. Agric. Can.* N.S., No. 105, 43 pp.

Sprague, R. (1950). *Diseases of Cereals and Grasses in North America*, 538 pp. Ronald Press, New York.

Snyder, W. C. and Hansen, H. N. (1940). The species concept in *Fusarium*. *Am. J. Bot.*, **27**, 64–7

Snyder, W. C. and Hansen, H. N. (1941). The species concept in *Fusarium* with reference to section Martiella. *Am. J. Bot.* **28**, 738–42

Snyder, W. C. and Hansen, H. N. (1945). The species concept in *Fusarium* with reference to Discolor and other sections. *Am. J. Bot.*, **32**, 657–66

Ullah, A. K. M. O. and Preece, T. F. (1966). Wheat root exudate and early stages of infection by *Helminthosporium sativum* Pamm. King and Bakke. *Nature, Lond.*, **210**, 1369–70

Verhoeff, K. and Weber, L. (1966). Foot-rot of tomatoes, caused by two *Phytophthora* species. *Neth. J. Pl. Path.*, **72**, 317–8

Waterhouse, G. M. (1956). The genus *Phytophthora*. Diagnoses (or descriptions) and figures from the original papers. 120 pp. Commonwealth Mycological Institute, Kew.

Waterhouse, G. M. (1967). Key to *Pythium* Pringsheim. *Mycol. Pap.*, No. 109, 15 pp.

Waterhouse, G. M. (1968). The genus *Pythium*. Diagnoses (or descriptions) and figures from the original papers. *Mycol. Pap.*, No. 110, 71 pp.

Watts Padwick, G. (1950). *Manual of Rice Diseases*, pp. 21–34. Commonwealth Mycological Institute, Kew.

Wollenweber, H. W. and Reinking, O. A. (1935). *Die Fusarien, ihre Beschreibung, Schadwirkung und Bekampfung*. Paul Parey, Berlin.

Wright, E. (1957). Influence of temperature and moisture on damping-off of American and Siberian elm, black locust and desert willow. *Phytopathology*, **47**, 658–62

CHAPTER 3

Root and foot rots

There are many individual diseases within this group but most of any economic importance are caused by fungi. In each there is a progressive rotting of the root system which often involves the basal portion of the stem (foot rot) and, as a result, the plant cannot obtain the water and nutrients it needs. This gives rise to a number of symptoms in the shoot: growth is checked and the plant becomes stunted, the leaves yellow and wilt, some drop and eventually the plant collapses and dies. The speed with which these symptoms appear depends not only on the progress of the rot but also on the ability of the host to produce new root growth in parts not yet affected, and to withstand the water shortage which results from the loss of roots. The type of plant attacked, therefore, largely determines disease development, and equally affects the control measures we can adopt, so it is convenient to consider root and foot rots in two sections: those of annual plants and of trees.

ROOT AND FOOT ROTS OF ANNUAL PLANTS

Once this division has been made it is the host range and the mode of survival of the fungal pathogen which determine the control measures, and it is possible on this basis to distinguish three groups of root rots affecting annual plants.

Group 1

One group comprises rots caused by fungi that perennate as sclerotia or resting spores and have a wide host range. There are four diseases of major economic importance which are caused by such fungi. They are:

Black root rot

The causal fungus is *Thielaviopsis basicola*, a hyphomycete (Moniliales) that forms endoconidia and short chains of thick-walled chlamydospores (Stover, 1950). These chlamydospores (Figure 3.1) become dispersed in the soil and provide inoculum for the infection of the next season's crop (Tsao and Bricker, 1966).

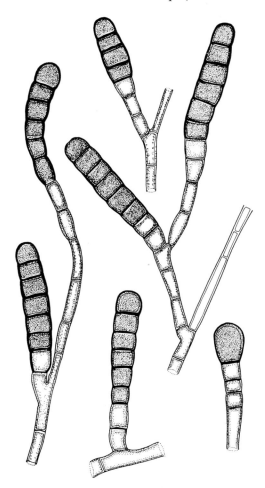

FIGURE 3.1 *Thielaviopsis basicola*, with chains of chlamy-dospores. ×600. From drawings by E. Punithalingam, Commonwealth Mycological Institute.

Tobacco is one of the most important crops attacked and amongst
the many other hosts are peas, tomatoes, celery and lettuce
(Johnson, 1916). Only rarely are plants killed but they remain
stunted and yellow. Although the disease is favoured by high soil
moisture it can develop in relatively dry soils and generally soil
temperature and pH are more important in determining its severity
(Lucas, 1965). For tobacco, the optimum temperatures for disease
development are 17°–23°; outside this range there is a marked
decline in severity and plants at 30° are little affected. In contrast
the disease is most severe in peas at 28° (Lloyd and Lockwood, 1963)
and it would appear that temperatures which are generally unfavourable for growth of the host are those likely to favour black
root rot. The disease is much less severe in soils of pH 5·6 or lower.
It is not fully understood why this is so, for the fungus grows well
in culture from pH 4–6·4 (Lucas, 1955).

Violet root rot

This is caused by the basidiomycete *Helicobasidium purpureum*, the
mycelial (sterile) form of which is *Rhizoctonia crocorum* (Buddin and
Wakefield, 1927). The disease gets its name from the colour of the
mycelium that invests the roots and shoot bases of infected plants.
Sugar beet, mangolds, clover, lucerne and carrots are some of the
more important crops attacked (Whitney, 1954; Hering, 1962;
Hull, 1960). The disease occurs on a wide range of soil types but,
like black root rot, is generally more severe on light, alkaline soils.
It also appears to be favoured by high soil moisture though there is
some disagreement in the literature on this point (Hull and Wilson,
1946). On the roots the fungus characteristically forms minute
hyphal aggregations at the point of entry, termed 'infection
cushions' (p. 22) or *'corps milaires'*. It also produces small, black
sclerotia which enable it to survive from one season to the next
(Valder, 1958).

Southern root rot

This disease is particularly important in the southern states of
America (hence the name), and also in other subtropical, and
tropical regions (Aycock, 1966). The causal fungus is *Sclerotium
rolfsii*, which has a basidiomycete perfect state (*Corticium rolfsii*),
rarely found in nature. Its important hosts include ground-nuts,
cotton, beans, potatoes and tomatoes. Young plants are usually
killed rapidly but older plants turn yellow and wilt before they die.
The mycelium often appears as a white mass at the stem bases of

dying plants and within this mycelium small, brown sclerotia are formed (Figure 3.2). The disease is favoured by high soil moisture and particularly by factors which increase moisture at the soil surface, such as heavy shading or crowding of plants. It is also most severe at relatively high soil temperatures, 27°–30°; below 20° and above 36° little infection occurs. There is little general agreement on the effect of soil type on the disease but the fungus is strongly aerobic and is more abundant in well-aerated soils.

Texas root rot

The causal fungus *Phymatotrichum omnivorum*, a hyphomycete (Moniliales), attacks a wide range of plants in Texas and neighbouring areas but cotton is probably the most important host (Streets, 1937; Rogers, 1942). All monocotyledons and a few dicotyledons are immune, possibly because their roots contain alkaloids which are toxic to the fungus (Greathouse and Rigler, 1940). With cotton a slight yellowing of the leaves is the first visible symptom of the disease and this is soon followed by wilting. When these plants are pulled up most of the roots are found to be dead and their surface covered with fungal strands and mycelial aggregates. During the summer rains the fungus may sporulate at the soil surface on conspicuous mycelial mats which are usually some 100–200 mm in diameter and about 25 mm thick. Like *S. rolfsii*, the fungus also forms small, brown sclerotia and these can persist in soil for many years. The northern limit of the disease appears to be determined by the winter temperatures which will permit survival of the sclerotia, and Ezekiel (1945) found that this corresponded well with a line linking points at which the lowest observed air temperature reached –23°, between the years 1899 and 1938. In the U.S.A. the disease is generally most destructive in alkaline soils and in the semi-arid areas of the south-west where the winter temperatures are not severe.

Group 2

Another group comprises root rots caused by fungi that perennate as resting spores but with a restricted host range. Two examples are root rot peas caused by *Aphanomyces euteiches*, and the dry root rot of *Phaseolus* bean caused by *Fusarium solani* f. sp. *phaseoli*.

Aphanomyces root rot

This is prevalent in most pea growing areas of the U.S.A., particularly in the Eastern and Central states. The fungus, a

member of the Saprolegniales, and the disease were first described
by Jones and Drechsler (1925). The shoot symptoms depend on the
stage of development at which the roots become thoroughly invaded
and on the degree of varietal resistance. If the roots and stem base

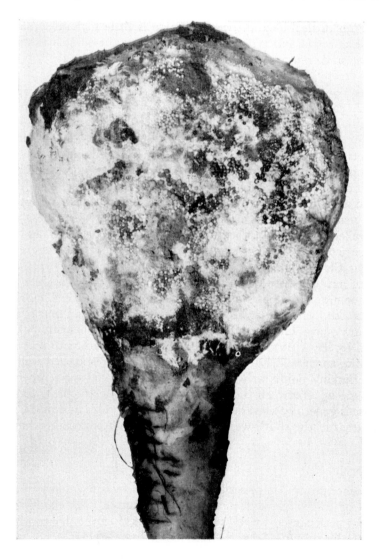

FIGURE 3.2 *Sclerotium rolfsii* on sugar beet with sclerotia
forming in mycelial mat. Photograph courtesy E. C. Tims,
from Aycock, 1966, *Tech. Bull. N. C. agric. Exp. Stn.*, no. 174

become invaded before the stem has formed three to four nodes there is often sudden wilting, but usually in the field invasion occurs later than this, resulting in a general check in growth and a progressive death of the leaves from the base of the stem. Frequently infected plants survive but produce only poorly filled pods. If infected plants are pulled up the vascular core of the tap root tends to come out in a long string, as a result of the soft decay of the root cortex. Oospores of the fungus (Figure 3.3) are found in great abundance within decaying tissue, and it is generally accepted that the fungus overwinters in this form. The disease is most serious in soils of high moisture content and at temperatures between 15° and 30°.

Bean dry root rot
This also causes serious losses in the U.S.A. The rot starts at the tips of the main and lateral roots, and there is subsequently a

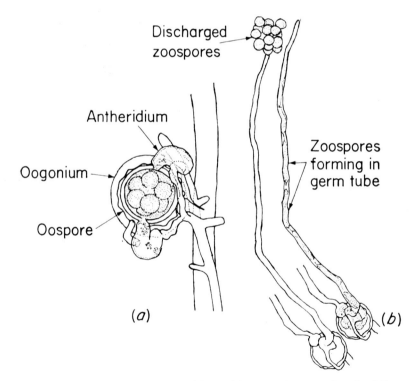

FIGURE 3.3 *Aphanomyces euteiches.* (*a*) oogonium and atheridia (*b*) germination of oospore ×340. Redrawn from Jones and Drechsler, 1925, *J. agric. Res.*, **24**, 641–740

gradual drying-out of the tissues to the stem bases. A reddish discolouration often appears on the tap root, sometimes as red streaks extending to soil level. Later these areas turn brown and longitudinal fissures appear in the cortex. The plant produces adventitious roots above the diseased area and, as a result, survives and shows few symptoms above ground other than a check in growth and some yellowing of the lower leaves. Affected plants tend to mature earlier than healthy ones but produce only a few pods of poor size.

The growth of the fungus in the root is relatively slow. For a short time after penetration it is intercellular in the cortex where strands tend to aggregate in the intercellular spaces; strands also develop on the root surface. However, the fungus soon becomes intracellular but only in the later stages invades the vascular tissue and it seldom extends in the stem much above soil level. Within the cortex, and particularly in the smaller roots, the fungus produces chlamydospores either singly or in short chains. When the roots decay these spores remain in the soil and provide inoculum for the infection of subsequent crops (Burkholder, 1919).

Group 3

A third group comprises root rots caused by fungi that perennate as mycelium in crop debris; these fungi are also fairly restricted in their host range.

Take-all

An example is 'take-all' caused by the ascomycete *Ophiobolus graminis*. Wheat and barley are the chief hosts of economic importance, together with oats which is attacked by a specific variety *avenae*. Some common grasses such as *Festuca rubra*, *Dactylis glomerata* and *Lolium* spp. also serve as hosts and are important as carriers of the fungus (Brooks, 1965*a*).

The cereal or grass roots may be attacked at any stage in the growth of the plant and, as indicated, the chief sources of inoculum are stubble and grass roots which have previously been infected. Hyphae of the fungus pass up the roots to the base of the tillers and spread on the root surface in this way precedes penetration. Eventually a dense mycelial mat is formed giving a characteristic black appearance to the roots and stem bases (Figure 3.4). Plants may be killed before the ears emerge but often the disease symptoms are not apparent until ear formation, when infected plants can be

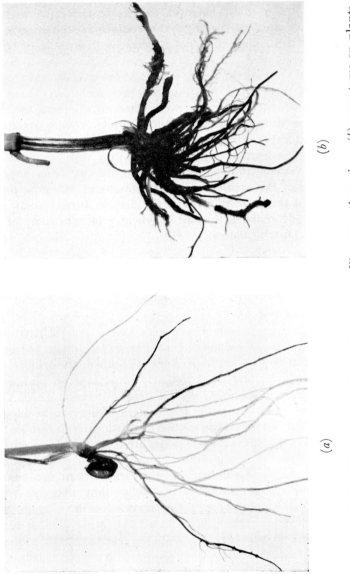

(b)

(a)

Figure 3.4 Take-all of wheat. *(a)* symptoms on seedling roots in spring. *(b)* symptoms on plants in July showing blackened stem bases. Photographs copyright Rothamsted Experimental Station.

readily spotted because the ears remain thin and papery, contain
very small grain if any at all, and have a bleached appearance
giving them their name 'whiteheads' (Davis, 1925; Fellows, 1928).
It should be borne in mind, however, that any interference with the
uptake of water and nutrients by the roots may cause poor ear
formation and this symptom is not necessarily diagnostic of *Ophiobolus* attack.

Perithecia of *O. graminis* develop on the lowermost leaf sheaths
as the host matures. It is doubtful whether ascospores normally
have any significance in the life cycle since all attempts to infect
roots of wheat seedlings in soil have failed. Brooks (1965*b*) concluded
that the normal soil microflora exerts a virtually complete biological
control of infection from ascospores by inhibiting their germination.
He showed, however, that ascospores were able to infect exposed
proximal parts of the seedling roots. Infections of this type might
be important in the establishment of the disease in new areas, and
could explain outbreaks of take-all in wheat grown in some of the
newly drained Dutch polders.

Root Rots of Trees

Armillaria root rot

Some fungi that cause root rots of trees have a general pattern of
infection similar to *O. graminis*. *Armillaria mellea* is one example.
This fungus attacks a wide range of plants both in the tropics and
in temperate regions, and is particularly important on plantation
crops such as tea and cacao.

The source of inoculum is the root system of previously infected
trees but whereas with *O. graminis* there is little spread outside the
infected stubble, the spread of *A. mellea* from its food base can be
considerable. This is accomplished by hyphae aggregated into
root-like structures or rhizomorphs, within which there is a certain
amount of tissue differentiation analogous to that of higher plant
roots. These rhizomorphs must be extremely efficient in conducting
food materials for some have been found extending 9 m or more.
However, as Garrett (1956) points out, radius of rhizomorph
spread may not necessarily be the same as the effective radius for
infection.

Under suitable conditions the rhizomorphs pass up the roots of
the host forming a rhizomorph mat and exploiting any structural

weakness, for instance, the junction of bark and wood (Figure 3.5*a*). This 'ectotrophic growth habit' occurs in advance of penetration, which is effected progressively by hyphal branches some distance behind the limit of rhizomorph advance. A similar type of infection occurs with other fungi causing tree root rots. Penetration by *Fomes lignosus*, an important pathogen of rubber in Malaya, occurs some 4.5 m behind the tips of the mycelial strands.

Once it has penetrated, *A. mellea* gradually colonizes the root tissues, and visible symptoms of disease appear such as yellowing, premature defoliation and eventually, death. These may occur slowly, branch by branch, depending largely on the site of infection.

When infection of the tree is advanced the sporophores of *A. mellea* are sometimes produced at the base of the tree in characteristic groups (Figure 3.5*b*) but basidiospores are not essential to the disease cycle, for in certain areas of Africa where *Armillaria* root rot is important, sporophores are not found. Where they do occur the contribution of the basidiospores to the general level of fungal inoculum is not clear. Individual spores are unable apparently to infect; whether they can *en masse* has not been determined. They may possibly initiate mycelial growth on stumps or fencing posts and this, in turn, provides additional inoculum for the infection of standing trees. Certainly it has been shown in a similar disease, white rot of pine caused by *Fomes annosus*, that infection of cut stumps arises from air-borne spores.

Sudden death of clove

With most root rots of trees symptoms appear gradually in the leaves and shoots but in sudden death of clove (*Eugenia aromatica*) they develop with remarkable rapidity. The first symptom is a slight chlorosis, an almost imperceptible change when considering individual leaves but noticeable in the mass to a practised observer. This is followed by a slight thinning and loss of turgidity of the leaves and then, within a few days, by a spectacularly rapid death. A mass of russet-brown leaves remains on infected trees, so that these stand out clearly against the dark green foliage of healthy ones (Figure 3.6).

An account of the various investigations of sudden death makes interesting reading for the cause was long disputed and there are still features of the disease which are not fully understood. Nutman and Roberts (1953*b*) concluded from the nature of disease spread that a relatively slow-moving pathogen was involved and that the symptoms were consistent with a disorganization of the absorbing

(b)

(a)

FIGURE 3.5 *Armillaria mellea.* (a) rhizomorphs beneath the bark of larch (b) sporophores at base of infected deodar. From Hiley, 1919, *The Fungal Diseases of the Common Larch*, by permission of The Clarendon Press, Oxford.

roots, a feature they demonstrated by numerous excavations of the root systems of infected trees. Death of the roots appears to be a comparatively slow process, and only the remarkable drought-resistance of the clove tree prevents the development of symptoms over an extended period. It seems that the tree can withstand a high degree of root disintegration to a certain point but then collapses giving the typical sudden death effect. Nutman and Roberts (1953*a*, 1954) found that diseased clove trees were invariably invaded by a fungus which they described as *Valsa eugeniae*. They were able to show in inoculation experiments that this was a primary parasite of mature clove trees and that seedlings were immune, while in saplings there was a slow response to fungal invasion, the symptoms of which they termed 'slow decline'.

V. eugeniae sporulates freely on dead tissue, producing perithecia and pycnidia some eight years after death of the tree, and infection is probably initiated by spores which are washed onto fibrous roots

(*a*)   (*b*)

Figure 3.6 Sudden death of cloves, showing marked contrast between (*a*) healthy tree (*b*) infected tree.

close to the soil surface. The role of hyphae in the soil is not known but inevitably in a plantation there is contact between roots and spread across them seems likely.

EPIDEMIOLOGY OF ROOT ROT DISEASES

Our knowledge of the behaviour of root-infecting fungi owes much to the work of Garrett and his associates, and the following is based chiefly on his review of this subject (Garrett, 1956). These fungi have two distinct phases: a parasitic phase on the roots of their hosts and a period of survival, which for some involves a saprophytic phase on plant residues. Some fungi such as *Thielaviopsis basicola* and *Fusarium solani* f.sp. *phaseoli* survive in soil as chlamydospores, others like *Helicobasidium purpureum*, *Sclerotium rolfsii* and *Phymatotrichum omnivorum* as sclerotia. Much attention has been given to the longevity of these structures and particularly to the conditions under which they germinate in the absence of the appropriate host because this might indicate ways of eradicating them. When chlamydospores of *T. basicola* are added to soil many appear to germinate for within the first two to three weeks there is a rapid decline in numbers but after this the population of chlamydospores remains stable in the absence of plant growth (Bateman, 1963). A similar spontaneous germination of the sclerotia of *P. omnivorum* occurs in well-aerated soil and can be induced by cultivation and by adding organic matter. In the latter instance the possibility of microbial antagonism cannot be ruled out, for it has been shown that fungal sclerotia in soil can be parasitized by a number of microorganisms (Curl and Hansen, 1964).

In contrast, *Ophiobolus graminis* and *Armillarea mellea* survive by colonizing the remains of the root systems of their hosts. The survival of *O. graminis* within infected wheat straws buried in soils has been studied at length by Garrett. He found generally that conditions favouring microbial activity such as high temperature, good aeration and suitable moisture were those that favoured the disappearance of *O. graminis*, although similar conditions favour its parasitic activity on living wheat roots. The supply of readily available nitrogen was found to be specially important; when some was added to the wheat straw *O. graminis* survived longer. Garrett suggested that the additional nitrogen enabled *O. graminis* to make continued slow growth and thus exploit further areas of the straw. This effect on fungal growth partly accounts for differences in the rate of disappearance of *O. graminis* and the rate of straw decomposition observed in some soils. Wheat straw contains little nitrogen, and so the nitrogen status of the soil is an important factor determining the degree of colonization and subsequent decomposition.

In Garrett's view, the survival of a pathogenic fungus like *O. graminis* in infected root tissue is determined largely by its ability to exploit the available food materials in the face of increasing activity by other soil organisms, some of which may be antagonistic. This he calls its 'competitive saprophytic ability'. Initially the pathogen has an advantage: it is already present in the tissues and these may take a while to die. The plant cells may therefore still retain some resistance which will exclude many microorganisms, while the pathogen because of its specific parasitic ability will be able to colonize them. With excised root systems of herbaceous plants this period is likely to be of short duration, but with the roots of woody plants it will be very much longer and in the colonization of the stump and roots of a felled tree, the pathogen has, comparatively, a greater advantage. None the less, in time, tree roots become colonized by microorganisms with the resulting suppression of the pathogen. Rishbeth (1951), with techniques basically similar to Garrett's, has shown that survival of *Fomes annosus* in pine roots depends mainly on factors influencing microbial activity. In particular, the antagonistic activities of *Trichoderma viride* feature largely in the suppression of these pathogens of woody plants.

The means by which the parasitic phase is initiated depends in part on the mode of survival. Where the pathogen is present in soil as a resting spore or sclerotium it presumably remains quiescent until it receives some stimulus. Apart from spontaneous germination this stimulus appears to be associated with the roots of the host plant as it is with some fungi causing damping-off (p. 20). The fact that bean seedlings become infected when planted in soil infested with chlamydospores of *T. basicola* suggests this is so in this instance (Bateman, 1963). Similarly, the chlamydospores of *F. solani* f. sp. *phaseoli* germinate most consistently in soil when close to germinating bean seeds and young bean roots (Schroth and Snyder, 1961).

There is an obvious biological advantage in a mechanism which induces germination in the presence of the appropriate host but the response is not always specific. For instance, Hering (1962) found that *Lotus corniculatus* stimulated the germination of sclerotia but did not function as a host for *H. purpureum*. Chlamydospores of *F. solani* f. sp. *phaseoli* also germinate near germinating seeds and roots of many non-susceptible plants and the fungus may grow to a limited extent and then produce additional chlamydospores (Schroth and Hendrix, 1962). In this instance, therefore, temporary supplies of nutrients from the root diffusates of non-susceptible plants favour survival.

For pathogens that survive in root residues there are two possible ways of initiating the parasitic phase, and these are illustrated by *A. mellea* and *O. graminis*. In some instances, the rhizomorphs of *A. mellea* grow out from the residues until the food reserves are exhausted or contact with a host is established. This seems to be so in woodlands in Britain. In other situations, for example in East Africa, the fungus forms few rhizomorphs and probably infection is most often initiated only when the host root comes into contact with an infected root. This pattern is normal for *O. graminis*; this fungus grows only in root residues and depends entirely on root contact by the host with the substrate it has colonized.

When we consider actual penetration of the host tissues it is clear, particularly with diseases of tree roots, that there must be a certain amount of the pathogen at any one site before this is achieved. Altson found, in experiments with *Fomes lignosus* (see Garrett, 1956), that no infection resulted when roots of young rubber trees were inoculated with pieces of infected tissue less than $\frac{1}{4}$ in³ (approx. 0.4×10^{-5} m³). When the size of inoculum was increased infection occurred, and the number of successful inoculations increased correspondingly with inoculum size, until with inocula of 5 in³ (approx. 8×10^{-5} m³) 100% infection was achieved. Garrett obtained similar results in a laboratory study of infection of potato tubers by *A. mellea*.

From a consideration of such data, Garrett has developed the idea of inoculum potential, which he defines as 'the energy of growth of a parasite available for infection of a host at the surface of the host organ to be infected'. Both the number and nutritional status of infecting units per unit area of root surface are factors which determine inoculum potential. Thus for *A. mellea* the aggregation of hyphae into rhizomorphs has the advantage of increasing inoculum potential, but the energy of growth is derived from the food base from which the rhizomorphs originate and if it is below a certain level no infection occurs.

CONTROL

Root diseases are among the most difficult to control. Once symptoms appear in the foliage it is usually too late to do anything and the aim of most methods is to eradicate the pathogen during its resting or saprophytic stage.

The efficiency of resting spores and sclerotia as inocula can be impaired and a measure of disease control achieved by encouraging germination in the absence of the susceptible host. Deep rotary tillage, for example, eliminates most sclerotia of *Phymatotrichum omnivorum* because these germinate spontaneously in a well-aerated soil, and deep ploughing and frequent cultivation have also been found beneficial in the control of *Helicobasidium purpureum* on beet.

A similar result could be achieved by a 'catch crop' which stimulates germination but does not itself act as a host. Hering's experiments (p. 41) suggest that *Lotus corniculatus* might be effective in this respect for *H. purpureum*. Two basic objections to this method are that the most suitable plants generally offer little monetary return to the grower and the degree of control obtained is not sufficiently great to compensate for this.

There are special ways of controlling the inoculum level of certain fungi that infect tree roots. With *Armillaria mellea* attempts are made to control the colonization of root debris. These depend largely on the form of the existing inoculum and its distribution. From experiments in tea plantations in Malawi, Leach (1937) deduced that the stump of a recently felled tree was an ideal site for *A. mellea* only if the roots contained abundant starch. Otherwise soil fungi with less exacting carbohydrate requirements invaded the roots and *A. mellea* was excluded. To take advantage of this Leach suggested that before clearing land for plantation crops trees should be ring-barked, that is a ring of tissues external to the wood is removed. This prevents the products of photosynthesis passing down to the roots but still enables food reserves of the roots, once mobilized, to pass to the leaf canopy via the xylem. When the tree dies the roots are thus depleted of food reserves and *A. mellea* does not successfully compete with other soil fungi in this situation. That it does not depends largely on the fact that in East Africa *A. mellea* is distributed sparsely through the soil in infected roots. In Britain, where it occurs in soil as an abundant population of rhizomorphs ring-barking is less effective. Here rhizomorphs are often already present on the roots of healthy trees and the comparatively rapid death of the tree by ring-barking enables *A. mellea* to invade the roots ahead of its competitors; its greater inoculum potential in this situation gives it an advantage of position. Provided that the land is to be cleared, however, and will remain so for some years before a tree-crop is planted, ring-barking may still be useful, for the early colonization of the stumps by *A. mellea* will also mean an early depletion of the food reserves and the fungus will then die of starvation. Where land cannot be left in this way, grubbing of felled-tree roots is the only practical alternative.

The colonization of freshly exposed surfaces of pine stumps by basidiospores of *Fomes annosus* is dealt with in East Anglia by different methods. Either the stump is painted with creosote or some other fungitoxic material or, immediately after felling, the stump is inoculated with a spore suspension of *Peniophora gigantea*, a basidiomycete which effectively competes with *F. annosus* in the colonization of the stump (Rishbeth, 1959, 1963).

Another approach to the control of these root diseases is to detect the sources of inoculum and then remove them. The best example is the scheme originally devised by Napper for the eradication of *Fomes lignosus* in the rubber plantations of Malaya. This relied on the fact that ectotrophic mycelial growth may be some 4·5 m in advance of the limit of penetration. Land required for rubber plantations or being replanted with rubber was cleared and the larger stumps removed. The young rubber trees were then themselves used to discover residual sources of inoculum. At intervals gangs of labourers went through the plantation and examined the tap roots, exposing them for about 50 mm in the first year to about 228 mm in the fourth year of growth. If rhizomorphs of *F. lignosus* were detected the whole root system was exposed and the rhizomorphs traced to their source, which was then removed. This method has now been modified in the light of more recent investigations. The current practices for controlling root diseases of rubber in Malaya are summarized by Fox (1965). Trees of the old planting are killed while standing, by treating them with sodium arsenite or 2,4,5-trichlorophenoxyacetic acid (2,4,5-T); alternatively, the trees are felled, the stump is poisoned with one or other of these chemicals and then treated with creosote. A mixed cover of creeping legumes such as *Pueraria phaseoloides*, *Centrosema pubescens* and *Calopogonium mucunoides* is also established between the new planting rows which are themselves maintained as clean weeded strips about 1·8 m across. Young rubber trees are still used to detect inoculum but 3-monthly inspections of the stand about a year after planting rely on foliage symptoms. Where these are found the diseased tree is removed and neighbouring trees along the row are also inspected at the collar region, i.e. junction of root and stem, until a disease-free tree is found. Any infected trees are treated, if possible, with a fungicide such as pentachloronitrobenzene and then the sources of inoculum which these operations reveal are eradicated from the clean-weeded planting rows and burnt, but sources outside this are left. Only if a stump within the leguminous cover consistently initiates new infections is it isolated by a trench and all lateral roots severed. This, however, is not common for the root-infecting fungi do not appear to survive long in these areas. Several factors probably account for this. Growth of these fungi is initially encouraged within the leguminous cover and they often produce fruit bodies, but as a result exhaust their food bases. The environment also favours microbial activity and their mycelia are liable to attack by antagonists of the microflora and by mycophagous species of the soil fauna such as nematodes.

Finally there are two general methods for controlling root diseases: crop rotations and eradication by chemicals.

Crop rotations are particularly useful in dealing with root diseases of annual crops in which stubble and roots of a previously infected crop are the chief sources of inoculum, because successive plantings of non-susceptible hosts allow time for the inoculum to die of starvation or to be eliminated by natural microbial activity. For example, the general experience is that one year free from crops or self-sown plants of wheat and barley and from susceptible grass-weeds is sufficient for the control of take-all, though oats may not precede wheat or barley in areas where *Ophiobolus graminis* var. *avenae* occurs (Glynne, 1965). It does not necessarily follow that successive plantings of wheat and barley result in increasing losses from take-all. Indeed in some areas the disease increased during the first 2–3 years of continuous cropping but it then declines with a corresponding improvement in yield. There are similar reports for the cotton root rot caused by *P. omnivorum*. The factors responsible for this apparent control are not clear but it may be that increases in these pathogens lead to a build-up of microorganisms antagonistic to them and some kind of an equilibrium between the two is eventually reached (see Lester and Shipton, 1967). In theory, crop rotations are also suitable for those diseases in which the pathogen survives as resting spores or sclerotia. Unfortunately many of these propagules are long-lived and the length of rotation required for their complete elimination would scarcely be acceptable as a practical proposition. Recent studies of *Aphanomyces* root rot showed, for example, that the disease could still be severe in some fields not cropped to peas for 6–8 years (Temp and Hagedorn, 1967). Also, some of the fungi have a wide host range which severely limits the choice of alternative crops. None the less, crop rotations are useful in conjunction with other cultural practices because the population of the pathogen is gradually diminished and a susceptible crop can then be grown without incurring severe losses.

Chemical treatment of soil to kill fungal sclerotia and resting spores is discussed in Chapter 19. As a method of controlling root diseases it has in the past been considered economically practical only on seedbed and glasshouse sites, though there have been a few attempts to use these methods on a field scale, for example, the application of carbon disulphide to soil in citrus plantations to eradicate *A. mellea* (Bliss, 1951). Field applications of materials such as chloropicrin and methyl bromide are now proving to be worthwhile in some areas. In California some 4000 m² of strawberry, tomato and vegetable land are regularly treated for the control of root-infecting pathogens, weeds and *Verticillium* (see Chapter 4). The treatment often results in high yields in situations where poor crop growth cannot be directly attributed to a major pathogen, a phenomenon generally described as a 'replant problem', and brought about by a prolonged monoculture. It seems likely that the beneficial effect results in part from the control of primitive pathogens like *Pythium ultimum* which infect the root tips and rootlets and induce a growth stasis suggestive of low soil fertility (Wilhelm, 1965).

REFERENCES

Aycock, R. (1966). Stem rot and other diseases caused by *Sclerotium rolfsii*. *Tech. Bull. N. C. agric. Exp. Stn.*, No. 174, 202 pp.

Bateman, D. F. (1963). Influence of host and non-host plants upon populations of *Thielaviopsis basicola* in soil. *Phytopathology*, **53**, 1174–7

Bliss, D. E. (1951). The destruction of *Armillaria mellea* in citrus soils. *Phytopathology*, **41**, 665–83

Brooks, D. H. (1965a). Wild and cultivated grasses as carriers of the take-all fungus (*Ophiobolus graminis*). *Ann. appl. Biol.*, **55**, 307–16

Brooks, D. H. (1965b). Root infection by ascospores of *Ophiobolus graminis* as a factor in the epidemiology of the take-all disease. *Trans. Br. mycol. Soc.*, **48**, 237–48

Buddin, W. and Wakefield, E. M. (1927). Studies on *Rhizoctonia crocorum* (Pers.) DC. and *Helicobasidium purpureum* (Tul.) Pat. *Trans. Br. mycol. Soc.* **12**, 116–40

Burkholder, W. H. (1919). The dry root rot of the bean. *Mem. Cornell agric. Exp. Stn.*, No. 26, 1003–33

Curl, E. A. and Hansen, J. D. (1964). The microflora of natural sclerotia of *Sclerotium rolfsii* and some effects on the pathogen. *Pl. Dis. Reptr.*, **48**, 446–50

Davis, R. J. (1925). Studies on *Ophiobolus graminis* Sacc. and the take-all disease of wheat. *J. agric. Res.*, **31**, 801–25

Ezekiel, W. N. (1945). Effect of low temperatures on survival of *Phymatotrichum omnivorum*. *Phytopathology*, **35**, 296–301

Fellows, H. (1928). Some chemical and morphological phenomena attending infection of the wheat plant by *Ophiobolus graminis*. *J. agric. Res.*, **37**, 647–61

Fox, R. A. (1965). The role of biological eradication in root disease control in replanting of *Hevea brasiliensis*. In *Ecology of Soil-borne Plant Pathogens* (Ed. K. F. Baker and W. C. Snyder), pp. 348–62. John Murray, London.

Garrett, S. D. (1956). *Biology of Root-infecting Fungi*, 293 pp. Cambridge University Press.

Glynne, M. D. (1965). Crop sequence in relation to soil-borne pathogens. In *Ecology of Soil-borne Plant Pathogens* (Ed. K. F. Baker and W. C. Snyder), pp. 423–35. John Murray, London.

Greathouse, G. A. and Rigler, N. E. (1940). The chemistry of resistance of plants to *Phymatotrichum* root rot. V. Influence of alkaloids on growth of fungi. *Phytopathology*, **30**, 475–85

Hering, T. F. (1962). Host range of the violet root rot fungus, *Helicobasidium purpureum* Pat. *Trans. Br. mycol. Soc.*, **45**, 488–94

Hull, R. (1960). Sugar beet diseases. *Bull. Minist. Agric. Fish Fd., Lond.*, No. 142, 41–3

Hull, R. and Wilson, A. R. (1946). Distribution of violet root rot (*Helicobasidium purpureum* Pat). of sugar beet and preliminary experiments on factors affecting the disease. *Ann. appl. Biol.*, **33**, 420–33

Johnson, J. (1916). Host plants of *Thielavia basicola*. *J. agric. Res.*, **7**, 289–300

Jones, F. R. and Drechsler, C. (1925). Root rot of peas in the United States caused by *Aphanomyces euteiches* (n.sp.). *J. agric. Res.*, **30**, 293–325

Leach, R. (1937). Observations on the parasitism and control of *Armillaria mellea*. *Proc. R. Soc.*, B. **121**, 561–73

Lester, E. and Shipton, P. J. (1967). A technique for studying inhibition of the parasitic activity of *Ophiobolus graminis* (Sacc.) Sacc. in field soils. *Pl. Path.*, **16**, 121–3

Lloyd, A. B. and Lockwood, J. L. (1963). Effects of soil temperature, host variety and fungus strain on *Thielaviopsis* root rot of peas. *Phytopathology*, **53**, 329–31

Lucas, G. B. (1955). The cardinal temperature and pH response of *Thielaviopsis basicola*. *Mycologia*, **47**, 793–8

Lucas, G. B. (1965). *Diseases of Tobacco*, pp. 200–25. Scarecrow Press, New York.

Nutman, F. J. and Roberts, F. M. (1953*a*). Two new species of fungi on clove trees in the Zanzibar protectorate. *Trans. Br. mycol. Soc.*, **36**, 229–34

Nutman, F. J. and Roberts, F. M. (1953*b*). Investigations into the diseases of the clove tree in Zanzibar. *E. Afr. agric. J.*, **18**, 146–54

Nutman, F. J. and Roberts, F. M. (1954). *Valsa eugeniae* in relation to the sudden death of the clove tree (*Eugenia aromatica*). *Ann. appl. Biol.*, **41**, 23–44

Rishbeth, J. (1951). Observations on the biology of *Fomes annosus* with particular reference to East Anglian pine plantations. II. Spore production, stump infection and saprophytic activity in stumps. *Ann. Bot.*, N.S. **15**, 1–21

Rishbeth, J. (1959). Stump protection against *Fomes annosus*. I. Treatment with creosote. *Ann. appl. Biol.*, **47**, 519–28; (1963). III. Inoculation with *Peniophora gigantea*. *Ann. appl. Biol.*, **52**, 63–77

Rogers, C. H. (1942). Cotton root rot studies with special reference to sclerotia, cover crops, rotations, tillage, seeding rates, soil fungicides and effects on seed quality. *Bull. Tex. agric. Exp. Stn.*, No. 614, 45 pp.

Schroth, M. N. and Snyder, W. C. (1961). Effect of host exudates on chlamydospore germination of the bean root rot fungus, *Fusarium solani* f. *phaseoli*. *Phytopathology*, **51**, 389–93

Schroth, M. N. and Hendrix, F. F. (1962). Influence of non-susceptible plants on the survival of *Fusarium solani* f. *phaseoli* in soil. *Phytopathology*, **52**, 906–9

Stover, R. H. (1950). The black root rot disease of tobacco. I. Studies on the causal organism *Thielaviopsis basicola*. *Can. J. Res.* C **28**, 445–70

Streets, R. B. (1937). *Phymatotrichum* (cotton or Texas) root rot in Arizona. *Tech. Bull. Ariz. agric. Exp. Stn.*, No. 71, 410 pp.

Temp, M. V. and Hagedorn, D. J. (1967). Influence of cropping practices on *Aphanomyces* root rot potential of Wisconsin pea fields. *Phytopathology*, **57**, 667–70

Tsao, P. H. and Bricker, J. L. (1966). Chlamydospores of *Thielaviopsis basicola* as surviving propagules in natural soils. *Phytopathology*, **56**, 1012–9

Valder, P. G. (1958). The biology of *Helicobasidium purpureum* Pat. *Trans. Br. mycol. Soc.*, **41**, 283–308

Whitney, N. J. (1954). Investigations of *Rhizoctonia crocorum* (Pers.) DC. in relation to the violet root rot of carrots. *Can. J. Bot.*, **32**, 679–704

Wilhelm, S. (1965). *Pythium ultimum* and the soil fumigation growth response. *Phytopathology*, **55**, 1016–20

CHAPTER 4

Wilts

In the advanced stages of many root diseases the infected plant wilts because the decaying root system cannot absorb enough water to replace that lost by transpiration. In other diseases wilting occurs before there is extensive root damage and it is with these that this chapter is principally concerned. Several types of pathogen are involved and the symptoms preceding wilt vary accordingly. Often the first indication is that the lower leaf-petioles bend downwards so that the angle between them and the main stem becomes obtuse (Figure 4.1). This is called epinasty (Wellman, 1941). There may also be slight vein clearing (Foster, 1946), followed by yellowing of the lower leaves. Progressively, these leaves become more chlorotic and eventually die while similar symptoms develop on younger leaves. During hot days individual leaves, even half-leaves, wilt and then recover at night. Eventually wilting is permanent and the plant shrivels and dies. Frequently, if stems of infected plants are cut, the vascular tissues are seen to be discoloured and a microscopical examination reveals other changes—tyloses and gums in the vessels, some collapse of the vessels, and disintegration of the adjoining parenchyma.

Wilt diseases are conveniently considered in relation to their pathogens. Viruses may cause wilting in some hosts, e.g. Tobacco-etch virus in Tabasco pepper (Greenleaf, 1953), but generally as a group they are not much associated with this type of symptom. Nematodes frequently cause wilts but usually because they disorganize the host root system. These two groups will therefore be omitted and the account limited to wilts induced by parasitic flowering-plants, insects, bacteria and fungi.

49

FIGURE 4.1 *Verticillium* wilt of tomato. The plant shows
marked epinasty of the leaf petioles, wilting and yellowing of
the terminal leaflets of the lower leaves and also the initiation
of adventitious roots along the stem which is an additional
feature of some wilt diseases. Photograph by T. V. Price.

WILTS CAUSED BY PARASITIC FLOWERING PLANTS

These differ from other wilts in two respects: the pathogen is
clearly visible with the naked eye, and although there is a tendency
for the infected plant to wilt on hot days, there are seldom any of
the other symptoms mentioned above.

Two main types of parasitic flowering plant are of economic significance—the Witchweeds and the Broomrapes. Dodder (*Cuscuta* sp.) is occasionally troublesome in tobacco seedbeds (Lucas, 1965) but seldom of significance elsewhere. Witchweeds belong to the genus *Striga* (Schrophulariaceae) of which there are some fifty species, but four only are important parasites of crops: *Striga asiatica* and *Striga hermonthica* on maize and sorghum especially in the Sudan, *Striga euphrasioides* on sugar cane in India and *Striga gesnerioides* on tobacco in Rhodesia (Wilson-Jones, 1953).

Broomrapes belong to the genus *Orobanche* (Orobanchaceae) and there are more than 150 species. Some have wide host ranges, others are restricted in the species they can parasitize. In the U.S.A. tobacco is attacked mainly by *Orobanche ramosa* and *Orobanche minor;* in India *Orobanche cernua* is the most common broomrape on this crop (Kumar, 1942). In Malta, *Orobanche crenata* is common on legumes especially broad bean (Wheeler, 1958).

The behaviour of these parasites follows a basically similar pattern. They produce large numbers of minute seeds which are blown by wind to adjacent areas and are also carried to new sites in contaminated seed samples of the crop. The seeds can remain dormant and viable for many years but are stimulated to germinate near plant roots, though the response is not host specific. In the presence of a suitable host, the parasite attaches itself to the root and then grows rapidly forming a thickened, underground stem full of starch reserves. Some weeks later it emerges, flowers and produces its seed (Figure 4.2). It then dies after the crop is harvested.

The occurrence of these parasites is sufficiently extensive on some crops, such as sorghum, to cause large losses in yield. Several methods of control have been tried, the most primitive being hand-weeding of the parasites before they set seeds. This is costly in terms of labour and impractical except on the smallest plantings. Trap-crops are sometimes of value. Two methods are used. In one a host of the parasite is planted, for example Sudan grass (*Sorghum sudanense*) for *S. hermonthica* in fields required for sorghum (*Sorghum vulgare*), it is allowed to grow for a limited period so that the parasite can become established, and is then ploughed-in well before the parasite produces flowers. In the other, a non-host of some economic importance is planted; this induces the seeds of the parasite to germinate but allows little further development. Groundnuts, cowpeas and dolichos bean have been suggested as trap-crops of this type for *S. hermonthica* (Andrews, 1947). Good control of witch-weed in the Sudan is also obtained by applying the herbicide

FIGURE 4.2 Parasitic flowering plants. (*a*) broomrape (*Orobanche crenata*) on broad bean (*Vicia faba*), showing the swollen underground stem. (*b*) witchweed (*Striga hermonthica*) on sorghum. Photograph of witchweed, courtesy F. T. Last.

(*a*)

(*b*)

2,4-dichlorophenoxyacetic acid (2,4-D) some 2–3 weeks after planting
sorghum and this method is generally preferred to trap-cropping
(Last, 1960, 1961). Heavy application of fertilisers are also beneficial.
Strains of sorgum resistant to witchweed have been bred in South
Africa. One of them, Framida, is of particular interest in that
resistance results from its inability to induce germination of the
parasite's seed (Williams, 1959).

Soil fumigation is another way in which seeds of parasitic
flowering plants may be destroyed, provided the crop merits the
relatively high cost of this treatment. For example, in the Coachella
Valley of California, treatment of large areas of valuable tomato
seedbed land with methyl bromide successfully eradicated Cooper's
broomrape, *O. ludoviciana* var. *cooperi* (Wilhelm and others, 1959).

WILTS CAUSED BY INSECTS

Mealybug wilt of pineapple is the only disease of importance in
this category. It occurs in most tropical areas where pineapples are
grown and is of special importance in Hawaii. The disease has been
reviewed by Carter (1962, 1963) and the information given here is
drawn largely from his accounts. The symptoms vary with the
pineapple variety and to a certain extent with the time of year but
for a susceptible variety such as Smooth Cayenne, which is grown
commercially in Hawaii, the first indications are a reddening of the
leaves and a slight incurving of the leaf margins. These symptoms
become more pronounced and are followed by a wilting of the
leaves and drying out of the leaf-tips (Figure 4.3). There is then
often a recovery stage in which new leaves are produced in the
centre of the plant. The above-ground symptoms are related to
changes in the root system, the first indication of which is that the
roots cease to elongate, and much of the root system then collapses.
Often before this stage, however, new roots appear above the old
ones and the renewed aerial growth is associated with their development.

Two species of mealybug are associated with the wilt, *Dysmicoccus
brevipes* and *Dysmicoccus neobrevipes* but the former probably includes
many closely related strains. Of the various factors influencing field
incidence the presence of the ant *Pheidole megacephala* is the most
important. Several other species of ant tend the mealybug but none
so favourably influences the build-up of the mealybug population,
and hence of the wilt. Climate, soil type, and pineapple variety

FIGURE 4.3 Mealybug wilt of pineapple. Diseased plants in the foreground, from Carter, 1962, *Insects in Relation to Plant Disease*, by permission of Interscience Publishers.

have smaller but significant effects. Heavy rains, by reducing the leaf populations of mealybugs, reduce wilt; for similar reasons so do low temperatures in regions at the limits of the economic range of the pineapple. On the other hand, root infection by *Pythium* spp. increases the severity of wilt.

For some years it was thought that wilt was induced by the prolonged feeding of large numbers of mealybugs on the pineapple because the insect secreted a toxin. The initial severity of the disease at the field edges was thus attributed to the movement of the mealybugs from wild hosts on the borders, and subsequent disease within the field to further encroachment by the insects. This simple hypothesis does not explain all the observations on the disease. For example, some field grown pineapples do not appear to be sources of wilt—if mealybugs are taken from them and placed on fresh plants these do not wilt; also seedlings not previously infested with mealybugs are negative sources of wilt. To explain this, Carter (1963) suggests that a transmittable latent factor, possibly a virus, is necessary to make the plant a source of wilt and that the toxic, wilt-inducing secretion is synthesized by the insect when feeding on a plant infected with this virus.

Though the etiology of the wilt is still not entirely understood, it is controlled most effectively in Hawaii by chemicals. The ants which encourage the mealybugs are killed with chlorinated hydrocarbons, and residual mealybugs with organophosphorus insecticides.

BACTERIAL WILTS

Mealybug wilt of pineapple, and plants parasitized by witchweed or broomrape are rather special examples of wilt. The wilt diseases most often encountered are caused by bacteria and fungi.

Wilts caused by Pseudomonas solanacearum

Of the bacterial wilts those caused by *Pseudomonas solanacearum* are particularly important. As a species this bacterium is known to attack a wide range of solanaceous and other hosts of which, economically, the most noteworthy are potato, tomato, eggplant, tobacco, groundnut and banana. The disease has been studied on various hosts over a number of years and has several names (Kelman, 1953). At the beginning of this century there were severe outbreaks on tobacco in Granville county, North Carolina, and hence on this crop it is often called 'Granville wilt'. Then it was found extensively on tomatoes in the southern states, where it became known as 'Southern bacterial wilt'. In the Caribbean area it was first noted on the Moko (or Buggoe) plantain in Trinidad and on plantain and bananas it is now called 'Moko disease' (Buddenhagen, 1961). The term 'brown rot' is often used for the disease on potatoes.

It is now clear that isolates of *Ps. solanacearum* differ in their host range (Buddenhagen and Kelman, 1964). Some attack many hosts (Race 1), others are restricted to bananas and species of *Heliconia* (Race 2), or to potato (Race 3). Moreover, some isolates are weakly pathogenic, others are markedly pathogenic. Fortunately these features correspond to certain cultural and biochemical characters which facilitate diagnosis. When grown on an agar containing 2,3,5-triphenyltetrazolium chloride weakly virulent or avirulent strains produce small, butyrous (butter-like) colonies which in obliquely transmitted light are distinctly dark; virulent strains develop irregularly round, fluidal colonies, which are white with light-pink centres. Virulent strains also produce large amounts of polysaccharide which appears extracellularly as a slime.

Lack of knowledge of races and strains and their respective host

C

ranges has undoubtedly resulted in some conflicting statements on the behaviour of *Ps. solanacearum*. Its longevity in soil is an example. Some reports of survival over many years are suspect because they take no account of susceptible wild hosts. On the other hand, finding *Ps. solanacearum* in indigenous hosts or isolating it from soil is not always relevant to the epidemiology of bacterial wilt of a particular crop; the pathogenicity of the isolates needs first to be established. Recent work (Sequeira, 1962) suggests that Race 2 survives in soil for a relatively short period; bananas planted in previously infested soil which had then remained fallow for 18–24 months were virtually free from wilt. In contrast strains of Race 1 attacking tobacco may survive in soil for many years (Buddenhagen, 1965).

While soil-borne inoculum may be important in certain situations, infected planting material is more often the means by which the pathogen is dispersed and the disease established. Young tomato transplants, potato tubers and banana rhizomes can harbour the pathogen yet show no obvious disease symptoms, but seed infection has not been established for any host. With bananas further spread often results from pruning when bacteria are transferred on the knife after cutting an infected plant. There is also evidence of insect dissemination in Honduras on the Buggoe variety, but this is unusual and involves a distinct strain of the bacterium. Spread from plant to plant is also possible where many bacteria are released into the soil from decaying roots. With soil-borne inoculum it is generally thought that the bacteria enter through some kind of wound incurred at transplanting, or made by the exit of a secondary root, or by nematodes.

Growth and movement of the bacteria within the plant takes place mainly in the vessels but pockets of infection develop in the parenchyma and sometimes cavities form in the pith at the stem base. In advanced stages of the disease on some hosts the root cortex disintegrates and becomes slimy. The bacteria can be detected in infected stems, tubers and rhizomes by cutting them across and either squeezing them or placing them in water when viscous drops or strands of bacteria exude from the vessels (Figure 4.4). On potato tubers the bacteria sometimes emerge *en masse* through the sprouts or eyes and soil adheres to these sites. This is also of some diagnostic value.

Symptoms follow the build-up of the bacteria within the vessels. The extracellular polysaccharide produced by virulent strains is considered to play a primary role in wilting. It increases the viscosity of the vascular stream and the vessels become plugged. This action is accentuated by the mass of bacterial cells. Other features, such as tylose formation and collapse of the vessels are thought to result from increased levels of indolacetic acid in infected plants and these accentuate wilting. Tissue degradation, which is a feature of the disease in herbaceous annuals such as tomato and potato, results from the action of pectic and cellulolytic enzymes produced by the bacterium, and aids its spread in the plant. Vascular browning also occurs in many hosts and this may result from the oxidation of phenolic substances released during the breakdown of the host tissue by hydrolytic enzymes. There are reviews of these physiological aspects by Sequeira (1963), Buddenhagen and Kelman (1964), and Beckman (1964).

The disease is generally most severe in the tropics and subtropics and in temperate areas with hot, humid summers. It is also generally

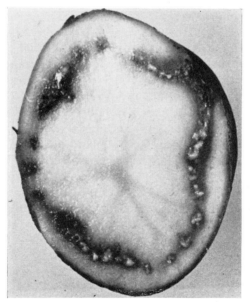

FIGURE 4.4 Potato infected with *Pseudomonas solanacearum*. The tissues around the vascular bundles show the browning commonly found on this host and masses of the bacteria are exuding from the cut ends of the vascular strands. Crown copyright.

favoured by high soil moisture. Certain strains attacking potatoes, however, have lower temperature optima and could possibly extend the known range of the disease were it not for legislation aimed at excluding them (Chapter 18). In areas where *Ps. solanacearum* is endemic wilt is controlled by crop rotation of varying length, by disinfecting pruning tools (Buddenhagen and Sequeira, 1958), and by planting resistant varieties. There are commercially acceptable resistant varieties of tobacco, groundnut and eggplant and so far these have not been attacked by new strains but suitable resistant varieties of tomato and banana are not yet available.

Wilt of sugar cane

Other bacterial wilts are more limited in their distribution but still of considerable economic significance. The wilt of sugar cane induced by *Xanthomonas vasculorum* is one: this is sometimes called gumming disease (Hughes, 1961). Pale yellow streaks develop on the leaves of infected plants and are most prominent on mature leaves which have not started to discolour. Later, portions of these streaks turn brown. Diseased plants appear unthrifty and the inflorescence seldom develops properly. If infected canes are cut a yellow, gummy mass exudes from the vascular bundles in which many bacteria are to be found. The gum interferes with the processing of the canes and results in losses additional to those directly incurred in the field. The vascular bundles appear red but this is not distinctive for it occurs also in other diseases of sugar cane.

The pathogen is introduced into plantations in cuttings (setts) taken unsuspectingly from infected plants which show few symptoms. It is at first confined to the vascular tissue but later invades the parenchyma and forms pockets of gum there. In wet weather or after heavy dews gum exudes from the streaks on fully turgid leaves via wounds caused by other leaves rubbing against them. The bacterium is then spread from these gummy exudates in wind blown rain or, passively, by flies. Inoculation experiments have shown that *X. vasculorum* can infect other plants such as sweet and dent corn (*Zea mays*) and sudan grass (*Sorghum sudanense*) but these do not appear to be important alternative hosts in the field. However, in Mauritius natural infections have been found on three palms (*Roystonea regia*, *Areca catechu*, and *Dictyosperma album*) and a grass (*Thysanolaena maxima*).

The disease is controlled mainly by planting resistant varieties. Particularly where a severe outbreak occurs the crop is ploughed in and planting of susceptible varieties near this area is prohibited.

Bacterial wilt of maize

This is also an important disease, particularly in the U.S.A. on sweet corn varieties (Robert, 1955; Pepper, 1967). It is caused by *Erwinia stewartii* (Bradbury, 1967). Like gumming disease of sugar cane the first symptoms are chlorotic stripes on the leaves (Figure 4.5) and these are followed by a progressive wilting of the leaves from the base of the plant. The staminate inflorescences tend to develop prematurely and wither, and another characteristic feature is the bright yellow, slimy exudate from the vascular bundles when infected stems are cut. Some plants are killed but others survive and often produce infected seed, infection occurring through the vascular strand of the funicle leading to the developing ovule. A few seeds give rise to diseased plants and there may be some spread of *E. stewartii* from these to adjacent seedlings by larvae of *Diabrotica longicornis* which feed on the roots (Ivanoff, 1933).

Insects also play an important part in the dissemination of the bacterium above ground (Poos and Elliott, 1936). Two species of flea beetle are involved, *Chaetocneme pulicaria* and *Chaetocneme denticulata*. *E. stewartii* overwinters in the intestinal tracts of these insects and is introduced into young plants when the beetles feed on them in the spring. There are a number of wild hosts which harbour the bacterium without apparently showing symptoms (Poos, 1939) and these may also serve as sources of inoculum since the beetles feed on some of them after emergence and before the corn seedlings have developed.

This disease is also controlled mainly by planting resistant varieties. Seed treatment is not generally effective because the bacteria are deep-seated.

FUNGAL WILTS

Dutch elm disease

Some fungi that cause wilts also enter their hosts largely through insect activity. *Ceratocystis ulmi* does so on elms and causes Dutch elm disease. This destructive disease was discovered in Holland in 1919 and found throughout Europe in the next few years. It was first noted in England in 1927 though it was probably present much earlier (Clinton and McCormick, 1936). In these territories, two species of bark-inhabiting beetles are vectors of the fungus, *Scolytus multistriatus* and *Scolytus scolytus*. These tunnel in freshly felled elm logs and in weakened trees (which are often diseased) and both

(a)   (b)

FIGURE 4.5 Bacterial wilt of maize. (a) Leaves showing chlorotic stripes (b) an infected ear. From C. Chupp and A. F. Sherf, 1960, *Vegetable Diseases and their Control*, copyright The Ronald Press, New York.

feed and lay their eggs there. The fungus can also live saprophytically on dead elm and produces its conidia (*Graphium* stage) abundantly in the insects' galleries. The net result is that when the beetles emerge they carry spores of *C. ulmi* with them and, in feeding, often success-fully inoculate healthy twigs (Parker and others, 1947). Once the fungus is in the vessels it produces small, yeast-like bodies by bud-ding and these are carried along in the transpiration stream, thus increasing the distribution of the pathogen (Banfield, 1941; Pomerleau and Mehran, 1966). The wilting of leaves on one or two limbs is usually the first indication of infection (Figure 4.6).

FIGURE 4.6 Dutch elm disease. Tree showing early symp-toms. One branch on the left and two branches on the right are beginning to die back as a result of infection by *Ceratocystis ulmi*. Photograph courtesy R. G. Strouts.

These leaves turn yellow, then brown, and finally shrivel and drop prematurely. Affected branches characteristically curved downwards at the tip giving a 'shepherd's crook' effect. It has been suggested that some of these effects result from the production of a toxin by the fungus (Feldman and others, 1950). Trees seldom die in one season; there is more often a progressive decline over a number of years.

C. ulmi and the vector *S. multistriatus* were introduced into the U.S.A. around 1930, probably on elm logs, and the first diseased elms were found in Cleveland and Cincinnati, Ohio, in that year. *S. multistriatus* became established in the New York area and initially disease outbreaks were associated with it. Another bark beetle, *Hylurgopinus rufipes*, native to the U.S.A., also proved to be an efficient vector of the fungus and in the following years both it and *S. multistriatus* were largely responsible for the extensive spread of the disease (Holmes, 1961). The movement of elm products through the States also helped in this respect. Attempts were made, on a very large scale, to eradicate the disease by felling infected trees and by clearing-up felled timber which might be sources of inoculum for the fungus and breeding sites for bark beetles. In terms of eliminating the disease the scheme was a failure (Zentmyer and others, 1946) but measures of this type may still be of value in limiting spread within a given locality (Marsden, 1953) particularly when combined with applications of insecticides in spring and autumn to reduce the bark-beetle populations and to prevent them feeding. Otherwise control relies on the introduction of elms that are resistant to *C. ulmi* and some have been obtained by selection and hybridisation (Went, 1938, 1954). Whether these will in turn be attacked by variants of the fungus remains to be seen (Holmes, 1965).

Oak wilt

Insects are also involved in oak wilt, which is caused by *Cerato-cystis fagacearum* [syn. *Endoconidiophora fagacearum* (Bretz, 1952); conidial state, *Chalara quercina*]. This disease is of considerable importance in the U.S.A. (Hepting, 1955; True and others, 1960). The fungus gains access to the tree via wounds, preferably those freshly made, and like *C. ulmi* develops in the vascular tissue. Spread from tree to tree may occur through natural root grafts but spread over greater distances results from the activities of various nitulid beetles. These feed in the mycelial mats of the fungus which eventually develop beneath the bark and by pressure crack it. The insects are apparently attracted by the odour of these mats and also to the oozing sap of fresh wounds (Morris and others, 1955). Since they carry fungus spores on their bodies they infect these wounds in some instances. The insects have a further role in the life cycle of the fungus. The mycelial mats are of two compatibility types called for convenience A and B, each bisexual and self-sterile, and producing perithecial initials and sticky endoconidia. Before perithecia and ascospores can form there must be a fertilization of the perithecial initials of type A by the endoconidia of type B or vice versa (Hepting and others, 1952) and it is by the movement of the nitulid beetles from the mycelial mats on one tree to those on another that the necessary transfers of endoconidia are made (Leach and others, 1952). When perithecia have developed and matured the ascospores ooze from them and they, too, are transferred to fresh sites by the nitulids. The conidia can survive for about 90 days and the asco-spores for about 150 days, long enough for survival during the insects hibernation (Stambaugh and Fergus, 1956). In addition, the fungus can survive in the infected tree for periods varying from 3 weeks in twigs to some 15–44 weeks in stumps and possibly longer in roots (Merek and Fergus, 1954).

Control of oak wilt aims to contain the disease rather than eliminate it. The treatment varies. In some states diseased trees and all oaks near the infected tree are cut and the stumps poisoned (Himelick and Fox, 1961). The felled wood is burnt or if any timber is retained it is sprayed with an insecticide–fungicide mixture. In other states, notably West Virginia, infected trees are deep-girdled to the heartwood: this prevents the formation of the fungal mats without damaging nearby trees as does felling (True and others, 1960).

Fusarium and Verticillium wilts

The remainder of the fungal wilts of any economic significance are caused by species of *Fusarium* and *Verticillium*.

The fusarial-wilt fungi are all forms of *Fusarium oxysporum* sensu Snyder and Hansen whose parasitism is limited usually to a single host species, e.g. f.sp. *lycopersici* on tomato, f.sp. *vasinfectum* on cotton, f.sp. *pisi* on peas, f.sp. *conglutinans* on cabbage (causing cabbage yellows), f.sp. *cubense* on banana (causing Panama disease). Many of these forms comprise races which attack only particular cultivars of the host, for example there are at least four races of *F. oxysporum* f. sp. *pisi* (Buxton, 1955; Bolton and others, 1966).

There are also different forms of *Verticillium* associated with wilt diseases but their status has been less clearly defined (Isaac, 1967). Some workers consider that most isolates of *Verticillium* from wilted plants can be referred to one species, *Verticillium alboatrum* (Rudolph, 1931). Others distinguish three principle species on cultural charac-teristics, and call isolates producing only dark, resting-type mycelium *V. alboatrum*, those forming small sclerotia in a particular way (microsclerotia) *Verticillium dahliae*, and isolates with chlamydo-spores, *Verticillium nigrescens* (Isaac, 1949, 1957). Whether these morphological divisions are accepted or not, there is abundant evidence that *Verticillium* isolates differ in their pathogenicity. For example, in *Verticillium* wilt of hops, two pathogenic strains (of *V. alboatrum*) are associated with two types of disease; one, which is relatively mild, has been known for many years and is called 'Fluctuating wilt', and the other 'Progressive wilt' which kills the hop bine and was first noted in certain areas of southeastern England in the 1930's (Keyworth, 1942; Isaac and Keyworth, 1948).

In contrast to the *Ceratocystis* species attacking elm and oak which are introduced mainly by insect vectors, the wilt-inducing forms of *Fusarium* and *Verticillium* enter their hosts through the roots. There is evidence that some of them can enter uninjured young roots but probably on older roots some injury is necessary (McClure, 1949). This may be one reason why plants infested with nematodes are often more severly attacked by these fungi (Porter and Powell, 1967). They also differ in their mode of survival. Most of them remain in soil for a long time without known host plants. They do so as dormant structures such as resting mycelium (*V. alboatrum*), chlamydospores (forms of *F. oxysporum*, *V. nigrescens*) and micro-sclerotia (*V. dahliae*). Infested soil is thus a major source of inoculum and local dissemination of these fungi results from the movement of this soil in drainage water and on implements. They are also disseminated in young transplants which show no obvious symptoms.

These fungi invade the root cortex but do not damage it to any great extent except under special conditions. They then become established in the vessels and are mostly confined there; only when the plant is becoming moribund do they grow out into the cortical tissues. At this stage there may be some spread in the field from an infected plant to an adjacent, healthy one especially where there is root contact (Roberts, 1943; Isaac, 1953). In any event the large amount of inoculum released into the soil places neighbouring plants at risk. In susceptible hosts the vascular system is often extensively colonized, even the leaf petioles (Scheffer and Walker, 1953), and the production and distribution of bud-conidia within vessels (as in elms infected with *C. ulmi*) accounts for this. Symptoms appear as the water-conducting system is invaded and cover the range outlined at the beginning of this chapter—epinasty, yellowing, vascular browning, tyloses and gums, and wilting. How these symptoms are produced is still not clearly understood. Increased levels of indolacetic acid, production of ethylene and enzyme activity may account for some changes, as in the disease caused by *Ps. solanacearum* (p. 57) but wilting does not appear to be associated with increased viscosity of the tracheal fluid in quite the same way. Although some plugging of the vessels occurs and may contribute to wilting many investigators consider that wilting is caused primarily by a fungal toxin. Although various fungal metabolites have been investigated they generally appear to be non-selective, that is culture filtrates from strains with low virulence cause symptoms comparable to those from a highly pathogenic strain, and they do not show the host-specificity which is such a feature of the wilt-inducing fusaria (Pringle and Scheffer, 1964).

Various environmental factors influence the degree to which the fusaria and verticillia colonize their hosts and therefore influence symptom expression. The fusarial wilts are favoured by high soil temperatures; those induced by *Verticillium* are more severe at cooler temperatures. For tomatoes the optimum for *Fusarium* wilt is 28°; disease development is poor below 21° and above 33° (Clayton, 1923*a*). The corresponding figures for *Verticillium* wilt of this host are approximately 20°, 12° and 25° (Bewley, 1922; Ludbrook, 1933); these figures may be modified by the prevailing air temperatures and vary also with the *Verticillium* isolate (Edgington and Walker, 1957). The effects of soil moisture are less distinctive. With tomatoes soil moistures which favour vegetative growth also favour *Fusarium* wilt (Clayton, 1923*b*) but subjecting plants to low soil moisture before inoculation predisposes them to *Fusarium* wilt (Foster and Walker, 1947). The connexion between water content of the soil and the severity of *Verticillium* wilt is more confused (Isaac, 1956). Some workers report that high soil moistures increase the intensity of the disease on tomato, others that the severity is decreased under these conditions. The same confusion appears with species of *Verticillium* on other hosts. The mineral status and the pH of the soil also affect wilt severity (Sherwood, 1923; Roberts, 1943; Walker and others, 1954; Walker and Foster, 1946) but often in different directions depending on the host and pathogen concerned. *Fusarium* and *Verticillium* wilts tend to be more severe at high nitrogen levels but apart from this, few useful generalizations can be made.

Exclusion of planting material which might harbour the pathogen is of some value where the disease is of limited distribution like progressive wilt of hops (p. 64), and soil sterilization can effectively deal with soil-borne inocula in seedbeds and glasshouses (Chapter 19), but usually the only practical way of controlling these wilt diseases in the field is by planting resistant varieties. Indeed some of the early work on breeding for disease resistance was concerned with this group (Chapter 21). Over the past two decades there has been an increasing interest in the factors responsible for resistance to *Fusarium* and *Verticillium* wilt. These include the action of root exudates on the fungal spores, the presence of inhibitory substances, the reduction of toxin and/or enzyme production by the pathogen in resistant hosts and histological changes which limit its spread. These aspects are reviewed by Wood (1967).

References

Andrews, F. W. (1947). The parasitism of *Striga hermonthica* Benth. *Ann. appl. Biol.*, **34**, 267–75

Banfield, W. M. (1941). Distribution by the sap stream of spores of three fungi that induce vascular wilt diseases of elm. *J. agric. Res.*, **62**, 637–81

Beckman, C. H. (1964). Host responses to vascular infection. *A. Rev. Phytopathol.*, **2**, 231–52

Bewley, W. F. (1922). 'Sleepy disease' of the tomato. *Ann. appl. Biol.*, **9**, 116–34

Bolton, A. T., Nuttall, V. W. and Lyall, L. H. (1966). A new race of *Fusarium oxysporum* f. *pisi. Can. J. Pl. Sci.*, **46**, 343–7

Bradbury, J. F. (1967). *Erwinia stewartii. Descriptions of pathogenic fungi and bacteria* No. 123. Commonwealth Mycological Institute, Kew.

Bretz, T. W. (1952). The ascigerous stage of the oak wilt fungus. *Phytopathology*, **42**, 435–7

Buddenhagen, I. W. (1961). Bacterial wilt of bananas: history and known distribution. *Trop. Agric., Trin.*, **38**, 107–21

Buddenhagen, I. W. (1965). The relation of plant-pathogenic bacteria to the soil. In *Ecology of Soil-borne Plant Pathogens* (Ed. K. F. Baker and W. C. Snyder), pp. 269–82. John Murray, London.

Buddenhagen, I. W. and Kelman, A. (1964). Biological and physiological aspects of bacterial wilt caused by *Pseudomonas solanacearum. A. Rev. Phytopathol.*, **2**, 203–30

Buddenhagen, I. W. and Sequeira, L. (1958). Disinfectants and tool disinfection for prevention of spread of bacterial wilt of bananas. *Pl. Dis. Reptr.*, **42**, 1399–1404

Buxton, E. W. (1955). *Fusarium* disease of peas. *Trans. Br. mycol. Soc.*, **38**, 309–16

Carter, W. (1962). *Insects in relation to Plant Disease*, 705 pp. Interscience (John Wiley), New York.

Carter, W. (1963). Mealybug wilt of pineapple; a reappraisal. *Ann. N.Y. Acad. Sci.*, **105**, 741–64

Clayton, E. E. (1923*a*). The relation of temperature to the *Fusarium* wilt of tomato. *Am. J. Bot.*, **10**, 71–88

Clayton, E. E. (1923*b*). The relation of soil mosture to the *Fusarium* wilt of the tomato. *Am. J. Bot.*, **10**, 133–47

Clinton, G. P. and McCormick, F. A. (1936). Dutch elm disease. *Bull. Conn. agric. Exp. Stn.*, No. 389, 701–52

Edgington, L. V. and Walker, J. C. (1957). Influence of soil and air temperature on *Verticillium* wilt of tomato. *Phytopathology*, **47**, 594–8

Feldman, A. W., Caroselli, N. E. and Howard, F. L. (1950). Physiology of toxin production by *Ceratostomella ulmi*. *Phytopathology*, **40**, 341–54

Foster, R. E. (1946). The first symptom of tomato *Fusarium* wilt: clearing of the ultimate veinlets in the leaf. *Phytopathology*, **36**, 691–4

Foster, R. E. and Walker, J. C. (1947). Predisposition of tomato to *Fusarium* wilt. *J. agric. Res.*, **74**, 165–85

Greenleaf, W. H. (1953). Effects of tobacco-etch virus on peppers (*Capsicum* sp.) *Phytopathology*, **43**, 564–70

Hepting, G. H. (1955). The current status of oak wilt in the United States. *Forest Sci.*, **1**, 95–103

Hepting, G. H., Toole, E. R. and Boyce, J. S., Jr. (1952). Sexuality in the oak wilt fungus. *Phytopathology*, **42**, 438–42

Himelick, E. B. and Fox, H. W. (1961). Experimental studies on control of oak wilt disease. *Bull. Ill. agric. Exp. Stn.*, No. 680, 48 pp.

Holmes, F. W. (1961). Recorded Dutch elm disease distribution in North America as of 1959. *Pl. Dis. Reptr*, **45**, 74–5

Holmes, F. W. (1965). Virulence in *Ceratocystis ulmi*. *Neth. J. Plant Path.*, **71**, 97–112

Hughes, C. G. (1961). Gumming disease. In *Sugar-cane Diseases of the World* (Ed. J. P. Martin, E. V. Abbott and C. G. Hughes), **1**, 55–76. Elsevier Publishing Co., Amsterdam.

Isaac, I. (1949). A comparative study of pathogenic isolates of *Verticillium*. *Trans. Br. mycol. Soc.*, **32**, 137–57

Isaac, I. (1953). The spread of diseases caused by species of *Verticillium*. *Ann. appl. Biol.*, **40**, 630–8

Isaac, I. (1956). Some soil factors affecting *Verticillium* wilt of antirrhinum. *Ann. appl. Biol.*, **44**, 105–12

Isaac, I. (1967). Speciation in *Verticillium*. *A. Rev. Phytopathol.*, **5**, 201–22

Isaac, I. and Keyworth, W. G. (1948). *Verticillium* wilt of the hop (*Humulus lupulus*). III. A study of the pathogenicity of isolates from fluctuating and from progressive outbreaks. *Ann. appl. Biol.*, **35**, 243–9

Ivanoff, S. S. (1933). Stewart's wilt disease of corn, with emphasis on the life history of *Phytomonas stewarti* in relation to pathogenesis. *J. agric. Res.*, **47**, 749–70

Kelman, A. (1953). The bacterial wilt caused by *Pseudomonas solanacearum*. *Tech. Bull. N.C. agric. Exp. Stn.*, No. 99, 194 pp.

Keyworth, W. G. (1942). *Verticillium* wilt of the hop (*Humulus lupulus*). *Ann. appl. Biol.*, **29**, 346–57

Kumar, L. S. S. (1942). Flowering plants which attack economic crops. *Indian Fmg*, **3**, 638–40

Last, F. T. (1960). Effect of cultural treatments on the incidence of *Striga hermonthica* (Del.) Benth. and yields of sorghum in the Sudan: Field experiments 1957/8. *Ann. appl. Biol.*, **48**, 207–29

Last, F. T. (1961). Direct and residual effects of *Striga* control treatments on Sorghum yields. *Trop. Agric., Trin.*, **38**, 49–56

Leach, J. G., True, R. P. and Dorsey, C. K. (1952). A mechanism for liberation of spores from beneath the bark and for diploidization in *Chalara quercina*. *Phytopathology*, **42**, 537–9

Lucas, G. B. (1965). *Diseases of Tobacco*, pp. 687–92. Scarecrow Press, New York.

Ludbrook, W. V. (1933). Pathogenicity and environal studies on *Verticillium* hadromycosis. *Phytopathology*, **23**, 117–54

Marsden, D. H. (1953). Dutch elm disease: an evaluation of practical control efforts. *Pl. Dis. Reptr.*, **37**, 3–6

McClure, T. T. (1949). Mode of infection of the sweet-potato wilt *Fusarium*. *Phytopathology*, **39**, 876–86

Merek, E. L. and Fergus, C. L. (1954). Longevity of the oak wilt fungus in diseased trees. *Phytopathology*, **44**, 328

Morris, C. L., Thompson, H. E., Hadley, B. L. Jr. and Davis, J. M. (1955). Use of radioactive tracer for investigation of the activity pattern of suspected insect vectors of the oak wilt fungus. *Pl. Dis. Reptr*, **39**, 61–5

Parker, K. G., Collins, D. L., Tyler, L. J., Connola, D. P., Ozard, W. E. and Dietrich, H. (1947). The Dutch elm disease: association of *Ceratostomella ulmi* with *Scolytus multistriatus*, its advance into new areas, methods of determining its distribution and control of the disease. *Mem. Cornell agric. Exp. Stn.*, No. 275, 44 pp.

Pepper, E. H. (1967). Stewart's bacterial wilt of corn. *Monogr. Am. phytopath. Soc.*, No. 4, 36 pp.

Pomerleau, R. and Mehran, A. R. (1966). Distribution of spores of *Ceratocystis ulmi* labelled with phosphorus-32 in green shoots and leaves of *Ulmus americana*. *Naturaliste can.* **93**, 577–82

Poos, F. W. (1939). Host plants harboring *Aplanobacter stewarti* without showing external symptoms after inoculation by *Chaetocnema pulicaria*. *J. econ. Ent.*, **32**, 881–2

Poos, F. W. and Elliott, C. (1936). Certain insect vectors of *Aplanobacter stewarti*. *J. agric. Res.*, **52**, 585–608

Porter, D. M. and Powell, N. T. (1967). Influence of certain *Meloidogyne* species on *Fusarium* wilt development in flue-cured tobacco. *Phytopathology*, **57**, 282–5

Pringle, R. B. and Scheffer, R. P. (1964). Host specific plant toxins. *A. Rev. Phytopathol.*, **2**, 133–56

Robert, A. L. (1955). Bacterial wilt and Stewart's leaf blight of corn. *Fmrs' Bull. U.S. Dep. Agric.*, No. 2092, 13 pp.

Roberts, F. M. (1943). Factors influencing infection of tomato by *Verticillium alboatrum*. *Ann. appl. Biol.*, **30**, 327–31

Rudolph, B. A. (1931). *Verticillium* hadromycosis. *Hilgardia*, **5**, 201–353

Scheffer, R. P. and Walker, J. C. (1953). The physiology of *Fusarium* wilt of tomato. *Phytopathology*, **43**, 116–25

Sequeira, L. (1962). Control of bacterial wilt of bananas by crop rotation and fallowing. *Trop. Agric.*, *Trin.*, **39**, 211–7

Sequeira, L. (1963). Growth regulators in plant disease. *A. Rev. Phytopathol.*, **1**, 5–30

Sherwood, E. C. (1923). Hydrogen-ion concentration as related to the *Fusarium* wilt of tomato seedlings. *Am. J. Bot.*, **10**, 537–53

Stambaugh, W. J. and Fergus, C. L. (1956). Longevity of spores of the oak wilt fungus on overwintered nitulid beetles. *Pl. Dis. Reptr.*, **40**, 919–22

True, R. P., Barnett, H. L., Dorsey, C. K. and Leach, J. G. (1960). Oak wilt in West Virginia. *Bull. W. Va Univ. agric. Exp. Stn*, No. 448T, 119 pp.

Walker, J. C. and Foster, R. E. (1946). Plant nutrition in relation to disease development. III. *Fusarium* wilt of tomato. *Am. J. Bot.*, **33**, 259–64

Walker, J. C., Gallegly, M. E. Jr., Broom, J. R. and Scheffer, R. P. (1954). Relation of plant nutrition to disease development. VIII. *Verticillium* wilt of tomato. *Am. J. Bot.*, **41**, 760–2

Wellman, F. L. (1941). Epinasty of tomato, one of the earliest symptoms of *Fusarium* wilt. *Phytopathology*, **31**, 281–3

Went, J. C. (1938). Compilation of the investigations on the susceptibility of different elms to *Ceratostomella ulmi* Buisman in the Netherlands. *Phytopath. Z.*, **11**, 181–201

Went, J. C. (1954). The Dutch elm disease—summary of fifteen years hybridization and selection work (1937–1952). *Tijdschr. PfZiekt.*, **60**, 109–27

Wheeler, B. E. J. (1958). *A Plant Disease Survey of Malta*. 30 pp. Department of Information, Malta.

Wilhelm, S., Storkan, R. C., Sagen, J. E. and Carpenter, T. (1959). Large-scale fumigation against broomrape. *Phytopathology*, **49**, 530

Williams, C. N. (1959). Resistance of sorghum to witchweed. *Nature, Lond.*, **184**, 1511–2

Wilson-Jones, K. (1953). The witchweeds of Africa. *Wld Crops*, **5**, 263–6

Wood, R. K. S. (1967). *Physiological Plant Pathology*, 570 pp. Blackwell Scientific Publications, Oxford.

Zentmyer, G. A., Horsfall, J. G. and Wallace, P. P. (1946). Dutch elm disease and its chemotherapy. *Bull. Conn. agric. Exp. Stn.*, No. 498, 70 pp.

CHAPTER 5

Downy mildews

One of the characteristic features of downy mildews is the development under humid conditions of a white or grey 'bloom' on the leaf and stem lesions owing to the production of sporangiophores by the causal fungi (Figure 5.1). Because it is a fungal structure which draws attention to these diseases rather than symptoms, it is convenient to start with the fungi concerned. Their relationships with other fungi are best considered first.

Within the Phycomycetes, the Peronosporales are differentiated largely on characters of zoospore formation and behaviour, the details of which need not concern us here. Suffice it to say that they comprise those fungi with biflagellate zoospores, and with reproductive structures that are specialized parts of the mycelium and which do not involve the entire somatic structure at any one time. Differentiation within the Peronosporales is primarily on sporangiophore structure. In the Pythiaceae the sporangiophores are either not very different from the somatic hyphae or are of indeterminate growth; in the Albuginaceae and Peronosporaceae the sporangiophores are markedly distinct structures, limited in their growth.

The Pythiaceae comprise the genera *Pythium* and *Phytophthora* which were briefly described in Chapter 2. The Albuginaceae cause diseases often called 'white blisters', because of the white, blister-like pustules produced on the host (Figure 5.2), or 'white rusts' because spores are formed in chains within the pustules and these are thus superficially similar to the aecia of some rusts (see Chapter 6). Generally they are comparatively unimportant as plant pathogens but in Illinois *Albugo candida* causes serious damage on

71

FIGURE 5.1   Downy mildew of vine. Groups of sporangiophores on the lower leaf surface. Photograph by A. Ironside.

horseradish (Endo and Linn, 1960) and similarly *Albugo occidentalis*
on spinach in Texas (Raabe and Pound, 1952). *A. candida* is otherwise common on brassicas and cruciferous weeds such as Shepherd's
Purse (*Capsella bursa-pastoris*).

The term downy mildews is normally restricted to diseases caused
by the Peronosporaceae and this family contains many important
plant pathogens.

Downy mildew fungi

These are all obligate parasites which typically invade the tissues
of their hosts intercellularly with only limited intrusions into the
host cells by specialized portions of the hyphae called haustoria
(Figure 5.3). In their simplest form haustoria are sac-like structures,

occasionally forked, but in some species they are much branched and it is often difficult to distinguish haustoria from host cytoplasm (Fraymouth, 1956). It is possible that the parasite obtains certain food materials from the plant cells via haustoria but there is as yet no experimental evidence for this either in the downy mildews or, for that matter, in any other group of fungi.

FIGURE 5.2 White rust of horseradish, showing the blister-like pustules of *Albugo candida*. From Endo and Linn, 1960, *Bull. Ill. agric. Exp. Stn*, no. 655.

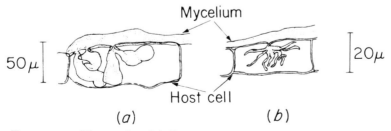

FIGURE 5.3 Haustoria. (*a*) *Peronospora parasitica* in wallflower leaf (*b*) *Peronospora grisea* in stem of *Veronica persica*. Redrawn from Fraymouth, 1956, *Trans. Br. mycol. Soc.*, **39**, 79–107.

Within the Peronosporaceae, genera are further delimited on sporangiophore morphology (Figure 5.4). In *Plasmopara* the branches and subdivisions are typically at right angles, irregularly spaced, and with blunt tips on which the sporangia are borne. In *Peronospora*, branching is dichotomous and at an acute angle; the sporangia are borne at the tips of finely tapered subbranches. *Pseudoperonospora* is similar in most respects to *Plasmopara* but the sporangiophores are dichotomously branched. In *Bremia* branching is similar to that in *Peronospora* but the ends are flattened into plate-like disks and the sporangia are borne on pointed extensions of these. In *Sclerospora* the sporangiophore consists of a long, stout hypha with many upright branches at its end, on which the sporangia are borne.

While it is generally true that symptoms in the downy mildews are less conspicuous than the sporangiophores *en masse*, there are exceptions. One is the downy mildew of millet caused by *Sclerospora graminicola*, which occurs widely in India. The fungus on this host (*Pennisetum typhoides*) causes the glumes and stamens of the flower head to develop into leaf-like structures, so that instead of a typical close spike with developing grains a loose, green structure results giving the name 'green-ear' disease (Butler, 1918; Tarr, 1962). On the leaves also, the fungus causes long, chlorotic streaks and the leaves tend to split. In downy mildew of hops, caused by *Pseudoperonospora humuli*, infected rootstocks give rise to swollen basal shoots, and these also are characteristic of the disease (Figure 5.5).

Downy mildew of the vine

One of the most important downy mildews, and certainly one of the most famous, is that caused by *Plasmopara viticola* on the vine. This disease devastated the French vineyards in the 1870's. The trouble started when, to control the root aphid *Phylloxera*, resistant rootstocks were imported from North America. It appears that *P. viticola* was introduced on these, and although in North America this fungus did not appear to be particularly destructive, it was on the varieties grown in the French vineyards. The occurrence of the disease was not, however, without some compensation for it led to the development of Bordeaux mixture by Millardet. The story of his discovery is a remarkable combination of luck and perspicacity and a translation of Millardet's papers on the subject are to be found in Volume 3 of the *Phytopathological Classics*.

The life-cycle of *P. viticola* illustrates the basic pattern in this group. There are two distinct phases. From spring to summer the young leaves and developing inflorescences become infected.

(a)

FIGURE 5.4 Sporangiophores of some downy mildew fungi. From drawings by E. Punithalingam, Commonwealth Mycological Institute. (a) *Peronospora destructor* × 480.

(*b*)

FIGURE 5.4 (*b*) Sporangiophore of *Bremia lactuae* × 400.

(c) (d)

FIGURE 5.4 Sporangiophores of (c) *Plasmopara viticola* and (d) *Sclerospora graminicola*. Both × 600.

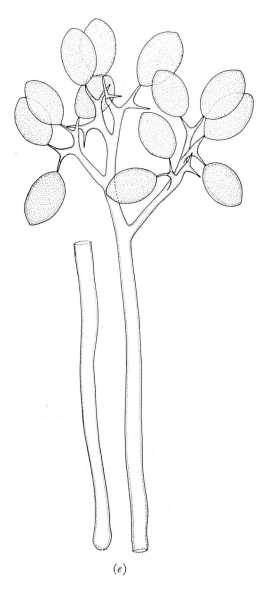

(e)

FIGURE 5.4 (e) Sporangiophore of
Pseudoperonospora humuli × 600.

Pale-green spots appear on the upper surfaces of the leaves and, under humid conditions, the typical downy mass of sporangiophores develops on the undersurface, beneath these chlorotic areas. Build-up of the disease to epiphytotic proportions is effected by the distribution of sporangia under wet conditions. Moisture is essential because the sporangia produce motile zoospores on germination.

The behaviour of these zoospores was first described by Arens (1929). They are actively motile for only a short period. At first their movement is erratic but when they approach a stoma they appear to be attracted to it in some way and eventually come to

FIGURE 5.5 Downy mildew of hop. A single, primary basal spike of the variety Northern Brewer showing typical shortened internodes and distorted, yellowish leaves. Photograph courtesy D. J. Royle.

rest over the stomatial opening. From this now non-motile spore a germ-tube emerges, penetrates the leaf via the stoma, and initiates hyphal growth in the substomal cavity. Stomatal penetration is fairly common in the downy mildews and the greater development of sporangiophores on the lower surfaces of leaves may be related to the greater number of stomata there in many host species. The fact that stomata provide a stimulus for penetration has been demonstrated only in two other downy mildews, *Pseudoperonospora cubensis* on cucumber and *P. humuli* on hops (Hickman and Ho, 1966), but zoospores of *Phytophthora syringae* on leaves of Fennel (*Foeniculum vulgare*) also congregate round stomata like those of *P. viticola* on vine (Noviello and Snyder, 1962).

The second phase in the life cycle starts towards the end of the growing season when oospores are formed in the senescent leaves which subsequently fall to the ground. In spring the oospores germinate to give a single, terminal sporangium (Gregory, 1912) from which zoospores are produced and these then infect the young vine leaves, thus completing the cycle:

Spring and summer / Autumn and winter — mycelium — sporangia / oospores — germination (zoospores)

Overwintering of other species

Within the Peronosporaceae there are two general changes from the pattern of behaviour outlined above for *P. viticola*:

1. The sporangia of some species germinate directly by producing a germ tube and thus function as conidia,
2. Oospore production is variable or may even be rare in some species.

The first is unlikely to be of great significance in relation to the behaviour of these fungi as pathogens. Although a water film on the leaf surface may no longer be essential for species in which sporangia germinate directly, high humidities at least appear necessary for germination and infection by all downy mildew fungi.

Variability in oospore production is much more important. For example, oospores of *Peronospora farinosa* have not been observed in all localities where beet downy mildew occurs; similarly in California the oospores of *Peronospora destructor*, which causes onion downy mildew, appear to be of minor importance in maintaining the disease cycle (Yarwood, 1943). How these and other similar species overwinter is of obvious interest since this influences the measures for controlling them.

There are several alternatives to oospores in plant debris and soil. The most common is perennation on the host itself. It has been suggested that *P. viticola* sometimes overwinters in this way on the shoots of the vine, but there is no convincing evidence that primary infections in the spring arise from such inoculum. With hops, however, there is now substantial evidence that *Pseudoperonospora humuli* overwinters in infected root-stocks and that primary infected shoots (the basal spikes) develop from dormant buds infected by this mycelium (Coley-Smith, 1962). Sporangia produced on these basal spikes then give rise to secondary infections. It has also been shown that *P. farinosa* can hibernate in the crowns of beet (Leach, 1931) and *P. destructor* in onion bulbs (Murphy and McKay, 1926). In some areas the planting of infected onion bulbs is one of the chief ways in which *P. destructor* is introduced into a new crop.

With both beet and onion infected 'ground-keepers', that is plants which for some reason have escaped harvesting, are also a potential danger to new crops.

The very nature of beet and onion production often results in a continuous supply of plants which the respective downy mildew fungi can parasitize. This is so where root crops of beet are grown close to the 'steckling beds' in which beet plants are raised for seed production, and where onions are sown in the autumn near diseased summer crops.

Another possible way of overwintering is on or in the seed of the host but this has been demonstrated for relatively few downy mildews Leach (1931) found mycelium and oospores of *P. farinosa* in the integuments of ovules, and also mycelium with haustoria inside the testa of viable seed taken from diseased beet plants. The number of infected seedlings obtained by planting seed from infected plants was small, no more than 0·25% in any one test of a series involving 34,000 seedlings. Nevertheless this might well be sufficient to initiate the disease in a crop. Oospores of *P. farinosa* (*P. effusa*) have also been found in commercial samples of spinach seed (Cook, 1935), but there is only circumstantial evidence that these initiate infections when the seed is sown.

A third method of overwintering is on an alternative host. Wild *Beta* species can be infected by inoculating them with conidia of *P. farinosa* from cultivated beet (Leach, 1931) and there is some evidence that in England *Beta maritima* is an inoculum source for this fungus. In a survey of beet crops in Suffolk, Blencowe (1956) found that all fields with more than 1% downy mildew were within 914 m of the foreshore where infected plants of *B. maritima* were common.

The indications are, however, that many of the downy mildew pathogens of economic crops are strictly limited in their host range and while fungi of similar morphology occur on a number of common weeds these are unable to infect the particular crop in question. Thus fungi morphologically similar to *Bremia lactucae* occur on wild *Lactuca* spp. and a range of Compositae (e.g. *Senecio* spp.) but only those from certain *Lactuca* spp. appear capable of infecting lettuce (Melhus, 1921; Wild, 1947). Similarly, fungi on some members of the Chenopodiaceae like *P. farinosa* are unable to infect spinach (Richards, 1939). Because of this specialization some care must be taken in assessing the importance of what appears to be an alternative host. Barrett (1939), for example, reported that *P. viticola* could apparently overwinter in the cortical tissue and buds of the wild grape (*Vitis californica*) and give rise to sporulating lesions on the new growth, but infection of cultivated grape even in close proximity to severely infected wild grapes was not observed. Barrett suggests that climatic conditions may have been unfavorable for the infection of the cultivated grape but a difference in races on the two hosts seems a more plausible explanation.

Factors influencing infection

Humidity and temperature are the two most important factors influencing infection by downy mildew fungi. Most require high humidities for sporulation and spore germination, and some require free water on the shoot surface for germination and hence infection, e.g. *P. farinosa* on spinach (Richards, 1939). The minimum temperatures for sporulation, germination of sporangia and infection are generally low within the group (Table 5.1); some species like *P. farinosa* can infect at temperatures near freezing-point.

The conditions necessary for infection of tobacco by *Peronospora tabacina* have been much studied particularly since the widespread outbreaks of this disease ('blue mould') in Europe during 1960 and 1961 (Peyrot, 1962). Sporulation occurs mainly at night and is influenced by the humidity during this period and the temperature during the previous day. A relative humidity over 95% for a minimum of 3 hours between midnight and dawn normally induces intense sporulation but if temperatures on the previous day remain at 30° or over for longer than 6 hours sporulation is significantly inhibited in spite of the favourable night humidities (Rider and

TABLE 5.1 Minimum temperature requirements (°C) of some downy mildew fungi.

Fungus	Host	Sporulation	Germination	Infection
Plasmopara viticola	vine	8–10	8	8–9
Peronospora farinosa	beet	6	<0·5	0·5
Peronospora destructor	onion	6	3	—
Peronospora tabacina	tobacco	1–2[1]	2[2]	c·5[3]
Pseudoperonospora humuli	hops	<5	c·4	4
Bremia lactucae	lettuce	1–2	1[4]	1–2[4]
Sclerospora graminicola	maize and millet	5–8	5–8	—

[1]Cruickshank (1961*b*), [2]Cruickshank (1961*a*), [3]Shepherd and Mandryk (1963), [4]Schultz (1937); remainder of data from Togashi (1949).

others, 1961). Spore dissemination shows a diurnal cycle with a peak release between 10.00 and 11.00 hours on the day of sporulation (Hill, 1961). As the conidiophore stalk dries out it twists violently and the conidia are flung into the air (Pinckard, 1942). The conidia require free moisture on tobacco leaves for germination, and temperatures between 15° and 25° are most favourable (Shepherd and Mandryk, 1963). Similar temperatures during both day and night also favour the development of symptoms, and under optimum conditions these appear some 4–5 days after inoculation. When temperatures drop below 16° either during the night or during both day and night the appearance of symptoms is correspondingly delayed (Hill and Green, 1965).

Losses and control

Damage caused by downy mildews is usually associated with the sporulation of the fungus. Quantitative studies by Yarwood (1941) indicated that the sporulation of *Peronospora destructor* caused a 55% reduction in the dry weight of onion leaves. The corresponding figures for *Pseudoperonospora humuli* on hops and *Peronospora farinosa* on spinach were 17% and 48% respectively. In one assessment on onions, the dry matter content of sporangiophores and sporangia produced during one night were found to correspond to 5% dry weight of infected leaves. Reduction in crop yield results from this massive transfer of nutrients from host to parasite and is accentuated by the host necrosis which often follows sporulation of the fungus.

Losses from downy mildews can be considerable. It is estimated that in 1962 downy mildew of tobacco reduced yields in Europe by at least 100,000 metric tons (Peyrot, 1962). This is one of the more spectacular examples. Where onions are grown for seed production heavy losses may result from infection by *P. destructor*. The fungus invades the flower stalks (Figure 5.6) and weakens these either directly, or indirectly by allowing the entry of other fungi: they keel over and no seed is set. Field trials with sugar beet in England indicated that downy mildew reduced root yields by as much as 25% and the sugar content was also reduced specially in plants which were infected early (Cornford, 1954).

Downy mildews are controlled chiefly by cultural methods, by spraying and by planting resistant varieties.

Where the fungus perennates chiefly as oospores, destruction of these is a possible method of control. In these instances, destruction

FIGURE 5.6 Downy mildew of onion. The light patches on the flower stalks are those invaded by *Peronospora destructor*.

of oospore-containing debris reduces the level of inoculum but some oospores get washed into the soil and except in seed bed sites it is not economically practical to do anything about them. How long these oospores remain effective as inoculum is of considerable interest, yet only for *P. destructor* is there substantial information on oospore longevity. Observations by McKay (1957) indicate that after separation from the host tissues an after-ripening or maturation period of some 2–3 years is necessary before the oospores of this fungus can germinate, and then they remain viable for at least 25 years. All attempts, however, to infect onions with oospores failed so even here there is no clear indication of longevity of effective inoculum.

Another possible cultural method of control is the regulation of temperature and humidity so that conditions are unfavourable for infection. This is of some value in the cultivation of lettuce under glass. Avoiding excessive moisture during the early stages of growth when there are low temperatures helps to reduce attack by *Bremia lactucae*.

It is, however, by the application of fungicides that most practical control of these diseases is achieved. Copper compounds are still widely used, especially Bordeaux mixture which was, of course, developed to control a downy mildew. With lettuce, spraying with thiram and zineb formulations has given very good control when applied to seedlings just after emergence and once, or more, after planting out (Powlesland and Brown, 1954). Zineb is also recommended for the control of tobacco downy mildew. In the seedbeds either dusts containing 6·5–7% or sprays with 0·25%–0·3% active ingredient are applied at 3-day intervals and after each rainfall. Treatments for field crops are similar although 0·10%–0·15% maneb is sometimes used in preference to zineb. This is applied at 5-day intervals during rapid growth and later at 7-day intervals (Peyrot, 1962). In Australia, benzol is frequently used in the seedbeds. This is spread in shallow pans above the plants at dusk and the seedbeds are covered with muslin or other material. The vapour produced kills the fungus spores and also eradicates incipient fungal infections in the leaves. Other volatile chemicals like paradichlorobenzene have also been used in the U.S.A. but have not been widely popular (Clayton and others, 1942); Lucas, 1965).

The timing of spray applications is all important in controlling these diseases. Attempts have been made to forecast the occurrence of mildew outbreaks based on the meterological conditions necessary for spore formation, germination and infection. In France, the use of a warning service for vine downy mildew has reduced the number of sprays necessary for control, thus substantially decreasing costs. Similar methods are used to predict outbreaks of tobacco downy mildew in the U.S.A., Europe and Australia (Waggoner, 1960; Rider and others, 1961; Peyrot, 1962).

With some downy mildews, spraying often fails to give satisfactory control. Onion downy mildew is an example; here the difficulty of obtaining a good coverage of fungicide on the host surface is one of the main problems. Similarly, fungicides give no more than partial control of beet downy mildew. Rapidly growing beet is very difficult to protect adequately, particularly if crops are near a large source of inoculum. Spraying of young plants (stecklings) in the seedbeds is practicable in areas where mildew occurs, because the fungicides can be applied with the routine insecticidal sprays (Byford and Hull, 1963).

So far there has been limited success in breeding varieties resistant to particular downy mildews. Onion varieties resistant to *P. destructor* are now available and there has been an intensification of breeding work with tobacco following the widespread outbreaks of downy mildew in Europe.

REFERENCES

Arens, K. (1929). Physiologische untersuchungen au *Plasmopara viticola*, unter besonderer berucksichtigung der Infectionsbegingungen. *Jb. wiss. Bot.*, **70**, 93–157

Barrett, J. T. (1939). Overwintering mycelium of *Plasmopara viticola* (B. and C.) Berl. and de T. in the Californian Wild Grape, *Vitis californica* Benth. *Phytopathology*, **29**, 822

Blencowe, J. W. (1956). Sugar-beet virus diseases. *Rep. Rothamsted exp. Stn.*, 1956, 110

Butler, E. J. (1918). *Fungi and Disease in Plants.* pp. 218–23. Thacker, Spink and Co., Calcutta.

Byford, W. J. and Hull, R. (1963). Control of sugar-beet downy mildew (*Peronospora farinosa*) by sprays. *Ann. appl. Biol.*, **52**, 415–22

Clayton, E. E., Gaines, J. G., Shaw, K. J., Smith, T. E., Foster, H. H., Lunn, W. M. and Graham, T. W. (1942). Gas treatment for the control of blue mold disease of tobacco. *Tech. Bull. U.S. Dep. Agric.*, No. 799, 38 pp.

Coley-Smith, J. R. (1962). Overwintering of hop downy mildew *Psuedoperonospora humuli* (Miy. and Tak.) Litson. *Ann. appl. Biol.*, **50**, 235–43

Cook, H. T. (1935). Occurrence of oospores of *Peronospora effusa* with commercial spinach seed. *Phytopathology*, **25**, 11

Cornford, C. E. (1954). Effect of downy mildew on yield of sugar beet. *Pl. Path.*, **3**, 82–3

Cruickshank, I. A. M. (1961*a*). Germination of *Peronospora tabacina*: effect of temperature. *Aust. J. biol. Sci.*, **14**, 58–65

Cruickshank, I. A. M. (1961*b*). Environment and sporulation in phyto-pathogenic fungi. II. Conidia formation in *Peronospora tabacina* Adam as a function of temperature. *Aust. J. biol. Sci.*, **14**, 198–207

Endo, R. M. and Linn, M. B. (1960). The white rust disease of horse-radish. *Bull. Ill. agric. Exp. Stn.*, No. 655, 56 pp.

Fraymouth, J. (1956). Haustoria of the Peronosporales. *Trans. Br. mycol. Soc.*, **39**, 79–107

Gregory, C. T. (1912). Spore germination and infection with *Plasmopara viticola*. *Phytopathology*, **2**, 235–49

Hickman, C. J. and Ho, H. H. (1966). Behaviour of zoospores in plant pathogenic Phycomycetes. *A. Rev. Phytopathol.*, **4**, 195–220

Hill, A. V. (1961). Dissemination of conidia of *Peronospora tabacina* Adam. *Aust. J. biol. Sci.*, **14**, 208–22

Hill, A. V. and Green, S. (1965). The role of temperature in the develop-ment of blue mold (*Peronospora tabacina* Adam.) disease in tobacco seedlings. *Aust. J. Agric. Res.*, **16**, 597–607

Leach, L. D. (1931). Downy mildew of the Beet, caused by *Peronospora schactii* Fuckel. *Hilgardia*, **6**, 203–51

Lucas, G. B. (1965). *Diseases of Tobacco*, pp. 308–58, Scarecrow Press, New York.

McKay, R. (1957). The longevity of the oospores of the onion downy mildew, *Peronospora destructor* (Berk.) Casp. *Scient. Proc. R. Dubl. Soc.*, **27**, 295–307

Melhus, I. E. (1921). *Bremia* on hothouse lettuce. *Phytopathology*, **11**, 54

Murphy, P. A. and McKay, R. (1926). The downy mildew of onions (*Peronospora schleideni*) with particular reference to the hibernation of the parasite. *Scient. Proc. R. Dubl. Soc.*, **18**, 237–61

Noviello, C. and Snyder, W. C. (1962). A *Phytophthora* disease of Fennel. *Phytopath. Z.*, **46**, 139–63

Peyrot, J. (1962). Tobacco blue mold in Europe. *FAO Plant Prot. Bull.*, **10**, 73–80

Phytopathological Classics No. 3. *The Discovery of Bordeaux Mixture.* A translation by F. J. Schneiderhan of three papers by Pierre Marie Alexis Millardet 1885. Published by the American Phytopathological Soc. 1933. Cayuga Press, Ithaca, N.Y.

Pinckard, J. A. (1942). The mechanism of spore dispersal in *Peronospora tabacina* and certain other downy mildew fungi. *Phytopathology*, **32**, 505–11

Powesland, R. and Brown, W. (1954). The fungicidal control of lettuce downy mildew, caused by *Bremia lactucae*. *Ann. appl. Biol.*, **41**, 461–9

D

Raabe, R. D. and Pound, G. S. (1952). Relation of certain environal factors to initiation and development of the White Rust disease of spinach. *Phytopathology*, **42**, 448–52

Richards, M. C. (1939). Downy mildew of spinach and its control. *Bull. Cornell agric. Exp. Stn.*, No. 718, 29 pp.

Rider, N. E., Cruickshank, I. A. M. and Bradley, E. F. (1961). Environment and sporulation in phytopathogenic fungi. III. *Peronospora tabacina* Adam: field environment, sporulation, and forecasting. *Aust. J. agric. Res.*, **12**, 1119–25

Schultz, H. (1937). Zur Biologie der *Bremia lactucae* Regel, des Erregers des Falschen Mehltaus des Salats. *Phytopath. Z.*, **10**, 490–503

Shepherd, C. J. and Mandryk, M. (1963). Germination of conidia of *Peronospora tabacina* Adam. II. Germination in vivo. *Aust. J. biol. Sci.*, **16**, 77–87

Tarr, S. A. J. (1962). *Diseases of Sorghum, Sudan Grass and Broom Corn*, pp. 180–2. Commonwealth Mycological Institute, Kew.

Togashi, K. (1949). *Biological Characters of Plant Pathogens. Temperature Relations.* 478 pp. Meibundo, Tokyo.

Waggoner, P. E. (1960). Forecasting epidemics. In *Plant Pathology: an advanced treatise* (Ed. J. G. Horsfall and A. E. Dimond), **3**, 291–312. Academic Press, New York.

Wild, H. (1947). Downy mildew disease of the cultivated lettuce. *Trans. Br. mycol. Soc.*, **31**, 112–25

Yarwood, C. E. (1941). Sporulation injury associated with downy mildew infections. *Phytopathology*, **31**, 741–8

Yarwood, C. E. (1943). Onion downy mildew. *Hilgardia*, **14**, 595–691

CHAPTER 6

Powdery mildews

Powdery mildews are also diseases that are recognized by the presence of fungal mycelium and conidiophores on the host (Figure 6.1). Like downy mildews the term powdery mildews is limited to diseases caused by fungi of one family, in this instance the Erysiphaceae. There have been several monographs and reviews of this group (Salmon, 1900; Blumer, 1933, 1967) and this chapter owes much to that of Yarwood (1957).

Powdery mildew fungi
In the Peronosporaceae genera are based on conidiophore morphology but in the Erysiphaceae the conidiophores are relatively simple and they also vary in size between collections of the same species on different hosts (Peries, 1966) and between collections on the same host in different environments. They are thus generally unsuitable for diagnostic purposes although this has been attempted (e.g. by Sawada, 1914).

Within the family Erysiphaceae three types of conidiophore can be recognized (Figure 6.2):

1. The *Oidium* type, which consists of a short stipe of one or more cells, a cell which gives rise to the conidia, i.e. a germinative or spore mother cell, and a chain of maturing conidia. This is most common, particularly in species of *Erysiphe*.

2. The *Ovulariopsis* type with clavate conidia which is formed by certain species of *Phyllactinia*.

3. The *Oidiopsis* type in which the conidiophores are branched and typically arise from a stoma as in *Leveillula*.

89

FIGURE 6.1 Powdery mildew of cucumber. The leaves on the left are completely covered with mycelium and conidiophores; those on the right have been sprayed and remain free of the fungus. Photograph courtesy Plant Protection Ltd., ICI copyright.

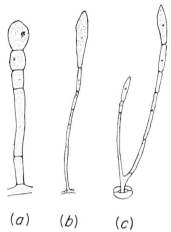

(*a*)   (*b*)   (*c*)

FIGURE 6.2 Types of conidiophore in the powdery mildews.
(*a*) *Oidium* (*b*) *Ovulariopsis* (*c*)
Oidiopsis. (*a*) based on Cook
and Wheeler, 1967, *Trans. Br.
mycol. Soc.*, **50**, 625–30; (*b*)
and (*c*) on Foex, 1912, *Miscel-
lanees, Montpellier.*

Where the ascospore stage is unknown, species are placed in
form-genera related to their conidiophore morphology, e.g. *Oidium
heveae.*

Since conidiophore structure is unsuitable as a basis for delimiting
genera three other features are generally used: the location of the
mycelium, the number of asci in the enclosed fruiting bodies
containing them, i.e. the cleistocarps, and the type of appendage on
the cleistocarps. The first is of limited value because with most
powdery mildews the mycelium remains as a superficial layer on
the host. In some, however, the hyphae also enter the stomata and
develop in the substomatal cavities, and there may be some penetration into the tissues surrounding these. It is mainly on the other two
features that genera are distinguished. There are two genera in
which the mycelium is superficial and the cleistocarp contains a
solitary ascus, but one, *Sphaerotheca*, has mycelium-like appendages
and the other, *Podosphaera*, has dichotomously branched appendages,
though the branching is often poorly developed or absent in *P.
leucotricha* which is one of the most important species. Of those genera
with several asci in the cleistocarp, two have simple appendages,

Erysiphe and *Leveillula*. In the former the mycelium is entirely superficial; in the latter it is partly intercellular, the hyphae enter the
stomata, and the branched conidiophores also emerge through the
stomata. The remaining three genera have distinct appendages:
these are dichotomously branched in *Microsphaera*, have coiled tips
in *Uncinula*, and arise from a bulbous base and taper to a fine point
in *Phyllactinia* (Figure 6.3). The mycelium is superficial in *Microsphaera* and *Uncinula* and partly intercellular in *Phyllactinia*.

Species differentiation is based largely on the sizes of the various
structures described.

Host range

These fungi attack most cultivated plants within the angiosperms
but there are some notable exceptions, e.g. maize, celery and
carrots. Some, like *Erysiphe polygoni*, apparently infect many plant
species but within the powdery mildew fungi there is considerable
evidence of the phenomenon known as physiologic specialization,
that is of morphologically similar isolates differing in their host
range. One of the earliest demonstrations of this was by Marchal
(1902). He showed that conidia of *Erysiphe graminis* from wheat
would infect certain other *Triticum* spp. but not barley, and similarly
that conidia of *E. graminis* from barley would infect other *Hordeum*
spp. but not wheat. He distinguished each as a *forma specialis*. It
soon became clear that further subdivisions could be made by
testing collections of conidia of these two forms on different cultivars
of wheat and barley. In 1930, Waterhouse distinguished two races
of *E. graminis* f.sp. *tritici* on wheat in Australia, and in the same year
Mains and Dietz reported five races of *E. graminis* f. sp. *hordei* on
barley in North America. There have been many investigations
since then in various countries and more races have been characterized. By 1966 thirty-eight races of *E. graminis* were identified on
wheat in Northwest Europe and twenty-two races on barley in
North America (Moseman, 1966).

Life history

In describing the life cycle of a typical powdery mildew it is
convenient to start with the arrival on the leaf of a conidium. With
suitable conditions germination starts in about two hours. A thick,
short germ-tube grows from the spore and terminates in a lobed or
wrinkled structure, the appressorium, in close contact with the host
surface. From this appressorium a thin hypha, the penetration tube,
grows through the cuticle and cell wall and then swells out in the

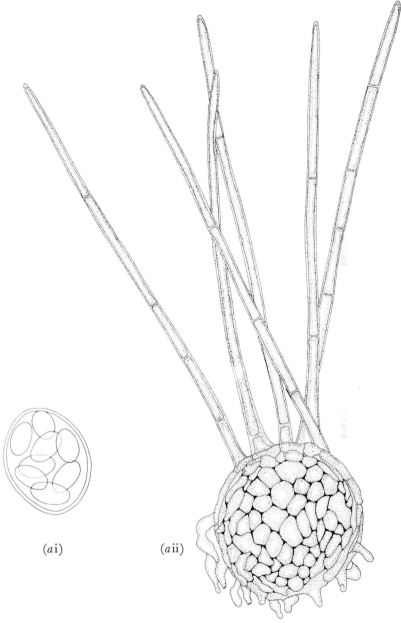

(ai)   (aii)

FIGURE 6.3 Cleistocarps and asci of some powdery mildews. From drawings by E. Punithalingam, Commonwealth Mycological Institute. (*a*) *Podosphaera leucotricha* ×460.

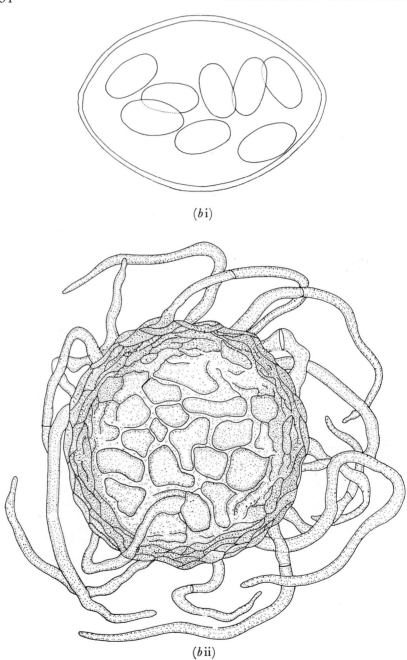

(*b*i)

(*b*ii)

FIGURE 6.3   (*b*) *Sphaerotheca mors-uvae* ×680.

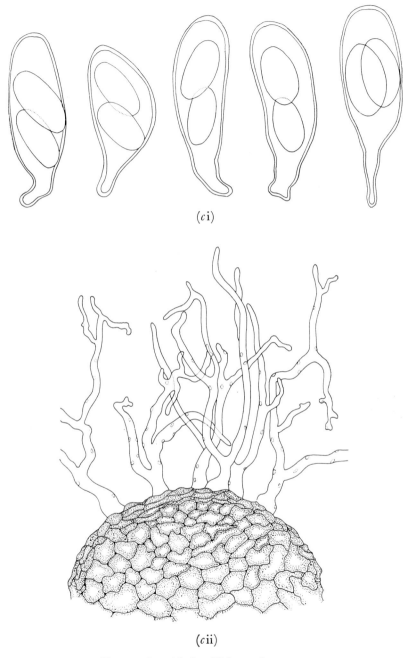

(*c*i)

(*c*ii)

FIGURE 6.3 (*c*) *Leveillula taurica* ×540.

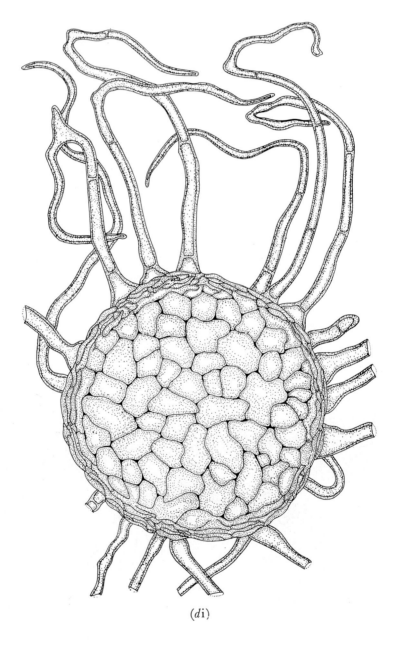

(*d*i)

FIGURE 6.3   (*d*i) *Erysiphe polygoni* ×545.

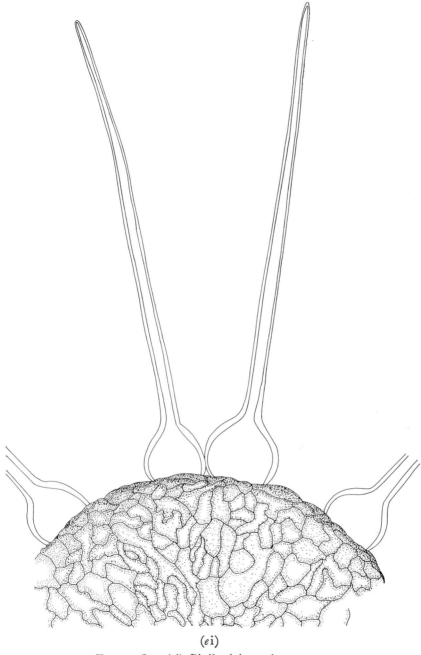

(*e*i)

FIGURE 6.3   (*ei*) *Phyllactinia corylea* ×540.

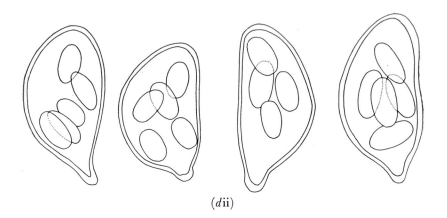

(*d*ii)

FIGURE 6.3   (*d*ii) *Erysiphe polygoni* ×545.

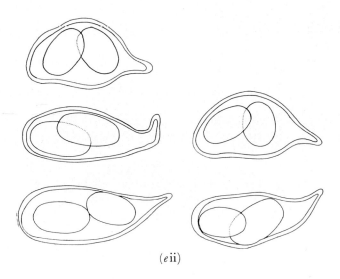

(*e*ii)

FIGURE 6.3   (*e*ii) *Phyllactinia corylea* ×540.

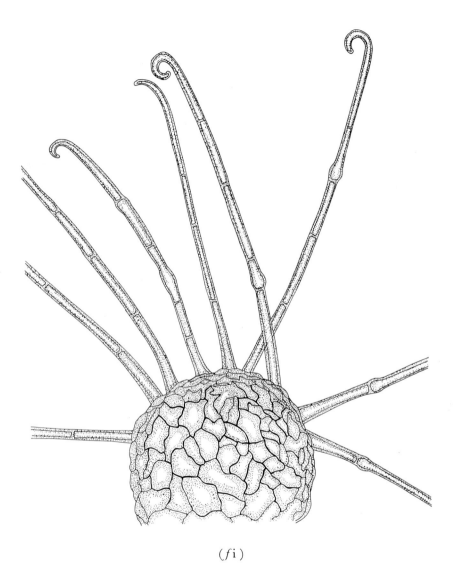

(*f* i)

FIGURE 6.3 (*f* i) *Uncinula necator* × 530.

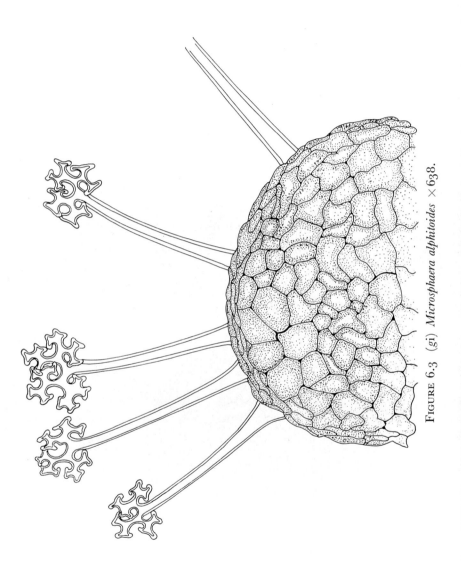

FIGURE 6.3 (gi) *Microsphaera alphitoides* ×638.

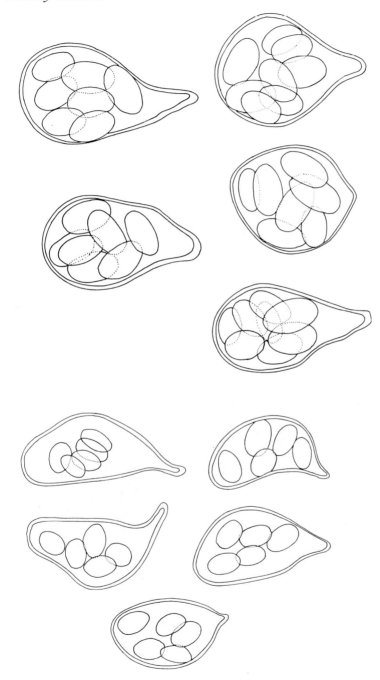

(gii) *Microsphaera alphitoides* ×638.

FIGURE 6.3 (ƒii) *Uncinula necator* ×530.

epidermal cell to form a haustorium. Haustoria are most commonly globular but in *E. graminis* they have long, fingerlike processes (G. Smith, 1900). (Figure 6.4). Usually the fungus penetrates only the epidermal cells but in those species where hyphae enter the stomata, haustoria develop from hyphae in the intercellular spaces. One species, *Uncinula salicis*, is unique in that several haustoria may arise from one appressorium and they may extend to the sub-epidermal layer of cells.

Once penetration has been effected further germ-tubes are produced from the conidium, and haustoria develop from appres-

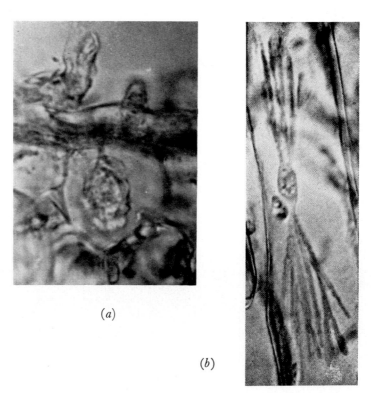

(a)

(b)

FIGURE 6.4 Haustoria. (a) *Erysiphe polygoni* in pea leaf. approx. × 1300. Photograph by C. G. Smith. (b) *Erisyphe graminis* in barley leaf approx. × 700. From Smedegaard-Petersen, 1967, *Åsskr. K. Vet.–Landbohøjsk.*, 1967, 1–28, by permission of the author and The Royal Veterinary and Agricultural College, Copenhagen.

soria borne laterally on them. The fungus thus grows out radially from the point of inoculation (Figure 6.5).

About four days after inoculation, sporulation starts near the site of inoculation and then extends outwards. An interesting feature is that many species show a marked diurnal cycle of conidial production (Yarwood, 1936a; Childs, 1940).

After the conidial stage has been apparent for some time, usually in late summer, cleistocarps develop in the same mycelial felt, but their formation is very variable. Some species form them frequently on certain hosts, e.g. *Sphaerotheca mors-uvae* on gooseberry and blackcurrant, *Sphaerotheca pannosa* on rose; some rarely do so, at least in certain localities, e.g. *Microsphaera alphitoides* on oak in Britain, and some never produce cleistocarps, e.g. *Oidium heveae* on rubber.

The factors influencing cleistocarp production have been much studied but with little indication of any general features. Probably the nutritional state of the host is as important a factor as any (Laibach, 1930). Some species at least appear to be heterothallic (Yarwood, 1935; Morrison, 1960), that is two particular strains need to combine in some way before cleistocarps are formed. Even when they are formed, viable ascospores are not always produced. Sometimes an examination of a collection of apparently mature cleistocarps will reveal asci containing only oil globules. In other instances, ascospores are produced but only an appreciable time after cleistocarp formation.

Only in relatively few instances, e.g. in blackcurrant mildew caused by *S. mors-uvae* (Jordan, 1966, 1967; Merriman and Wheeler, 1968), is there convincing experimental evidence that cleistocarps overwinter and provide inoculum for infection of next season's crop. In other instances all the evidence suggests they play no significant part in the life cycle, e.g. *Sphaerotheca macularis* on strawberry (Peries, 1962). There must then be other ways of overwintering and the most common is as mycelium in the dormant buds of the host (Figure 6.6). This occurs with *Podosphaera leucotricha* on apple (Woodward, 1927), *Sphaerotheca pannosa* var. *persicae* on peach (Weinhold, 1961), and *S. mors-uvae* on gooseberry (Merriman and Wheeler, 1968).

In warm climates survival from season to season may be achieved by mycelium, or by active infections on volunteer plants, which appear also to be important in maintaining some powdery mildews in temperate regions. Turner (1956) has shown that in Britain much of the infection of winter wheat by *E. graminis* arises from inoculum

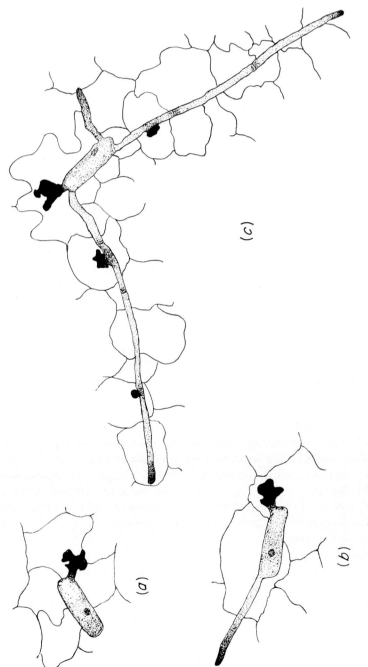

FIGURE 6.5 Germination of a conidium of *Erysiphe polygoni* on a pea leaf. (*a*) 12 hours (*b*) 24 hours (*c*) 48 hours, approx. × 1280. Drawn from stained epidermal strips prepared by C. G. Smith.

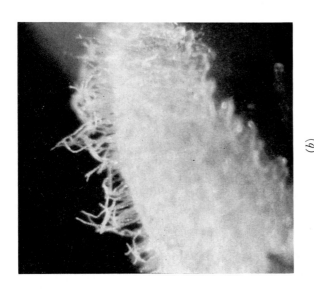

(b)

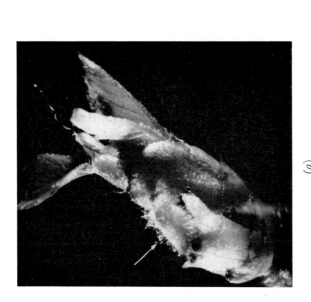

(a)

FIGURE 6.6 Bud infection of rose. (a) shows a bud on a shoot which was surface sterilized. The bud scale arrowed has emerged already white with mildew. A close-up (b) shows the conidial chains of *Sphaerotheca pannosa* arising from the surface of the bud scale. $a \times 9$, $b \times 30$. Photographs by T. V. Price.

produced on volunteer plants, left from the previous spring wheat crop; the same appears to happen in Denmark (Smedegaard-Peterson, 1967). These are examples of oversummering rather than overwintering and similarly for some crops there are other sources of inoculum which do not necessarily involve survival through the winter. Stone (1962) found, for example, that conidia of *Erysiphe cichoracearum* from *Sonchus asper, Sonchus arvensis* and some other Compositae infected cucumbers, and these alternative hosts could well be sources of inoculum for glasshouse crops. Here conidia are thought to come from plants growing near the glasshouses but in other instances infections may be initiated by conidia blown by wind over comparatively long distances. Recent evidence suggests this is so with *E. graminis* on spring barley in Denmark for winter barley is seldom grown there and volunteer barley plants are rarely found to be infected with mildew in the spring (Hermansen, 1964; Hermansen and others, 1965).

Factors influencing disease development

Of a large number of factors, four are most important: moisture, temperature, light and soil fertility. It is not always easy to distinguish the individual effects of the first three, and experiments designed to elucidate the effects of soil fertility have often given variable results.

The effects of moisture on fungal development and disease are most controversial but two generalizations can be made. One is that while there are reports to the contrary most evidence suggests that disease incidence is generally higher during dry weather; indeed, Boughey (1949) has shown that the incidence of powdery mildews throughout the world can be related to the mean annual rainfall. The other is that germination of the conidia of most species is poor in free water.

The effects of different atmospheric humidities on germination and growth are more complex especially since the conidial population of a given species is often heterogeneous in its response to moisture. Much of the information has been critically reviewed by Schnathorst (1965). He considers that the responses observed in germinating conidia of various species are best related to vapour pressure deficit as a measure of moisture stress rather than relative humidity. Vapour pressure deficit (VPD) is calculated from the formula

$$VPD = (1-RH)E$$

where E is the vapour pressure at saturation at a given temperature and RH is the relative humidity. On this basis he divides the powdery mildews into three groups:

1. Those that germinate only at low moisture stress, that is roughly between 0·5–6·0 mm VPD with an optimum of 0·5–1·0 mm VPD. In terms of relative humidity this is a range of 75%–99% and an optimum of 96%–99% at 23°. The conidia of *S. pannosa* behave in this way.

2. Those with an optimal germination at low moisture stress but with a small percentage of conidia capable of germinating at high moisture stress. In terms of relative humidity, optimum germination occurs (at c. 23°) between 75%–99%, there is a sharp decline in germination between 50% and 75% RH but a few spores germinate at lower humidities right down to 0% RH. Examples are *E. cichoracearum*, *E. graminis*, *S. macularis* and *Leveillula taurica*.

3. Those that germinate well throughout a wide range of moisture stress, from 0·5–36 mm VPD, i.e. over a range 0%–99% RH at c. 23°. *Uncinula necator* and *E. polygoni* fall in this group.

Once germination has occurred, the moisture stresses normally encountered under natural conditions probably have little effect on colony development.

The ability of the conidia of some species, e.g. *E. polygoni*, to germinate at high moisture stress or conversely low relative humidity (Yarwood, 1936*b*) may well be one reason why powdery mildews are most severe in dry weather. They owe this ability possibly to their high water content. The conidia of *E. polygoni*, for example, contain about 70% water and they lose this slowly (Yarwood, 1952).

Most powdery mildew fungi will infect plants within a temperature range 11°–28°, with an average about 21° (Yarwood and others, 1954). *E. graminis* has probably the lowest optimum for infection within the group at about 17°. The temperature range for infection is often narrower than that for spore germination. Conidia of *S. macularis*, for example, will germinate over a range 2°–35°, but infection of strawberries does not occur below 5° (Peries, 1962). There are indications that the distribution of powdery mildews is influenced by temperature, e.g. rubber mildew is more serious at high elevations in Malaya, but it is difficult to separate temperature from other factors, in this instance rainfall.

The higher incidence of mildew on shaded than on exposed leaves, seen particularly with tobacco (Hopkins, 1956), suggests that light is also an important factor but this may in part be a temperature effect, since under tropical conditions there may be considerable

differences in temperature between such leaves. Several direct
effects of light on powdery mildew fungi have been reported. These
include increased conidial germination, negative phototropism of
germ-tubes to white light at low intensities, and positive phototropism to green light (Yarwood, 1932). There may also be indirect
effects through the host. Yarwood (1936*b*) found, for example, that
less mildew developed on clover plants if these were held in darkness
after inoculation.

The effects of soil fertility are equally complex as might be
expected. The most convincing evidence that mineral nutrition
influences susceptibility comes from water culture experiments. For
example, Cole (1964), found that the leaves of tobacco (var. Hicks)
were more susceptible to *E. cichoracearum* when grown in media
containing 50, 38 and 50 p.p.m. of nitrogen, phosphorus and
potassium, respectively, than in media with smaller concentrations
of these elements. He also found that leaves were least susceptible in
media with a low ratio of potassium to nitrogen, but this is contrary
to the generally held view that potassium deficiency increases
susceptibility to these diseases.

In some instances increased susceptibility following various
fertilizer treatments appears to be linked with a growth response.
Last (1953) found that when cereal plants of two size groups were
given the same amount of nitrogen, the initially smaller plants
increased in growth more than the others and became more heavily
infected. Experiments such as these suggest that mildew severity is
related to host vigour and that factors which favour plant growth
correspondingly favour mildew development. Support for this comes
from the work of Cole (1966) on the effect of irrigation on powdery
mildew of tobacco in Rhodesia. He found that more disease
developed on irrigated plants than on non-irrigated ones and this
was related mainly to the effect of irrigation on leaf growth. It
must be made clear that other experiments do not support this view,
for instance Trelease and Trelease (1928), in a detailed investigation
of the influence of mineral nutrition on wheat powdery mildew,
found no close relationship between disease severity and host
vigour. Yarwood (1957) after reviewing the conflicting evidence
concludes that while it may be true in a general way that susceptibility to mildew and host vigour are related, the many exceptions
do not make this a very useful generalization.

Control
There are two main ways in which these diseases are controlled,

by fungicides and by resistant varieties. Powdery mildew fungi are unique amongst plant pathogens in that their superficial growth makes them vulnerable to chemical action through most of their life cycle. Sulphur, in various forms, was the most popular of the many chemicals previously used. Its chief disadvantage is that on certain plants such as cucurbits and some apple varieties, it causes injury: such plants are said to be 'sulphur-shy'. For these, there are now various alternatives, the most important of which is dinocap [2-(1-methyl-n-heptyl)-4, 6-dinitrophenyl crotonate], known in its commercial form as 'Karathane'. This is used as a wettable powder or dust. Recently some systemic fungicides have been developed which appear particularly effective against certain powdery mildews, and these are likely to replace the existing materials (Elias and others, 1968; Hammett, 1968).

Breeding mildew-resistant varieties has met with varied success, and there is an ever increasing volume of literature on this aspect of control. Useful references are to be found particularly for cereals in the review by Moseman (1966), and for tobacco in Lucas (1965). The difficulties involved are not special to this group of diseases and are discussed generally in Chapter 21.

REFERENCES

Blumer, S. (1933). Die Erysiphaceen Mitteleuropas. *Beitr. KryptogFlora Schweiz.*, **7**, 1–483

Blumer, S. (1967). *Echte Mehltaupilze (Erysiphaceae). Ein Bestimmungsbuch für die in Europa vorkommenden Arten.* 436 pp. Gustav Fischer Verlag, Jena.

Boughey, A. S. (1949). The ecology of fungi which cause economic plant diseases. *Trans. Br. mycol. Soc.*, **32**, 179–89

Childs, J. F. L. (1940). Diurnal cycle of spore maturation in certain powdery mildews. *Phytopathology*, **30**, 65–73

Cole, J. S. (1964). Powdery mildew of tobacco (*Erysiphe cichoracearum* DC). I. Effects of nitrogen, phosphorus and potassium on susceptibility, growth and chemical composition of infected and healthy tobacco grown in water culture. *Ann. appl. Biol.*, **54**, 291–301; (1966). III. Some effects of irrigation on disease development. *Ann. appl. Biol.*, **57**, 435–44

Elias, R. S., Shephard, M. C., Snell, B. K. and Stubbs, J. (1968). 5-n-butyl-2-dimethylamino-4-hydroxy-6-methylpyrimidine: a systemic fungicide. *Nature, Lond.* **219**, 1160

Hammett, K. R. W. (1968). Root application of a systemic fungicide for control of powdery mildews. *Pl. Dis. Reptr*, **52**, 754–8

Hermansen, J. E. (1964). Notes on the appearance of rusts and mildew on barley in Denmark during the years 1961–1963. *Acta. agric. Scand.*, **14**, 33–51

Hermansen, J. E., Johansen, H. B., Hansen, H. W. and Carstensen, P. (1965). Notes on the trapping of powdery mildew conidia and urediospores by aircraft in Denmark in 1964. *Årsskr. K. Vet.-Landbohøjsk.*, 1965, 121–9

Hopkins, J. C. F. (1956). *Tobacco Diseases*, p. 94. Commonwealth Mycological Institute, Kew.

Jordan, V. W. L. (1966). Observations on American gooseberry mildew on black currants. II. Primary infection. *Rep. agric. hort. Res. Stn. Univ. Bristol*, 1965, 178–83; (1967) IV. Source of primary infection. *Rep. agric. hort. Res. Stn. Univ. Bristol*, 1966, 180–3

Laibach, F. (1930). Über die Bedingungen der Perithezienbildung bei den Erysiphaceen. *Jb. wiss. Bot.*, **72**, 106–136. [*Rev. appl. Mycol.*, **9**, 548–7]

Last, F. T. (1953). Some effects of temperature and nitrogen supply on wheat powdery mildew. *Ann. appl. Biol.*, **40**, 312–22

Lucas, G. B. (1965). *Diseases of Tobacco*. pp. 64–93. Scarecrow Press, New York.

Marchal, Em. (1902). De la specialization du parasitisme chez *l'Erysiphe graminis*. *C.r. hebd. Seanc. Acad. Sci., Paris*, **135**, 210–2

Merriman, P. R. and Wheeler, B. E. J. (1968). Overwintering of *Sphaerotheca mors-uvae* on blackcurrant and gooseberry. *Ann. appl. Biol.*, **61**, 387–97

Morrison, R. M. (1960). Studies on clonal isolates of *Erysiphe cichoracearum* on leaf disk culture. *Mycologia*, **52**, 388–93

Moseman, J. G. (1966). Genetics of powdery mildews. *A. Rev. Phytopathol.*, **4**, 269–90

Peries, O. S. (1962). Studies on strawberry mildew, caused by *Sphaerotheca macularis* (Wallr. ex Fries) Jaczewski. I. Biology of the fungus. *Ann. appl. Biol.*, **50**, 211–24

Peries, O. S. (1966). Host induced change in the morphology of a powdery mildew fungus. *Nature, Lond.*, **212**, 540–1

Salmon, E. S. (1900). A monograph of the Erysiphaceae. *Bull. Torrey bot. Club*, No. 9, 292 pp.

Sawada, K. (1914). The classification of the Erysiphaceae based on the conidial stages. *Spec. Rep. Formosa agric. Exp. Stn.*, **9**, 1–102 (In Japanese)

Schnathorst, W. C. (1965). Environmental relationships in the powdery mildews. *A. Rev. Phytopathol.*, **3**, 346–66

Smedegaard-Peterson, V. (1967). Studies on *Erysiphe graminis* DC with a special view to the importance of the perithecia for attacks on barley and wheat in Denmark. *Åsskr. K. Vet.-Landbohøjsk.*, 1967, 1–28

Smith, G. (1900). The haustoria of the Erysiphaceae. *Bot. Gaz.*, **29**, 153–84

Stone, O. M. (1962). Alternate hosts of cucumber powdery mildew. *Ann. appl. Biol.*, **50**, 203–10

Trelease, S. F. and Trelease, H. M. (1928). Susceptibility of wheat to mildew as influenced by salt nutrition. *Bull. Torrey bot. Club.*, No. 55, 41–67

Turner, D. M. (1956). Studies on cereal mildew in Britain. *Trans. Br. mycol. Soc.*, **39**, 495–506

Weinhold, A. R. (1961). The orchard development of peach powdery mildew. *Phytopathology*, **51**, 478–81

Woodward, R. C. (1927). Studies on *Podosphaera leucotricha* (Ell. and Ev.) Salm. I. The mode of perennation. *Trans. Br. mycol. Soc.*, **12**, 173–204

Yarwood, C. E. (1932). Reversible phototropism of the germ tubes of clover powdery mildew. *Phytopathology*, **22**, 31

Yarwood, C. E. (1935). Heterothallism of sunflower powdery mildew. *Science, N.Y.*, **82**, 417–8

Yarwood, C. E. (1936a). The diurnal cycle of the powdery mildew *Erysiphe polygoni*. *J. agric. Res.*, **52**, 645–57

Yarwood, C. E. (1936b). The tolerance of *Erysiphe polygoni* and certain other powdery mildews to low humidity. *Phytopathology*, **26**, 845–59

Yarwood, C. E. (1952). Some water relations of *Erysiphe polygoni* conidia. *Mycologia*, **44**, 506–22

Yarwood, C. E. (1957). Powdery mildews. *Bot. Rev.*, **23**, 235–301

Yarwood, C. E., Sidky, S., Cohen, M. and Santilli, V. (1954). Temperature relations of powdery mildews. *Hilgardia*, **22**, 603–22

CHAPTER 7

Rusts

Rust diseases are caused by fungi belonging to the Uredinales and derive their name from the orange-brown spore masses which many of these fungi produce on their hosts. Most rust fungi parasitize Angiosperms or Gymnosperms, a few attack Ferns, and they colonize the host chiefly by intercellular mycelium with intracellular haustoria, as in the downy mildews. As far as is known, most are obligate parasites. Williams and others (1966, 1967) have grown an isolate of *Puccinia graminis* from wheat on a synthetic medium and similar claims have been made by Cutter (1959, 1960) for *Gymnosporangium juniperi-virginianae* and *Uromyces ari-triphylli* but so far this latter work has not been successfully repeated.

Spore forms

One feature of rust fungi is that each species may have from one to five spore forms and associated fruiting structures, and the recognition of these is obviously important. The terms used here for the forms are those of Cummins (1959), but they are by no means universally accepted: some reasons why they are not are discussed by Laundon (1967). For convenience the forms are given the Roman numerals O to IV.

O. Spermagonium (pl. spermagonia). This is frequently a flask-shaped structure (see Figure 7.3*a*), rather like the pycnidium of the Sphaeropsidales (p. 183), but it can also be lens or cone-shaped. The spores produced (spermatia) are usually minute and are discharged in a sweet exudate.

I. The aecium (pl. aecia) arises from the same thallus as the spermagonium and frequently on the opposite leaf-surface to it.

The aeciospores are 1-celled, and these germinate to give a mycelium on which other spore forms are produced but never further aecia. Within the rust fungi there are five different morphological types of aecium and each may be used as the basis for a 'form-genus' (Figure 7.1) in the absence of other, definitive structures, viz.

(i) *Aecidium.* The aeciospores are produced in chains in a short

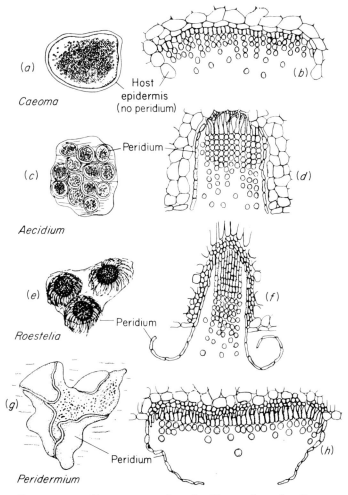

FIGURE 7.1 Four types of aecia illustrating the form-genera *Caeoma, Aecidium, Roestelia, Peridermium.* From C. J. Alexopoulos, 1962, *Introductory Mycology,* John Wiley.

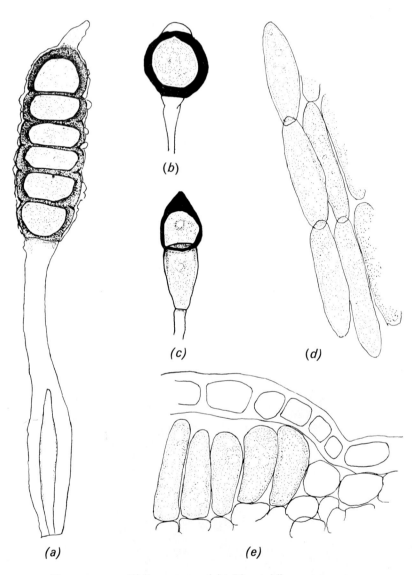

FIGURE 7.2 Teliospores. (*a*) *Phragmidium mucronatum* from rose, (*b*) *Uromyces appendiculatus* from dwarf bean, (*c*) *Puccinia graminis* from wheat, (*d*) *Cronartium ribicola* from black currant (part only of a telial column), (*e*) *Melampsoridium betulinum* from *Betula pubescens*. All × 650.

cup-like structure bordered by a layer of cells, called the peridium. This is the typical 'cluster cup' seen in many species of *Puccinia*.

(ii) *Peridermium*. The peridium is typically long and much more developed than in *Aecidium* which it otherwise resembles. It is common in certain rust species with aecial stages on Gymnosperms and the term is restricted to these rusts.

(iii) *Roestelia*. The peridium is long and well developed as in *Peridermium*, but generally more horn-like, and tends to split longitudinally at maturity. The term is usually restricted to aecia produced by species of *Gymnosporangium*.

(iv) *Caeoma*, in which there is no peridium and the pustule appears diffuse or indeterminate. This type is common in species of *Phragmidium* and *Melampsora*.

(v) *Uraecium*, in which there is also no peridium but the aeciospores are stalked and resemble the next spore form.

II. Uredium (pl. uredia). This arises initially on mycelium produced by aeciospores. The spores are 1-celled and on germination give rise to further uredia: they are thus a 'repeating form'. Typically urediospores are relatively short-lived and serve to enlarge the distribution of the parasite on its host, though in some species, e.g. *Puccinia vexans*, thick-walled urediospores (amphispores) are formed which can survive adverse conditions (Arthur, 1929). In many rusts, the mycelium from which uredia are derived later produces the fourth spore stage.

III. Telium (pl. telia). Most rust genera are based on the morphology of the telium and the teliospores because of the diversity of types which occur. For example, in *Uromyces* the teliospore is 1-celled and borne singly on a stalk or pedicel; in *Puccinia* it is also stalked but divided into 2 cells by a horizontal septum, in *Phragmidium* the stalked teliospore has several horizontal septa. In *Melampsoridium* the teliospores are sessile, 1-celled, and in 1-layered crusts; in *Cronartium* they are also 1-celled but become attached one to another so that a telial column is formed (Figure 7.2). Many other examples are clearly illustrated by Cummins (1959).

Teliospores of many species are thick-walled and capable of surviving adverse conditions, and so the teliospore is often regarded as a 'resting' or 'winter' spore. Overwintering appears to be necessary for teliospore germination in some rusts but not in others. On germination, teliospores give rise to a basidium on which basidiospores are formed and this stage is denoted by the numeral IV.

Rust species which have the four spore-forms O–III, or those in which only the spermagonia are missing, are termed macrocyclic.

Those with aecia and uredia, or these plus spermagonia are termed demicyclic, and those with telia only or telia plus spermagonia, microcyclic. Other terms are sometimes used for different combinations of spore forms (Laundon, 1967).

Some rust species have all their spore-forms on one host, and each spore-form is capable of infecting the same host. Such a species is said to be autoecious. Other rust species alternate between two, often unrelated, hosts, and both are necessary for the completion of the life cycle. These species are called heteroecious. Amongst fungi only *Sclerotinia rhododendri* and *Sclerotinia heteroica* have a similar requirement (Gaumann, 1950).

Black stem rust of cereals

This rust disease, caused by *Puccinia graminis*, has probably been studied more than any other. *P. graminis* is macrocyclic and heteroecious, with spermagonia and aecia on the barberry (*Berberis* spp.), occasionally on *Mahonia* spp., and with uredia and telia on wheat, barley, oats, rye and many grasses (Figure 7.3). Our knowledge of the different stages in the life cycle particularly the cytological aspects owes much to the work of Craigie (1927, 1931) and Allen (1930, 1933). It can be summarized as follows. The basidiospores are uninucleate and of two types designated + and −, there being two of each type per basidium. Basidiospores germinate on the barberry and each produces a mycelium on which spermagonia and aecial initials are formed. This mycelium or thallus is bisexual but it is self-sterile. Pairing of nuclei occurs only between spermatia and aecial initials derived from different (+ and −) thalli and this is initiated through the chance movement of spermatia of one strain, by insects, to the receptive hyphae of an aecial initial of the other strain. At this stage there is no nuclear fusion but the egg-cell of the aecial initial becomes binucleate. Aeciospores are formed from this binucleate cell and they in turn give rise to a mycelium with binucleate cells from which binucleate urediospores are produced. Binucleate teliospores develop later within the same sorus but at this stage nuclear fusion occurs followed by meiosis so that the basidial cells and the basidiospores formed from them contain a single, haploid nucleus. There is thus an alternation between a gametophytic or sexual generation which is uninucleate and haploid (basidiospores, spermagonia and aecial initials) and a sporophytic or asexual generation which is binucleate or dikaryotic in the aecia, uredia and young telia, and diploid in the mature teliospore.

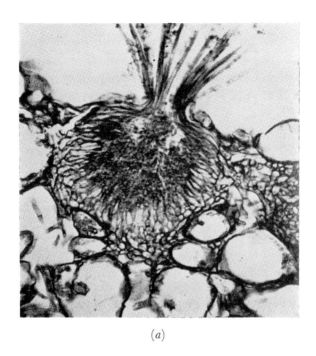

(a)

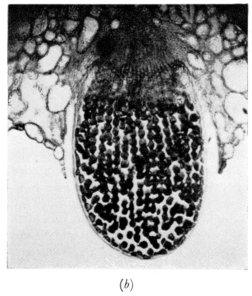

(b)

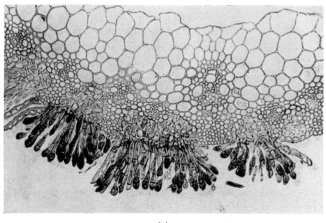

(*c*)

FIGURE 7.3 *Puccinia graminis.* Sections of (*a*) spermagonium on barberry approx. × 260, (*b*) aecium on
barberry, with the peridium not yet ruptured × 300,
(*c*) telia on wheat approx. × 260. From A. H. R.
Buller, 1950, *Researches on Fungi*, Vol. 7, by permission
of the University of Toronto Press.

The hybridization process on the barberry ensures a redistribution of characters possessed by *P. graminis* and those which may arise
by mutation. It is hardly surprising, therefore, that within this
species, and indeed in other species of rust fungi, there are many
strains that differ in pathogenicity. It was Eriksson who first demonstrated it in *P. graminis* in 1894. He distinguished several *formae
speciales* which could attack one particular crop but not others, e.g.
tritici on wheat, *secalis* on rye, *avenae* on oats. There are small
differences in urediospore size of these forms which some workers
consider sufficient to justify varietal status but it is generally agreed
that they are best separated on their pathogenicity. The form of
P. graminis on wheat thus became known as *P. graminis* f. sp. *tritici*
or simply *P. graminis tritici*, and the others accordingly. Further
work particularly by Stakman and his associates at Minnesota
showed that these forms themselves comprise a number of races
that can be distinguished on different cultivars of the host like the
forms of *Erysiphe graminis* (p. 92) (Johnson and Newton, 1946).

The identification of these races is a specialized aspect of plant
pathology but, taking *P. graminis* on wheat as an example, the
procedure is basically as follows. A standard set of 12 wheat varieties

are inoculated with urediospores (or aeciospores). These are called differential varieties (Stakman and others 1962). The type of infection produced on these varieties by a single spore collection is then graded (Figure 7.4):

   0 — no pustules produced, nor other evidence of infection.

   ; — only faint, light flecks with either some chlorosis or necrosis.

   1 — small pustules, rather scattered, with some chlorosis or necrosis.

   2 — small to medium pustules with some chlorosis.

   3 — medium size pustules.

   4 — large and confluent pustules.

These grades thus indicate varying degrees of susceptibility. In addition there is a grade X, an intermediate or mesothetic reaction, with pustules of variable size but mainly a mixture of types 1 and 4. Small deviations from that normally accepted for the grade are indicated by one or two plus and minus signs. For each type except 0 it is thus possible to indicate five degrees of infection, e.g. 3− −, 3−, 3, 3+, 3+ +.

It is sometimes possible to subdivide a physiologic race by adding another variety to the standard differentials. Race 15B was distinguished from Race 15 in this way by its reaction on the variety 'Lee'.

Other cereal rust diseases

Black stem rust is not the only cereal rust disease of importance. In certain areas, e.g. Britain, yellow rust caused by *Puccinia striiformis* is generally more serious (Macer and others, 1967). The yellow pustules on mature leaves are characteristically in long lines and the disease is frequently called stripe rust. Only urediospores and teliospores are found and no alternate host is known, but the basidiospores are incapable of infecting wheat and barley. It is generally supposed that in areas where the winters are relatively mild urediospores from volunteer plants infect autumn sown crops and the fungus overwinters on them as a dormant uredomycelium (Mehta, 1923; Hungerford, 1923). Further development of the disease then occurs in the spring. In other instances infections in the spring are initiated by wind-borne urediospores from warmer areas (Sanford and Broadfoot, 1932). However, *P. striiformis* cannot withstand high temperatures. During the summer in California, for example, it is found only in the cooler, coastal areas or on wild grasses at altitudes of 1829 m or more in the Sierra Nevada. Then in autumn, wind-blown urediospores from these sources infect

E

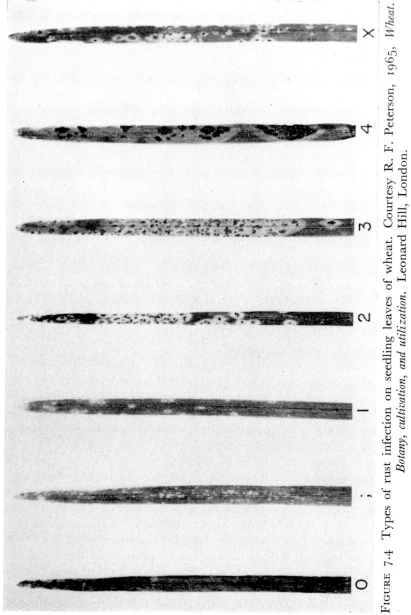

FIGURE 7.4 Types of rust infection on seedling leaves of wheat. Courtesy R. F. Peterson, 1965, *Wheat. Botany, cultivation, and utilization.* Leonard Hill, London.

early-sown wheat and volunteer plants; the fungus overwinters on these and spreads on the wheat crop in the spring (Tollenaar and Houston, 1967).

A third rust disease of wheat is brown leaf rust caused by *Puccinia recondita* (Chester, 1946). The pustules are initially bright orange but later turn brown and are scattered chiefly over the upper surfaces of leaves. *P. recondita* is a heteroecious species with aecia on *Isopyrum fumarioides* and species of *Thalictrum* but this stage is not always found in areas where the disease occurs e.g. in Britain. In these areas infections in the spring are initiated, like those of *P. striiformis*, by urediospores produced on mycelium that has over-wintered in the host or by urediospores carried by wind from warmer areas.

Most of the other cereal rusts are heteroecious. *Puccinia hordei* which causes brown rust of barley has its aecial stage on *Ornithogalum pyrenaicum*; *Puccinia coronata*, causing crown rust of oats on species of *Rhamnus*, and the form of *P. recondita* causing brown rust of rye on *Lycopsis arvensis* and *Anchusa officinalis* (Arthur and Cummins, 1962; Wilson and Henderson, 1966).

Rust diseases of other hosts

While the cereal rusts have quite rightly received most attention particularly in the grain producing areas of North America, it would be wrong to suggest that they are the only rust diseases of significance. Rust fungi attack a wide range of commercially important crops; some of the more important are:

Vegetables;	*Uromyces appendiculatus* on bean,
	Puccinia asparagi on asparagus,
	Puccinia allii on onion, leek, and garlic,
	Puccinia menthae on peppermint
Grain;	*Puccinia polysora* on maize
Fibres;	*Melampsora lini* on flax
Fruit;	*Tranzschelia pruni-spinosae* f. *discolor* on plum,
	Gymnosporangium juniperi-virginianae on apple,
	Cronartium ribicola on currant
Ornamentals;	*Puccinia antirrhini* on antirrhinums,
	Puccinia chrysanthemi on chrysanthemums,
	Puccinia malvacearum on hollyhocks and other malvaceous hosts
	Phragmidium mucronatum on rose
	Endophyllum sempervivi on houseleek

Apart from the cereal rusts, the one rust disease which has had most impact on humanity is the leaf rust of coffee caused by *Hemileia vastatrix* (Figure 7.5) This was first recorded in Ceylon in 1868 and it spread so rapidly throughout the coffee plantations that these ceased to be profitable and were replaced by tea (Large, 1940).

H. vastatrix is apparently autoecious but the basidiospores do not infect coffee and this has led to speculation regarding the existence of an alternate host. Only the leaves are attacked but because of defoliation bushes with rust produce small berries which often fail to ripen. A 50% loss in yield is not uncommon in areas where the

FIGURE 7.5 Coffee leaf rust. A Shell photograph, copyright.

disease is severe, for example in Kenya it has been estimated that the annual loss from this disease is some 4.5 Mkg of coffee.

The spores of *H. vastatrix* are somewhat bizarre and are produced in a characteristic way (Figure 7.6). Hyphae aggregate in the substomatal cavities on the lower surfaces of leaves, and then emerge as stalks through the stomata. Each stalk becomes swollen at the tip, forming a basal cell with sterigmata on which the urediospores arise. These resemble a segment of an orange in shape. The teliospores are produced in the same sorus but are turnip-shaped and thin-walled. They germinate without a resting stage to produce a typical basidium and basidiospores.

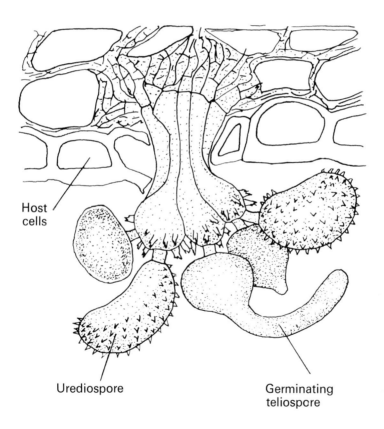

Host cells

Urediospore

Germinating teliospore

FIGURE 7.6 *Hemileia vastatrix*. Section through a pustule about ×800. From G. B. Cummins, 1959, *Illustrated Genera of Rust Fungi*. Burgess Publishing Co., Minneapolis.

Infection by rust fungi

In most parasite–host combinations which have been investigated penetration by rust urediospores and aeciospores occurs through stomata. Examples are *P. graminis* and *P. striiformis*/wheat (Allen, 1923; 1928), *P. hordei*/barley (D'Oliveira, 1938), *P. coronata*/oats (Ruttle and Fraser, 1927), and *C. ribicola*/currant (Anderson, 1939). In each the process is basically similar. The tip of the germ-tube becomes swollen and closely adpressed to the surface of the guard cells. From this swollen tip (the appressorium), a fine penetration tube emerges and enters the substomatal cavity where it swells to form a vesicle. In susceptible hosts hyphae then develop from this vesicle and colonize the host tissue intercellularly (Figure 7.7).

Basidiospores, on the other hand, frequently enter the hosts by direct penetration of the cuticle. The process has been described in detail for *P. graminis* and barberry by Waterhouse (1921). The germ-tube becomes flattened over the cuticle and from this area of contact a fine penetration tube passes through the cuticle and epidermal wall into the epidermal cell. Here it increases in diameter forming a hypha which then colonizes the palisade mesophyll.

So far little is known about the mechanism by which rust germ-tubes or those of other fungi are stimulated to enter their hosts by these two processes. Some early work with *P. striiformis* (Balls, 1905) suggests that a growth response to water vapour (hydrotropism) is involved in stomatal entry but does not explain the formation of appressoria and penetration hyphae. The nature of the plant surface may be an important factor in stomatal entry as well as in direct penetration of the cuticle. Dickinson (1960) suggested that growth of germ-tubes, appressoria and penetration tubes are responses to a contact stimulus (thigmotropism) because he found it possible, by varying the physical structure of artificial membranes, to induce responses in rust germ-tubes ranging from simple directional changes in growth to structures resembling appressoria and substomatal vesicles.

Whereas with the downy and powdery mildews it is possible to make some general statements regarding the environmental conditions conducive to penetration and infection, within the rusts there is so much variation not only from one species to another but between form species and races that generalizations serve no useful purpose. For each individual species or race, particular regimes of temperature and humidity determine infection.

For some, like *Puccinia graminis* on wheat, much is now known of the factors influencing disease severity. The effect of temperature on

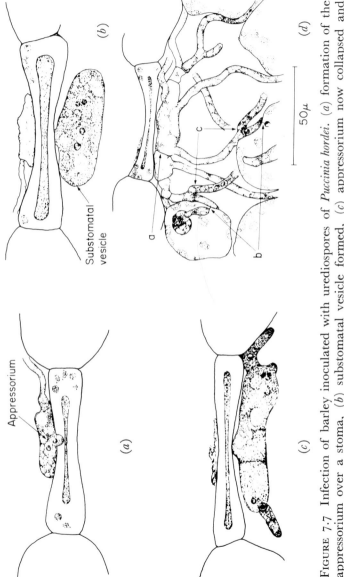

FIGURE 7.7 Infection of barley inoculated with urediospores of *Puccinia hordei*. (*a*) formation of the appressorium over a stoma, (*b*) substomatal vesicle formed, (*c*) appressorium now collapsed and substomatal vesicle beginning to branch, (*d*) infection after 3 days. The substomatal vesicle (*a*) now has several cells and has produced a mycelium (c) with haustoria penetrating the host cells (b). From D'Oliveira, 1938, *Revta agron., Lisb.* **26**, 1–54, by permission of the Sociedade de Ciencias Agronomicas de Portugal.

outbreaks of black stem rust in the spring wheat area of Minnesota, North and South Dakota was critically examined by Stakman and Lambert (1928) for the period 1904–1925. They found that in the three states the average temperature throughout the growing season was consistently above the normal (22 year average) in years in which stem rust was epidemic and below normal in other years. Generally epidemics developed in seasons with average temperatures above 17·8° but not in seasons during which the average temperature was below 16·1°. There were exceptions, for example in 1910 the temperature was comparatively high yet there was no rust epidemic. In this instance, a low rainfall undoubtedly limited the disease. A similar study was carried out by Lambert (1929) for the Mississippi valley, and by Levine (1928). In Canada Craigie (1945) also found that there was a similar relationship between the mean minimum temperature for the period June 20 to August 4 and rust severity, and also an association between medium and heavy stem rust infection and years of high rainfall in spring and summer.

Control of rust diseases

For a heteroecious rust one possible method of control is the elimination of the alternate host for theoretically, at least, this stops the fungus completing its life cycle.

With black stem rust, the biggest campaign for the eradication of the barberry has taken place in the United States. It began effectively in 1917 when several wheat growing states passed laws forbidding the planting of barberries as ornamentals and making obligatory the removal of bushes already present (Fulling, 1943). These schemes were later taken over and extended by the Department of Agriculture, and there is now a group of states centred on Minnesota, Iowa, Wisconsin and Illinois in which barberry eradication is enforced.

Removing the barberry has undoubtedly been of value in limiting the development of new races through the sexual process on this host but it has not by any means eliminated black stem rust. Obviously there are other sources of inoculum. It is now known that urediospores are blown by wind over long distances (Stakman and Christensen, 1946; Stakman and Harrar, 1957). In North America wheat growing extends from the Gulf of Mexico to the Canadian Prairies, and with the different climates there is a succession of crops from the south to the north. Urediospores formed on autumn-sown crops in the south can be blown in stages northwards and infect spring-planted crops as these develop. Given favourable conditions black stem rust can become epiphytotic throughout the entire wheat belt. The movement of urediospores is not only northwards; in late summer and autumn spores from spring-sown wheat in the north can be carried south and infect autumn-sown wheat in Texas and neighbouring states. This explains why stem rust is still severe in areas below the 39th parallel where the barberry does not grow.

A similar state of affairs obtains in Britain. Surveys showed that although barberries were to be found, notably in southeastern Scotland, they were not sources of *P. graminis tritici* although they carried the oat, rye, and grass forms of *P. graminis* (Ogilvie and Thorpe, 1961). This suggested that urediospore inoculum was involved in the occasional epidemics of stem rust on wheat: yet urediospores do not survive the English winter. There is now evidence that these come from the Iberian peninsula and possibly also from North Africa. Outbreaks of black stem rust occur in Britain in years with high summer temperatures and prevailing southwesterly air streams and it is often severe in the southwestern districts which are in a favourable position with regard to this inoculum. The movement of *P. graminis* urediospores over the English Channel has recently been plotted by Hirst and others (1967) by relating counts obtained from surface spore traps and those mounted on aircraft to detailed meteorological observations. The results provide the most detailed information to date on the factors involved.

Another rust disease in which large-scale eradication of the alternate host has been attempted is blister rust of pine caused by *C. ribicola*, which has aecia on species of five-needle pines such as *Pinus strobus* and uredia and telia on currants (*Ribes*). In North America the campaign has been directed against the currant bushes to prevent infection of pines grown for timber. Initially, it was not successful in restricting the overall spread of *C. ribicola* because the aeciospores can be carried many miles by wind but it has considerably lessened the damage caused by this disease on pine (Fulling, 1943).

Long-distance dissemination of spores has been established for other rust species of which *P. polysora* is the most striking example. This occurs commonly on maize in Central and South America and causes the disease known as South American leaf rust. Before 1949 the fungus was restricted to the Americas but in that year appeared in West Africa (Cammack, 1958). By late 1952 it had spread across

Africa to Kenya and Tanzania, and by 1953 to Mauritius and the Malagasy Republic. In 1956 it was reported from Thailand, the Philippines and islands in the Indian Ocean. An examination of urediospore collections from many parts of the world suggested that the fungus had spread both westwards and eastwards from the Caribbean area, where it was endemic, and it seems probable that its movement initially, e.g. across the Atlantic, was facilitated by air transport (Cammack, 1959).

Rust diseases can also be controlled by fungicides. With cereals, however, not only does their growth habit present special problems in application but also the costs are likely to be prohibitive. In these instances a systemic fungicide is required which could be applied with fertilizers or in a seed-dressing. Alternatively, if such a fungicide is applied to leaves it should both eradicate existing lesions and persist in the plant at a fungitoxic level for some time. Certain nickel compounds appear promising in this respect (Forsyth, 1962) because they are absorbed by plants and are fungicidal, but the difference between a dose which kills rust fungi and that which damages the host is not large and may make them commercially unacceptable. Spraying of wheat might, however, be economic in a situation where existing varieties were threatened by new races (Forsyth and Peturson, 1960).

For broad-leaved plants spraying with fungicides is often the only method of control at present available. This is so for coffee and leaf rust (Firman, 1965). Here copper fungicides are generally most effective but the timing of the applications is particularly critical. Although there has been some controversy regarding the action of rain in the liberation and dispersal of spores it is generally agreed that outbreaks of leaf rust are associated with rain. In a study of the disease in Kenya, Bock (1962 *a*) distinguished three phases in the disease cycle. The first phase which occurs at the end of the dry season is one of low disease incidence in which few fresh infections take place. The second starts at the onset of the rains when many new infections arise as spores from existing rust pustules are dispersed throughout the bush. During this period disease incidence reaches its maximum. The third phase, usually of short duration, is characterized by a rapid decline in disease incidence. This results from the shedding of leaves both naturally and prematurely as a result of infection. Within this general pattern the course and severity of seasonal outbreaks are determined by the distribution and intensity of rainfall, the degree of leafiness of the tree and the amount of residual inoculum at the end of the dry season. In extensive trials,

Bock (1962 *b*) found that maximum control of leaf rust was obtained by spraying before commencement and during the early period of the rains. When sprays were applied within 7 days of the first rains effective in dispersing spores (> 6mm), almost complete control resulted. Under these conditions it would appear that the inoculum is reduced to a very low level indeed and a considerable period must elapse before there are sufficient urediospores of the fungus to initiate many new infections.

One special method of control is that for *P. menthae* on mint (*Mentha villoso-nervata*) and spearmint (*Mentha spicata*). The rust persists on the runners of the host mainly as urediospores and to obtain rust-free planting material, runners are selected during dormancy; these are washed and placed in water at 44·4° for 10 minutes, and then plunged into cold water. This treatment effectively kills the rust fungus without seriously damaging the host tissue (Ogilvie and Brian, 1936; Niederhauser, 1945). This fungus is also important on field crops of peppermint (*Mentha piperata*) in Oregon but here it overwinters as teliospores and different methods of control are involved (Horner, 1963).

The development of resistant varieties is by far the most common method of rust control, especially for the cereal rusts. Since the problems involved are those commonly encountered in breeding for resistance to many diseases a discussion of them is deferred to Chapter 21.

REFERENCES

Allen, R. F. (1923). A cytological study of infection of Baart and Kanred wheats by *Puccinia graminis tritici*. *J. agric. Res.*, **23**, 131–51
Allen, R. F. (1928). A cytological study of *Puccinia glumarum* on *Bromus marginatus* and *Triticum vulgare*. *J. agric. Res.*, **36**, 487–513
Allen, R. F. (1930). A cytological study of heterothallism in *Puccinia graminis*. *J. agric. Res.*, **40**, 585–614
Allen, R. F. (1933). Further cytological studies of heterothallism in *Puccinia graminis*. *J. agric. Res.*, **47**, 1–16
Anderson, O. C. (1939). A cytological study of resistance of Viking currant to infection by *Cronartium ribicola*. *Phytopathology*, **29**, 26–40
Arthur, J. C. (1929). *The Plant Rusts* (*Uredinales*), p. 16. John Wiley, New York.

Arthur, J. C. and Cummins, G. B. (1962). *Manual of the Rusts in the United States and Canada*, 438 pp. Hafner, New York.

Balls, W. L. (1962). Infection of plants by rust fungi. *New Phytol.*, **4**, 18

Bock, K. R. (1962 *a*). Seasonal periodicity of coffee leaf rust and factors affecting the severity of outbreaks in Kenya colony. *Trans. Br. mycol. Soc.*, **45**, 289–300

Bock, K. R. (1962 *b*). Control of coffee leaf rust in Kenya colony. *Trans. Br. mycol. Soc.*, **45**, 301–13

Cammack, R. H. (1958). Studies on *Puccinia polysora* Underw. I. The world distribution of forms of *P. polysora*. *Trans. Br. mycol. Soc.*, **41**, 89–94, (1959). II. A consideration of the method of introduction of *P. polysora* into Africa. *Trans. Br. mycol. Soc.*, **42**, 27–32

Chester, K. Starr (1946). *The Cereal Rusts*, 269 pp. Chronica Botanica, Waltham, Mass.

Craigie, J. H. (1927). Discovery of the function of the pycnia of the rust fungi. *Nature, Lond.*, **120**, 765–7

Craigie, J. H. (1931). An experimental investigation of sex in the rust fungi. *Phytopathology*, **21**, 1001–40

Craigie, J. H. (1945). Epidemiology of stem rust in Western Canada. *Scient. Agric.*, **25**, 285–401

Cummins, G. B. (1959). *Illustrated Genera of Rust Fungi*, 131 pp. Burgess Publishing Co., Minneapolis.

Cutter, V. M. Jr. (1959). Studies on the isolation and growth of plant rusts in host tissue cultures and upon synthetic media. I. *Gymnosporangium*. *Mycologia*, **51**, 248–95; (1960). II. *Uromyces ari-triphylli*. *Mycologia*, **52**, 726–42

Dickinson, S. (1960). The mechanical ability to breach the host barriers. In *Plant Pathology: an advanced treatise* (Ed. J. G. Horsfall and A. E. Dimond), **2**, 203–32. Academic Press, New York.

D'Oliveira, B. (1938). Studies on *Puccinia anomala* Rost. II. Histological and cytological variation in susceptible and resistant barleys inoculated with physiologic races 12 and 17. *Revta agron., Lisb.*, **26**, 1–54

Firman, I. D. (1965). A review of leaf rust and coffee berry disease control in Kenya. *Trop. Agric., Trin.*, **42**, 111–9

Forsyth, F. R. and Peturson, B. (1960). Control of leaf and stem rust of wheat by zineb and inorganic nickel salts. *Pl. Dis. Reptr.*, **44**, 208–11

Forsyth, F. R. (1962). Inhibition by nickel of the respiration and development of established infections on Thatcher wheat caused by *Puccinia recondita* Rob. ex Desm. *Can. J. Bot.*, **40**, 415–23

Fulling, E. H. (1943). Plant life and the law of man. IV. Barberry, currant and gooseberry, and cedar control. *Bot. Rev.*, **9**, 483–592

Gaumann, E. (1950). *Principles of Plant Infection* pp. 82–3 (English Edtn, W. B. Brierley), Crosby Lockwood, London.

Hirst, J. M., Stedman, O. J. and Hogg, W. H. (1967). Long-distance spore transport: methods of measurement, vertical spore profiles and the detection of immigrant spores. *J. gen. Microbiol.*, **48**, 329–55

Horner, C. E. (1963). Field disease cycle of peppermint rust. *Phyto-pathology*, **53**, 1063–7

Hungerford, C. W. (1923). Studies on the life history of stripe rust, *Puccinia glumarum* (Schm.) Erikss. and Henn. *J. agric. Res.*, **24**, 607–20

Johnson, T. and Newton, M. (1946). Specialization, hybridization and mutation in the cereal rusts. *Bot. Rev.*, **12**, 337–92

Lambert, E. B. (1929). The relation of weather to the development of stem rust in the Mississippi valley. *Phytopathology*, **19**, 1–71

Large, E. C. (1940). *Advance of the Fungi*, pp. 196–207. Jonathan Cape, London.

Laundon, G. F. (1967). Terminology in the rust fungi. *Trans. Br. mycol. Soc.*, **50**, 189–94

Levine, M. N. (1928). Biometrical studies on the variation of physiologic forms of *Puccinia graminis tritici* and the effects of ecological factors on the susceptibility of wheat varieties. *Phytopathology*, **18**, 7–123

Macer, R. C. F., Johnson, R. and Wolfe, M. S. (1967). Pathology. *Rep. Pl. Breed. Inst.*, 1965–66, 116–24

Mehta, K. C. (1923). Observations, and experiments on cereal rusts in the neighbourhood of Cambridge, with special reference to their annual recurrence. *Trans. Br. mycol. Soc.*, **8**, 142–76

Neiderhauser, J. S. (1945). The rust of greenhouse-grown spearmint, and its control. *Mem. Cornell agric. Exp. Stn.*, No. 263, 30 pp.

Ogilvie, L. and Brian, P. W. (1936). Diseases of mint. *Rep. agric. hort. Res. Stn Univ. Bristol*, 1935, 115–7

Ogilvie, L. and Thorpe, I. G. (1961). New light on epidemics of black stem rust of wheat. *Sci. Prog., Lond.*, **49**, 209–27

Ruttle, M. L. and Fraser, W. P. (1927). A cytological study of *Puccinia coronata* Cda. on Banner and Cowra 35 oats. *Univ. Calif. Publs Bot.*, No. 14, 21–72

Sanford, G. B. and Broadfoot, W. C. (1932). Epidemiology of stripe rust in western Canada. *Scient. Agric.*, **13**, 77–96

Stakman, E. C. and Lambert, E. B. (1928). The relation of temperature during the growing season in the spring wheat area of the United States to the occurrence of stem rust epidemics. *Phytopathology*, **18**, 369–74

Stakman, E. C. and Christensen, C. M. (1946). Aerobiology in relation to plant disease. *Bot. Rev.*, **12**, 205–53

Stakman, E. C. and Harrar, J. G. (1957). *Principles of Plant Pathology*, pp. 207–57. Ronald Press, New York.

Stakman, E. C., Stewart, D. M. and Loegering, W. Q. (1962). Identification of physiologic races of *Puccinia graminis* var. *tritici*. *Bull. agric. Res. Serv., Wash.*, No. E–617

Tollenaar, H. and Houston, B. R. (1967). A study on the epidemiology of stripe rust, *Puccinia striiformis* West. in California. *Can. J. Bot.*, **45**, 291–307

Waterhouse, W. L. (1921). Studies in the physiology of parasitism. VII. Infection of *Berberis vulgaris* by sporidia of *Puccinia graminis*. *Ann. Bot., Lond.*, **35**, 557–64

Williams, P. G., Scott, K. J. and Kuhl, J. L. (1966). Vegetative growth of *Puccinia graminis* f. sp. *tritici* in vitro. *Phytopathology*, **56**, 1418–9

Williams, P. G., Scott, K. J., Kuhl, J. L. and Maclean, D. J. (1967). Sporulation and pathogenicity of *Puccinia graminis* f. sp. *tritici* grown on an artificial medium. *Phytopathology*, **57**, 326–7

Wilson, M. and Henderson, D. M. (1966). *British Rust Fungi*, 384 pp. Cambridge University Press.

CHAPTER 8

Smuts

Smut diseases are caused by fungi belonging to the Ustilaginales and are so called because of the soot-like masses of spores which many of these fungi produce on their hosts. The morphology of these spores, the way they germinate, and the variety and position of the sori in which they are produced are the main features for determining species. The biology of these fungi has been fully covered by Fischer and Holton (1957) and there are excellent monographs dealing with the smuts of particular regions, (e.g. Ainsworth and Sampson, 1950; Mundkur and Thirumalachar, 1952; Fischer, 1953).

Smut spores and their germination

The smut spores (brand spores or chlamydospores as they are sometimes called) may be smooth-walled or sculptured in various ways. They are all 1-celled, but some are produced singly, e.g. *Ustilago* spp., and others in groups called spore balls (Figure 8.1). In some genera, these spore balls consist entirely of spores, e.g. *Tolyposporium*, in others there are sterile elements which cover the viable spores, e.g. *Urocystis*. The sori in many genera are initially covered only by host tissue, e.g. *Ustilago*, *Tilletia*, but in others a peridium of fungal tissue is also formed over the developing spores, e.g. *Sphacelotheca*, *Sorosporium*.

On germination most smut spores give rise to a germ-tube of limited growth called a promycelium but the further development of this differs with the species (Figure 8.2). For example, in *Ustilago avenae*, which causes loose smut of oats, the promycelium becomes septate, and each cell by budding gives rise to a number of small, hyaline, thin-walled cells or sporidia. After these are released they fuse in pairs and produce a mycelium capable of infecting the host. In *Ustilago nuda* which causes loose smut of wheat and barley there are no sporidia but mycelia develop from the promycelial cells and fusion occurs between adjacent branches or with branches of promycelia from other germinating spores. In *Tilletia caries*, which causes wheat bunt the promycelium remains aseptate and eight

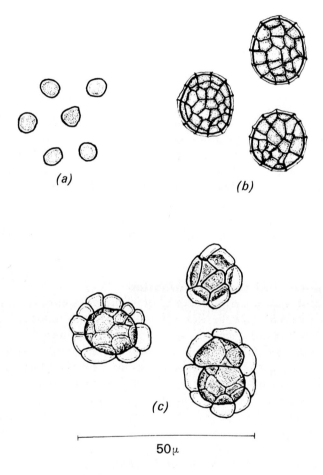

FIGURE 8.1 Smut spores. (*a*) *Ustilago avenae* from oats (*b*) *Tilletia caries* from wheat (*c*) *Urocystis agropyri* from *Holcus*.

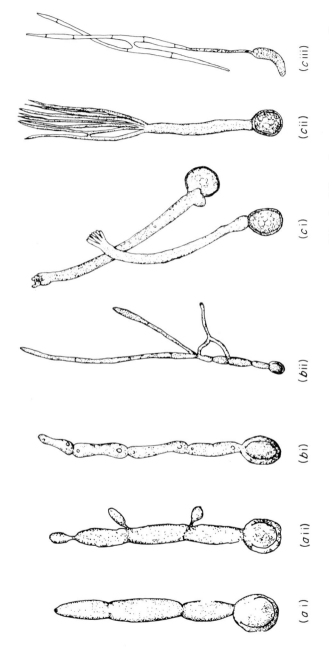

FIGURE 8.2 Germination of smut spores. (*a*) *Ustilago avenae*, sporidia budding from septate promycelium, (*b*) *Ustilago nuda*, septate promycelium and fusion of promycelial branches, (*c*) *Tilletia caries*, formation of sporidia terminally on non-septate promycelium, fusion of two sporidia and formation of secondary sporidium. From Stakman, 1913, *Bull. Univ. Minn. agric. exp. Stn.*, No. 133.

filiform, septate sporidia develop terminally. Fusion then occurs between cells of adjacent sporidia, and from the fused cells secondary sporidia are formed capable of infecting wheat.

In each species a binucleate (dikaryotic) mycelium results from these fusions between sporidia, mycelia or cells, and generally in the smuts only this mycelium is capable of infecting, and sporulating on, the host. The smuts then, like the rusts, are heterothallic. The parasitic mycelium is binucleate and so are the young spores formed from it; on germination these give rise to haploid sporidia or hyphae with haploid cells. The smuts contain fewer obligate parasites than the rusts, for many have now been grown on artificial media, particularly in the haploid phase and much is known of the behaviour and genetics of these fungi (Halisky, 1965).

Although the mycelium of many smuts may be distributed throughout the host (except for a few instances to be discussed later) sporulation is generally restricted to certain parts of the plant. In all the economically important smuts sporulation occurs on stems and leaves and within inflorescences. The inflorescence smuts are by far the largest group, within which several types can be distinguished. Some like *U. nuda* more or less destroy the entire inflorescence, some leave the rachis intact, e.g. *Ustilago hordei* in covered smut of barley, oats and other grasses, some sporulate in the ovaries only, e.g. *T. caries*, and others sporulate in the stamens of their hosts like *Ustilago violacea*, the cause of anther smut of carnation and other species of the Caryophyllaceae.

Modes of infection

Basically there are three ways in which smut fungi infect their hosts and they are best considered in terms of specific diseases.

1. *Embryo infection.* The best example is loose smut of wheat and barley caused by *U. nuda*. Generally it is not possible to determine whether a plant is diseased or not until the ears emerge when in infected plants the inflorescence is replaced by a mass of black, smut spores. Only in extremely susceptible varieties is the flag leaf itself infected. In a few resistant varieties infection may be limited to the glumes and then the sori occur in lines. Once the spores are exposed they are blown by wind to the flowers of healthy plants and only at this stage can plants become infected. Penetration usually takes place through the ovary wall and not via the stigma and style as was previously supposed (Batts, 1955). The hyphae cross the cells of the pericarp (fruit coat), enter the testa (seed coat) and then move towards the ovary. On reaching the ovary the hyphae

turn sharply from the testa, enter the scutellum and pass into the growing point of the embryo. Within the pericarp and testa the mycelium is intracellular, but is intercellular within the embryonic tissues.

The presence of the fungus apparently has no effect on grain development and it is impossible to tell from external appearances that a seed is infected, but there are techniques for the microscopical detection of the fungus in excised embryos (Russell and Popp, 1951; Laidlaw, 1961). The mycelium remains dormant until the seed is sown and begins to germinate, then it also becomes active. It passes into the crown node of the seedling and permeates the tissues including the developing inflorescences. When the tillers lengthen by the growth of the lowest internodes the fungus is carried up in the inflorescence primordia (Batts and Jeater, 1958). Spore formation begins some weeks before the ears emerge and is complete at emergence. With this smut then, colonization of the host is initiated by mycelium already present within the embryo and this inoculum becomes established during flowering in the previous season.

2. *Seedling infection.* With many smuts infection occurs at the seedling stage but the exact mode of infection varies with the species involved. In loose smut of oats, caused by *U. avenae* (Figure 8.3*a*), the spores are dispersed at flowering like those of *U. nuda*, but on germination the mycelium becomes established in the glumes and the outer parts of the seed, i.e. in the pericarp; it does not invade the embryo (Gage, 1927). When this seed is planted the dormant mycelium renews its activities and invades the young seedling (Mills, 1966). There is also evidence that spores which become lodged at flowering between the hull and caryopsis of the seed, but do not germinate, also act as inoculum for the infection of the developing seedlings in the following spring (McKay, 1936). Spores on the seed surface appear not to be important in infection by this fungus.

The reverse is true of bunt of wheat caused by *T. caries* (Figure 8.3*b*). This is sometimes called stinking smut because the spores *en masse* have an odour of bad fish due to the presence of trimethylamine. Losses by bunt arise from the replacement of all parts of the grain, except the coat, by smut spores. Infected grains are known as bunt balls and they are shorter and plumper than healthy seed. The bunt balls often remain intact until threshing when they become broken, and millions of spores are released and contaminate the healthy seed. Machinery also becomes contaminated and endangers successive harvestings. When this seed is sown the spores on the seed coat germinate and the binucleate hyphae which result from the fusion of sporidial cells infect the young coleoptile. The subsequent development of the fungus within the seedling is basically similar to that of *U. nuda* in wheat and barley. The inflorescence primordia are colonized at a very early stage in their development and the fungus is carried in these when the internodes elongate (Swinburne, 1963). The smut spores develop in place of the embryo and endosperm but unlike loose smut of wheat it is not possible to tell whether an ear is infected when it emerges from its sheath. Symptoms become apparent as the ear gets older. Infected ears are a darker green and remain green longer than healthy ones, and they have a loose and open appearance owing to the greater divergence of the chaff, bunt balls being fatter than healthy grains.

In contrast to bunt in which the grain coat remains intact and the smut spores are not visible until threshing, in covered smut of barley caused by *U. hordei* the dark mass of spores is enclosed only by the thin glumes and is clearly visible. Spores are liberated *en masse* during threshing but splits in the covering membrane may permit an earlier dissemination of spores while grain is developing

(a)   (b)

FIGURE 8.3 Two cereal smuts. (a) loose smut of oats, (b) bunt of wheat. Five bunted grains have been removed and two of them crushed to show the mass of black smut spores. Photograph by A. Ironside.

on healthy plants in the field. In this instance mycelium may develop in the pericarp or spores become lodged beneath the seed hulls as with *U. avenae* and oats (Tapke, 1940). Infection then proceeds when the seed germinates. Seedling infection from spores and/or mycelium also occurs with stripe smut of grasses caused by *Ustilago striiformis* (Davis, 1926) and flag smut of wheat and grasses caused by *Urocystis agropyri* (Purdy, 1965).

For some smut fungi that infect their hosts at the seedling stage seed-borne inoculum is relatively unimportant. Two examples are *Tilletia contraversa* causing dwarf bunt of wheat (Holton and others, 1949; Meiners, 1959) and *Urocystis cepulae* causing onion smut (Anderson, 1921). With these, infections arise predominantly from soil-borne spores which may persist for many years. Those of *U. cepulae*, for example, are reported to remain viable for 15 years. This fungus attacks seedlings only during the first 2–3 weeks after germination. After this the cotyledon becomes resistant and provides a barrier to infection. The immature tissue beneath the cotyledon remains susceptible, however, and if the cotyledon is removed infection can occur. On infected plants dark coloured spots or streaks are clearly visible on the cotyledons and sometimes on successive leaves (Figure 8.4). These are the spore masses beneath the epidermis. Eventually the epidermis bursts, and the spores are liberated and contaminate the surrounding soil.

3. *Shoot infection*. A few smut fungi enter their hosts through the young shoots, particularly through the buds. This mode of infection was first demonstrated for *U. violaceae* on *Melandrium album* (Fischer and Holton, 1957, p. 154). Once established, the mycelium of this fungus perennates in the host root-stock, grows up with the young shoots and subsequently sporulates in the anthers. The spores fall to the ground but do not germinate until the following spring. Then they produce many sporidia which infect young shoots of healthy plants. *Ustilago scitaminea* also infects sugarcane through buds on the young offshoots or sets (Ajrekar, 1916). The spores adhere to the planting material and this is one way in which the fungus is distributed throughout the plantation. Shoot infection also occurs in the long smut of sorghum caused by *Tolyposporium ehrenbergii* (Prasad, 1945).

In the smuts mentioned so far infection of the hosts is 'systemic' in the sense that the mycelium becomes established in several parts of the plant and sporulation occurs often at a site far removed from the point of entry. With some smuts infection is localized and sporulation is restricted to the part of the plant penetrated. The

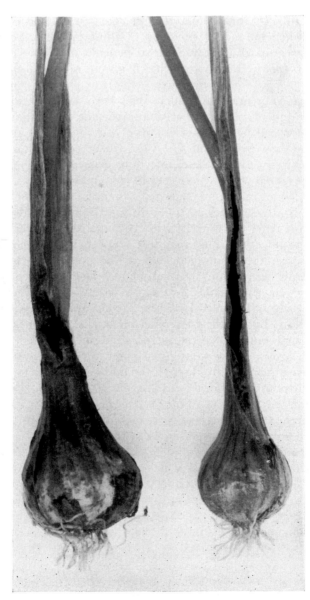

FIGURE 8.4 Onion smut.
Photograph copyright D. E. Green.

best known example is boil smut or common smut of corn (Figure 8.5) caused by *Ustilago maydis* (Christensen, 1963). Another example is rice bunt caused by *Tilletia barclayana* (Chowdhury, 1946); each bunted grain represents a separate infection and all infections remain localized. The spores of *T. barclayana* survive on stubble left in the fields and germinate to give large numbers of sporidia. The sporidia are then blown by wind and infect the developing grains of the new crop. The sori caused by *Entyloma* spp. are generally assumed to result from local infections because of their discrete appearance (Figure 8.6). There is some evidence to support this for *Entyloma calendulae* f. *dahliae* (Pape, 1926), but otherwise the group has been neglected because few species are of economic importance.

FIGURE 8.5 Maize smut. Only the top grains of the cob have been infected by *Ustilago maydis*. Photograph copyright D. E. Green.

FIGURE 8.6 Dahlia smut, showing the discrete lesions of *Entyloma calendulae* f. *dahliae*,
each with a surrounding, chlorotic zone.
Photograph copyright D. E. Green.

Effects on the host

In the inflorescence smuts, particularly those of cereals, e.g. loose
smut of wheat and barley, there is a direct loss in yield through the
replacement of the flowering parts, but before this there are few
indications of any adverse effect on host growth. With the bunts
there may be excess tillering and some dwarfing, the latter particularly with *T. contraversa*, but there is a remarkable balance
between host and parasite until the later stages of host growth.
Then, for reasons not yet known, the smut fungi rapidly colonize
the embryonic grain tissues and sporulate.

Other smut fungi have more striking effects on host growth. *U. maydis*, for example, induces large, blister-like galls on corn and *Sphacelotheca reiliana* on the same host results in leaf-like structures in the staminate and pistillate flowers, a phenomenon known as phyllody. One of the most interesting effects is hermaphroditism induced by *U. violacea* in dioecious members of the Caryophyllaceae. When this fungus infects the pistillate flowers it causes stamens to develop but then colonizes them so that they contain only smut spores.

Control

The cereals smuts have received most attention as regards control because of their great economic importance. Seed treatment of some kind is frequently employed, the nature of this depending on the seed-borne inoculum.

A hot-water treatment is generally used to eliminate *U. nuda* from wheat and barley seed. Seed is placed in hot water under controlled conditions so that the smut mycelium within the embryo is killed but the seed is not. Jensen first treated barley in this way in 1888. He immersed seed for 5 minutes in water at $52 \cdot 8°$, then poured cold water over it. There have been many modifications since then. Some employ several tanks. For example, in one the grain is presoaked for 4–6 hours in cold water, then for a few minutes in water at about $48 \cdot 9°$ and finally in water at $53 \cdot 9°$ for 10 minutes. The figures given are for wheat; slightly lower temperatures, $51 \cdot 1°–52 \cdot 2°$ are used in the hot tank for barley. The short immersion at $48 \cdot 9°$ prevents undue cooling by the seed of the water in the last tank. After the final hot treatment the seed is plunged into cold water (Batts, 1956).

Other methods use only one tank and the presoaking is replaced by a longer period in warm water. The length of soaking depends on the temperature. The effective and practical range for wheat is from $1\frac{1}{2}$–2 hours at $48 \cdot 9°$ to 5–6 hours at $40 \cdot 6°$; the corresponding range for barley is $1\frac{1}{2}$ hours at $48 \cdot 9°$ to 5 hours at $40 \cdot 6°$ (Doling, 1965).

Hot-water treatment is basically simple but with large quantities there are considerable practical difficulties in ensuring that all the seeds receive the appropriate treatment. If the grain temperature does not reach the required level the fungus is not killed; on the other hand if the temperature exceeds those stated seed germination is drastically reduced. In this respect single-tank treatments allow a greater margin of error. Another difficulty is that treated seed has to be dried relatively quickly to stop mould development.

Soaking seed for much longer periods in comparatively cold water can also be effective. With barley, successful elimination of *U. nuda* has been achieved by soaking for 56–64 hours at 22·2°–25·0° (Tyner, 1953). Why the fungus is killed by this treatment is not entirely clear but one suggestion is that quinones are formed as germination begins and these are responsible (Tyner, 1957).

A variation of the water soaking involves storage under anaerobic conditions. Seed is soaked in water at room temperatures for periods up to 4 hours and then stored in air-tight containers. The length of storage depends on the temperature: 36 hours at 32°, 48 hours at 28°, and 60 hours at 24°. Hebert (1956) who devised this method considers that the removal of oxygen by the respiring seed in the closed container is an important factor in eliminating the fungus.

The general relationship between temperature and length of treatment for the single-tank, hot-water method and the water-soaking and anaerobic-wetting methods can be expressed as $t = k \log h + c$ where t = temperature, h = minimum number of hours and k and c are constants. Doling (1965) found that most of the satisfactory treatments reported in the literature gave points close to the curve represented by this equation.

Fungicides are not generally of any value in dealing with loose smut because the mycelium is internal but a systemic fungicide would obviously be of value. Recently, control of this disease by treating wheat and barley seed with such a substance, vitavax (2,3,-dihydro-5-carboxanilido-6-methyl-1,4-oxathiin), has been reported (Jones and Barnett, 1967).

With some bunts and covered smuts the fungus is present only in or on the outer parts of the seed, and treating the seed with a chemical has long been a standard method of control. Copper sulphate was used in some of the early methods. A 2% solution was sprinkled over the heaped grain which was turned until all the seed became wet. The seed was then dried. Formalin (99·7 kg commercial formalin/m³ water) was often used in place of copper sulphate and alternatively, grain was soaked in these solutions in large containers. In 1919, a dry seed dressing of copper carbonate was introduced. This was not only less injurious to the seed than the copper sulphate and formalin steeps but met a popular demand for a dry treatment. Work in Germany at this time produced another type of material, an organomercurial compound containing about 18% mercury, which was called 'Upsulun'. This was intended for use in water but the demands for dry treatments were such that similar mercurial compounds were incorporated in dry seed dressings, the first of which was called 'Tillatin R'. Subsequently other mercurial compounds were developed notably ethylmercury chloride ('Ceresan') ethylmercury phosphate ('New Improved Ceresan') and other ethylmercury derivatives, phenylmercury urea and methyl-mercury dicyanadiamide ('Panogen'). Over the last two decades more organomercurials have been produced, many for use as liquid seed dressings which have again found favour mainly because the poisonous dusts are too easily inhaled. The search continues for materials equally effective as seed dressings but less toxic than mercury. Hexachlorobenzene is one which has been found useful for dwarf bunt control in the Pacific Northwest (Purdy, 1957). It appears particularly effective against the soil-borne spores.

Where the smut spores persist in the soil control is usually more difficult. Treatment of the soil with chemicals has been used to control onion smut, for example by trickling 40% formalin in the seed drills before covering them, but more recently there has been some success with seed dressings particularly with ferric dimethyl-dithiocarbamate (ferbam), tetramethylthiuram disulphide (thiram), applied with a potash resin sticker (Linn, 1951; Croxall and Hickman, 1953; Larson and Walker, 1953), and hexachlorobenzene (Duran and Fischer, 1959).

Apart from fungicides smut diseases, especially in the cereals, are controlled by planting resistant varieties. A useful review of varietal reactions and smut resistance is given in Fischer and Holton (1957).

REFERENCES

Ainsworth, G. C. and Sampson, K. (1960). *The British Smut Fungi*, 137 pp. Commonwealth Mycological Institute, Kew.

Ajrekar, S. L. (1916). On the mode of infection and prevention of the smut disease of sugarcane. *Agric. J. India*, **11**, 288–95

Anderson, P. J. (1921). Development and pathogenesis of the onion smut fungus. *Tech. Bull. Mass. agric. Exp. Stn.*, No. 4, 99–133

Batts, C. C. V. (1955). Observations on the infection of wheat by loose smut (*Ustilago tritici* (Pers.) Rostr.). *Trans. Br. mycol. Soc.*, **38**, 465–75

Batts, C. C. V. (1956). The control of loose smut in wheat and barley. *Ann. appl. Biol.*, **44**, 437–52

Batts, C. C. V. and Jeater, A. (1958). The development of loose smut (*Ustilago tritici*) in susceptible varieties of wheat, and some observations on field infection. *Trans. Br. mycol. Soc.*, **41**, 115–25

Chowdhury, S. (1946). Mode of transmission of the bunt of rice. *Curr. Sci.*, **15**, 111

Christensen, J. J. (1963). Corn smut caused by *Ustilago maydis*. *Monogr. Am. phytopath. Soc.*, No. 2, 41 pp.

Croxall, H. E. and Hickman, C. J. (1953). The control of onion smut (*Urocystis cepulae*) by seed treatment. *Ann. appl. Biol.*, **40**, 176–83

Davis, W. H. (1926). Life history of *Ustilago striaeformis* (Westd.) Niessl. which causes a leaf smut in Timothy. *J. agric. Res.*, **32**, 69–76

Doling, D. A. (1965). Single-bath hot-water treatment for the control of loose smut (*Ustilago nuda*) in cereals. *Ann. appl. Biol.*, **55**, 295–301

Duran, R. and Fischer, G. W. (1959). The efficacy and limitations of hexachlorobenzene for the control of onion smut. *Pl. Dis. Reptr.*, **43**, 880–8

Fischer, G. W. (1953). *Manual of North American Smut Fungi*, 343 pp. Ronald Press, New York.

Fischer, G. W. and Holton, C. S. (1957). *Biology and Control of the Smut Fungi*, 622 pp. Ronald Press, New York.

Gage, G. R. (1927). Studies of the life history of *Ustilago avenae* (Pers.) Jensen and of *Ustilago levis* (Kell. and Swing.) Magn. *Mem. Cornell agric. Exp. Stn.*, No. 109, 35 pp.

Halisky, P. M. (1965). Physiologic specialization and genetics of the smut fungi III. *Bot. Rev.*, **31**, 114–50

Hebert, T. T. (1956). Mode of action of the wet anaerobic storage treatment for the control of loose smut in barley. *Phytopathology*, **46**, 14

Holton, C. S., Bamberg, R. H. and Woodward, R. W. (1949). Progress in the study of dwarf bunt of winter wheat in the Pacific Northwest. *Phytopathology*, **39**, 986–1000

Jones, J. P. and Barnett, R. D. (1967). A promising new control for wheat and barley loose smut. *Arkans. Fm Res.*, **16**, 2 (*Rev. appl. Mycol.*, **47**, 133)

Laidlaw, W. M. R. (1961). Extracting barley embryos for loose smut examination. *Pl. Path.*, **10**, 63–5

Larson, R. H. and Walker, J. C. (1953). Thiram for smut control in onion set plantings. *Phytopathology*, **43**, 596–7

Linn, M. B. (1951). Control of smut in bulb onions by pelleting the seed with technical thiram. *Pl. Dis. Reptr*, **35**, 94–6

McKay, R. (1936). Method of infection of oat grain with *Ustilago avenae* and the influence of external factors on the incidence of the disease. *Sci. Proc. R. Dublin Soc.*, N.S. **21**, 297–307

Meiners, J. P. (1959). Methods of infecting wheat with the dwarf bunt fungus. *Phytopathology*, **49**, 4–8

Mills, J. T. (1966). The development of loose smut (*Ustilago avenae*) in the oat plant with observations on spore formation. *Trans. Br. mycol. Soc.*, **49**, 651–63

Mundkur, B. B. and Thirumalachar, M. J. (1952). *Ustilaginales of India*. 84 pp. Commonwealth Mycological Institute, Kew.

Pape, H. (1926). Eine für Deutschland neue Blattfleckenkrankheit der Dahlien. *Gartenwelt*, **30**, 632–4 (*Rev. appl. Mycol.*, **6**, 97)

Prasad, N. (1945). Long smut of sorghum—method of infection. *Curr. Sci.*, **14**, 239

Purdy, L. H. (1957). Differential response of dwarf bunt to seed and soil surface treatment with hexachlorobenzene. *Pl. Dis. Reptr.*, **41**, 916–8

Purdy, L. H. (1965). Flag smut of wheat. *Bot. Rev.*, **31**, 565–606

Russell, R. C. and Popp, W. (1951). The embryo test as a method of forecasting loose smut infection in barley. *Scient. Agric.*, **31**, 559–65

Swinburne, T. R. (1963). Infection of wheat by *Tilletia caries* (DC.). Tul., the causal organism of bunt. *Trans. Br. mycol. Soc.*, **46**, 45–56

Tapke, V. F. (1940). Studies on the natural inoculation of seed barley with covered smut (*Ustilago hordei*). *J. agric. Res.*, **60**, 787–810

Tyner, L. E. (1953). The control of loose smut of barley and wheat by Spergon and by soaking in water at room temperature. *Phytopathology*, **43**, 313–6

Tyner, L. E. (1957). Factors influencing the elimination of loose smut from barley by water-soak treatments. *Phytopathology*, **47**, 420–2

CHAPTER 9

Blight

Death of the tissues is a common feature of plant disease and the next three chapters are concerned with particular diseases in which this symptom predominates. The term 'blight' is applied, often indiscriminately, to a number of different diseases and insect attack but especially when leaf damage is sudden and serious. Given the right conditions many pathogens can cause blights in this sense but there are a select few whose effects on their hosts are so regularly devastating that the diseases they cause fully merit this term.

LATE BLIGHT OF POTATOES

The role this disease played in the Irish Potato famine of the mid 19th Century is reason enough for its inclusion here, and is well described by E. C. Large (1940) in '*The Advance of the Fungi*' and by C. Woodham-Smith (1963) in '*The Great Hunger*'. Ironically plant pathology has benefitted from this disaster because it gave the necessary impetus for an intensive study of the disease which continues today and from which is derived much information basic to our understanding of plant diseases in general.

The fungus *Phytophthora infestans* causes late blight of potatoes; it also attacks tomatoes but it will be considered here only in relation to potatoes. On leaves and stems it results in dark-brown lesions of varying size and shape, and under moist conditions produces at the edges of these lesions on the lower leaf surfaces a mass of sporangio-phores visible to the naked eye as a white bloom (Figure 9.1).

FIGURE 9.1 Late blight of potatoes. The under surface of an infected leaf with *Phytophthora infestans* sporulating at the edge of the lesion. From R. McKay, 1955, *Potato Diseases* by permission of Mrs. R. McKay and The Three Candles Limited.

With favourable conditions the number of lesions increases rapidly, they coalesce and the potato haulms (shoots) are killed (Figure 9.2). The whole process, when the disease is most severe, takes some 3–4 weeks.

Tubers may be infected by spores which are washed into the soil from leaves and stems or by coming into contact with infected haulms at lifting. Symptoms on the tubers vary—there may be irregular areas that are dark, slightly sunken and associated with a reddish-brown rot or the tubers may appear sound. Rotting often occurs during storage mainly from the invasion via the blighted areas of other microorganisms notably bacteria.

Sources of inoculum

The early stages of the disease in the field, and particularly the methods by which the fungus overwinters, have received much attention. Considering that the fungus is a member of the Peronosporales it might be thought that it overwinters as oospores, but while these can be produced in culture (Clinton, 1911) and on potato tubers (Murphy, 1927) it seems that in most potato growing regions of the Northern Hemisphere they play no part in the life cycle. Oospores may, however, contribute to the survival of *P. infestans* in Mexico (Gallegly and Galindo, 1957).

In New Zealand *P. infestans* can overwinter on wild perennial species of *Solanum* (Driver, 1957) and these may be important as sources of inoculum. In Britain there is still no convincing evidence for alternative hosts. *P. infestans* has been found on certain other plants, e.g. *Petunia hybrida*, *Datura stramonium*, *Solanum nigrum* and *Solanum dulcamara* but only late in the potato growing season and on senescent leaves that have soon fallen (Hirst and Moore, 1957).

Infected tubers have been considered to be the principal source of inoculum since de Bary demonstrated in 1893 that the fungus could grow from such tubers into the developing sprouts. In the field, where there may be as many as 12,000 shoots per acre, this is difficult to demonstrate because by the time a group of plants is sufficiently infected to be visible it is usually too late to locate the source. This was partly overcome in some experiments by Hirst and Stedman (1960b). They planted a high proportion of diseased tubers in plots small enough to examine all plants each week. They were not able to trace completely the continuation of mycelium from shoot to tuber but they did follow lesions as far as possible below ground without disturbing the root system. To confirm that these lesions were those of *P. infestans* they waited until a leaf petiole was infected, then removed this and incubated it in a damp chamber to induce sporangia. From experiments over 5 years they found that under normal conditions small loci of blighted plants developed around plants with stem lesions. Generally the first lesions appeared 62 days after planting and 38 days before blight became general in the district.

FIGURE 9.2 Late blight of potatoes. Severe infection of the variety Ulster Torch. A Shell photograph, copyright.

F

These particular experiments gave another interesting result. On irrigated plots loci of blighted plants occurred that were not associated with stem lesions, at a time when infection by spores coming from outside the experimental area could be discounted. It seemed that the source might be blighted tubers which had not produced infected stems. This was an interesting observation because other investigators had doubted whether continuous mycelial growth from tubers to stem was necessary for establishing infection (e.g. Naoumova, 1939).

Hirst and Stedman investigated this by infecting tubers of the variety Pentland Ace with a race of *P. infestans* which could be readily distinguished from those normally encountered in the area. The 'eyes' of these tubers were removed so that they could not produce any shoots and they were interplanted with healthy tubers of the variety Majestic. Hirst and Stedman found that loci of infected Majestic plants developed in which the inoculum must have come from the blighted Pentland Ace tubers. Other data suggested that this occurred only when the soil moisture was maintained at a high level for certain periods. The most plausible explanation seems to be that under these conditions zoospores are produced which splash from soil onto the lower leaves. In the experimental plots lesions appeared first on these leaves, a feature which lends weight to this view.

It has been calculated that one primary focus of infection is sufficient to establish blight in a square kilometre of potatoes. On this basis and on data from their own experiments Hirst and Stedman (1960*b*) calculate that as few as 0·01% blighted tubers in the field stocks are sufficient and an elimination of such a small contamination is obviously more than could be expected of any commercial inspection.

Infected potato tubers may, however, serve as sources of inoculum in other ways for often at harvesting some are discarded in the borders of the fields or at the end of the winter partly rotten tubers from potato stores are dumped on waste piles. Some of the tubers give rise to blighted shoots, and sporangia are blown from them to nearby crops of potatoes. It is odd that in Britain and other countries little attention has been paid to these sources of inoculum for there is impressive evidence from North America, more specifically from Aroostook County, Maine, of the association of local outbreaks of blight with piles of discarded potatoes, or cull piles as they are called (Bonde and Schultz, 1943).

Factors influencing disease development

During the past 40 years there has been much research on the factors influencing disease development. Van Everdingen (1926) was one of the first to define the weather conditions necessary for an outbreak of blight in a potato crop. His work was developed by Beaumont (1947) who examined critically the meteorological data for the periods preceding blight outbreaks in southwestern England. He found that if for 2 days there was a temperature not less than 10° and a relative humidity of 75% or above then blight could be expected approximately 10 days afterwards. These periods are called 'Beaumont periods' and are the basis of a blight forecasting system in England and Wales. Alternatively predictions are based on 'Smith periods' (Smith, 1956), in which a relative humidity of 90% or above for at least 11 hours on each of the 2 days replaces the 75% R.H. level of Beaumont. The temperature requirement is the same.

Slightly different criteria for forecasting the first appearance of blight have been developed in other countries (Cox and Large, 1960). The common factor of these methods is that they attempt to predict the conditions under which free water will be present on the leaves for a period of approximately 15 hours which allows the sporangia to germinate and infect the host (Melhus, 1915).

Secondary development of the disease may or may not be dependant on further Beaumont or Smith periods. Whereas sporangia first entering the crop from outside (not from the internal loci of infection previously discussed) are relatively dry and need free water for germination, those produced on the first-formed lesions are turgid and about 1% of them can germinate at relative humidities between 95% and 100%. This may not seem important but a blight lesion frequently produces 150 sporangia/mm² and a well-grown potato plant has approximately 3 million mm² of leaf. If one assumes that only 1% of this area is blighted and that only 1% of the sporangia which, potentially, can be produced from this infected tissue are capable of germinating at high relative humidities, this still gives 45,000 sporangia per plant for which presumably Beaumont periods are not essential for infection (Glendinning and others, 1963).

In addition to any fungal factor, there are changes in microclimate which result from the development of the crop itself. Hirst and Stedman (1960a) found that above crops (where Beaumont and Smith periods are recorded) the number of hours per day with a relative humidity not less than 90% rose and fell with the passing of wet spells. Initially this was true within crops, but when foliage was dense, the rise in relative humidity after rain often persisted through intervals of dry weather. Such conditions usually preceded blight epidemics by 1–3 weeks. In a sense then, the growth of the potato crop is self-destructive.

There are other factors connected with the potato plant. In Scotland, Grainger (1956) found that some early Beaumont periods were not followed by outbreaks of blight in the potato crop. He showed that there was a relationship between the Cp/Rs ratio of the host and the development of *P. infestans*, where Cp is the total carbohydrate of the whole plant and Rs is the residual dry weight of the shoot. No blight occurred when this ratio was less than unity even though inoculum was present. Grainger calls this phase, when Beaumont periods are ineffective, the 'physiological barrier', and forecasts of blight must take account of this. A method of estimating the Cp/Rs ratio in the field has been devised by Grainger and Rutherford (1963).

Control

One effect of *P. infestans* is to reduce the photosynthetic area of the potato plant and so limit the growth of the tubers. For all practical purposes it can be assumed that when 75% of the foliage is attacked, translocation of synthesised materials to the tubers ceases and they stop growing. The earlier in the season that this point is reached the greater will be the loss in yield (p. 306). Conversely, if the destruction of the foliage can be delayed for a while there is likely to be a corresponding improvement in yield. This is the basis on which protective sprays are applied. A number of materials are used, particularly Bordeaux and Burgundy mixtures and other copper fungicides, also some of the dithiocarbamates such as maneb, and organic tin compounds. To be effective the first spray should be made when there are only a few plants infected here and there (0·1% infection). The progress of blight under these circumstances is depicted in Figure 9.3. The delay in reaching the 50% blight point is called the 'mean prolongation of growth'. The timing of the first sprays is thus all important and hence the need for some system of accurately forecasting blight.

Another type of spraying is that designed to kill off the haulms before lifting and so decrease tuber infection. This treatment is particularly important with outbreaks late in the season where direct losses of yield by blight are small but tuber infection can be considerable. It is also important with potato varieties whose tubers are particularly susceptible such as King Edward. Experiments at

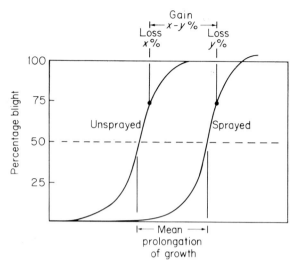

FIGURE 9.3 Effect of correct spraying on the progress of blight. Based on Large, 1952, *Pl. Path.* **1**, 109–17

Rothamsted by Hirst and others (1965) showed that tuber infection in this variety can cause greater losses than premature defoliation. In the 1960 epidemic, yield was highest in trial plots in which the haulms were killed when there was 5% blight present. Yields were not increased by allowing haulms to survive beyond this stage even in other seasons (1959–1963) when blight was late or slow in developing.

Sulphuric acid (77%) is often used to destroy haulms either at a dilution of 3m³ acid/17m³ water for high volume applications or without diluting at 1l./44.4m² (20 gal./acre) low volume application (Large, 1952a). This has been partly replaced in recent years by bipyridyl herbicides such as diquat (1, 1'-ethylene-2, 2'-dipyridinium dibromide).

All varieties grown on a commercial scale are susceptible to *P. infestans* but there are considerable differences among them. Some show relatively little damage compared with others under similar conditions. This field resistance, as it is frequently called, is distinct from the type of resistance which hitherto has occupied the attention of plant breeders in which a hypersensitive reaction to *P. infestans* has been transferred from clones of *Solanum demissum*. The two types of resistance are discussed in Chapter 21.

FIREBLIGHT OF PEARS

There are three reasons for selecting this disease as a second example of 'blight': it was the first disease shown to be caused by a bacterium, one of the earliest in which an insect vector was demonstrated, and it is still one of the most important and destructive diseases of pomaceous fruit trees (Curtis, 1934; Parker and others, 1956; Crosse and others, 1960). The bacterium concerned is *Erwinia amylovora*. Its chief hosts are pear, apple and quince but it also occurs on other Rosaceae such as *Crataegus* and these alternative hosts can be important sources of inoculum (Rosen and Groves, 1928). The disease will be considered here with reference mainly to pears.

Disease development

There are several common names for the disease, each describing one particular phase or symptom (Thomas and Parker, 1933). The disease syndrome can be summaried as follows. In the spring, when the flowers open, individual blossoms or entire trusses appear water soaked, They shrivel and turn black (blossom blight). As the bacteria progress down the fruiting spur they enter the leaf petioles and midribs. The leaves become scorched at the margins and shrivel (Figure 9.4), but do not drop (leaf blight). Finally the whole spur is infected and dies (spur blight). Terminal shoots, and suckers, also become infected (twig blight) and in these the progress of the pathogen is usually much more rapid than in the fruiting spur. Recently invaded bark appears dark green or oily and drops containing masses of the bacteria frequently exude from it. The leaves on these twigs, like those on the fruiting spurs, do not drop, and an infected tree with numerous twigs bearing these dead leaves resembles one scorched by fire, hence the name fireblight.

The downward extension of bacteria from infected spurs and twigs is restricted by various host reactions such as cork formation, and a canker (see Chapter 14) develops at the base of the dead spur or twig. Some cankers which arise from early spring infections may eventually extend for several feet; others, particularly those from late infections of secondary blossoms, remain small. The cankered area appears watersoaked at first, then as the bark dries becomes slightly depressed with a definite line of demarcation between diseased and healthy tissue (Figure 9.5). There is usually some exudate from an active canker and the bark when cut shows characteristic reddish-brown (or 'foxy-red') lines and mottling. In an inactive or dormant canker there is often a definite crevice or

FIGURE 9.4 Fireblight of pear. The infection has spread from the blossom on the lateral twig (right of the photograph). Photograph copyright East Malling Research Station.

crack in the bark or a raised, marginal callus separating the living and dead tissue. Cankers are difficult to spot on scaly or rough bark but can usually be detected by the stub of the dead·spur or twig through which infection occurred. In the Pacific Northwest of the United States cankers are formed on the roots, similar to those on the main stems, by invasion of bacteria through suckers.

Young fruit may also be attacked, particularly with pears (fruit blight). The fruit appears watersoaked, drops exude from it, and gradually it dries and mummifies (Figure 9.6).

FIGURE 9.5   Fireblight of
pear. A dormant canker,
with cracks separating the
diseased area (top) from
healthy bark (bottom).
Photograph copyright East
Malling Research Station.

Sources of inoculum

Early investigations showed that the bacteria could overwinter
in some cankers which were therefore called 'hold-over' cankers
(Tullis, 1929; Parker, 1936). These cankers are only a fraction of
the total formed and are often those with indeterminate margins.
Apparently the bacteria must be in contact with living tissue to
remain viable. In spring the bacteria renew their activity in the
tissues adjacent to the 'hold-over' cankers and drops containing
bacteria exude from the canker margin. The bacterial ooze appears
attractive to various insects such as flies, aphids and wasps. They

become contaminated with it, and when they collect pollen or nectar they effectively transfer the bacteria to the flowers. Rain splashing on the ooze also helps to disseminate the bacteria and is considered to be important in initiating infections in some areas (Rosen, 1933).

There is some evidence that *E. amylovora* can also overwinter in blighted twigs especially those infected late in the season and these may be an important source of inoculum (Rosen, 1929). It has also been found in buds of apple on apparently symptomless twigs (Baldwin and Goodman, 1963).

It was thought at one time that the bacteria might overwinter in beehives to which they were transferred by bees from infected flowers. A number of investigations disproved this: the bacteria live only for short periods, 5–11 days at the most, in honey and probably less in the beehive (Pierstoff and Lamb, 1934). Their survival in soil is similarly of short duration.

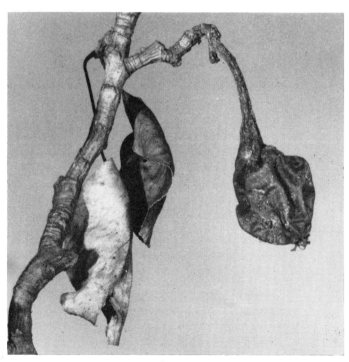

FIGURE 9.6 Fireblight of pear. A mummified fruit. Photograph copyright East Malling Research Station.

Spread of the pathogen and factors influencing it

Once the disease has been initiated on the flowers, secondary infections result mainly through the activities of bees moving from flower to flower. The bacteria enter via the nectaries (Rosen, 1936), and growth in the nectar depends on the sugar concentration (Ivanoff and Keitt, 1941; Keitt and Ivanoff, 1941). With high humidities, nectar is abundant and the sugar concentration is low: this favours bacterial growth. Under drier conditions there is less nectar, the sugar concentration is increased, and bacterial growth is inhibited.

On shoots *E. amylovora* enters via the trichomes, hydathodes and lenticels. It may also be washed into wounds by rain or introduced by boring insects.

Once in the tissue the bacteria multiply rapidly and insinuate themselves between the cells probably by producing pectic enzymes which degrade the middle lamellae. At first the contents of the separated cells appear relatively unaffected but then the starch grains disappear, and the cells plasmolyse and collapse. The rate of progress is largely influenced by the degree of maturity or 'succulency' of the tissues. In young apple shoots a rate of 15·25 cm in 6 h 42 min has been recorded. Here, movement occurs via the phloem (Lewis and Goodman, 1965).

The severity of fireblight is to a large extent determined by the prevailing weather conditions. Frequent rain, ensuring prolonged periods of high humidity, and a temperature between 18° and 29° during blossoming particularly favour the disease (Brooks, 1926).

Disease severity is also affected by cultural practices and soil conditions. Surveys of orchards in New York State showed that fireblight was generally less severe on well-drained soils. On the other hand, mulch treatments and extra applications of nitrogen favoured blight, in the latter instance probably by inducing more succulent shoot growth (Parker and others, 1961).

Control

Several control methods are used in the United States where fireblight has been known for the past 150 years. The eradication of the bacteria in the 'hold-over' cankers is most important. In one method the bark is shaved off until nearly all the discoloured streaks are removed. The cut surface is then treated with an aqueous mixture of mercuric chloride and mercuric cyanide to which glycerin is added to prevent rapid drying and thus allow greater penetration. When dry the exposed wood is coated with a permanent wound dressing. Active cankers are sometimes treated *in situ*, without removing diseased tissue, by painting the surface with zinc chloride dissolved in a mixture of alcohol, water and concentrated hydrochloric acid (Thomas and Parker, 1933).

Trees are also sprayed during blossoming, but often with indifferent results. A weak Bordeaux mixture (1–3–50) has proved to be as effective as any material tried though in recent years good control has been obtained with streptomycin and organic fungicides (Ark, 1953; Fronek and Klos, 1963; Jones and Parker, 1963).

None of the commercial pear varieties of high quality are immune but there are now some such as Waite with considerable resistance (Moon and others, 1957). Top-working the more susceptible varieties on resistant rootstocks is one way in which total loss of trees through fireblight can be avoided. In England, where the disease has only recently become established, growers are by law obliged to remove and destroy infected trees and are not now permitted to grow the very susceptible pear variety, Laxton's Superb (Statutory Instrument, 1966).

REFERENCES

Ark, P. A. (1953). Use of streptomycin dust to control fireblight. *Pl. Dis. Reptr*, **37**, 404–6

Baldwin, C. H. Jr. and Goodman, R. N. (1963). Prevalence of *Erwinia amylovora* in apple buds as detected by phage typing. *Phytopathology*, **53**, 1299–303

Beaumont, A. (1947). The dependence on the weather of the dates of outbreak of potato blight epidemics. *Trans. Br. mycol. Soc.*, **31**, 45–53

Bonde, R. and Schultz, E. S. (1943). Potato refuse piles as a factor in the dissemination of late blight. *Bull. Me agric. Exp. Stn.*, No. 416, 229–46

Brooks, A. N. (1926). Studies of the epidemiology and control of fireblight of apple. *Phytopathology*, **16**, 665–96

Clinton, G. P. (1911). Oospores of potato blight, *Phytophthora infestans*. *Rep. Conn. agric. Exp. Stn.*, 1909–1910, 753–74

Cox, A. E. and Large, E. C. (1960). Potato blight epidemics throughout the world. *Handbk U.S. Dep. Agric.*, No. 174, 230 pp.

Crosse, J. E., Bennett, M. and Garrett, C. M. E. (1960). Investigations of fireblight of pear in England. *Ann. appl. Biol.*, **48**, 541–58

Curtis, K. M. (1934). Fireblight. A survey of current knowledge and recent advances. *Cawthron Inst. mycol. Publ.*, No. 10, 8 pp.

Driver, C. M. (1957). Infection of native *Solanum* by the potato blight fungus. *Nature, Lond.*, **180**, 1367

Fronek, F. R. and Klos, E. J. (1963). The performance of several new chemicals for the control of fireblight on pears. *Pl. Dis. Reptr*, **47**, 348–51

Gallegly, M. E. and Galindo, J. (1957). The sexual stage of *Phytophthora infestans* in Mexico. *Phytopathology*, **47**, 13

Glendinning, D., MacDonald, J. A. and Grainger, J. (1963). Factors affecting the germination of sporangia in *Phytophthora infestans*. *Trans. Br. mycol. Soc.*, **46**, 595–603

Grainger, J. (1956). Host nutrition and attack by fungal parasites. *Phytopathology*, **46**, 445–56

Grainger, J. and Rutherford, A. A. (1963). Rapid determination of host receptivity in potato blight forecasting. *Eur. Potato J.*, **6**, 258–67

Hirst, J. M. and Moore, W. C. (1957). *Phytophthora infestans* on *Petunia* and *Datura*. *Pl. Path.*, **6**, 76

Hirst, J. M. and Stedman, O. J. (1960a). The epidemiology of *Phytophthora infestans*. I. Climate, ecoclimate and the phenology of disease outbreak. *Ann. appl. Biol.*, **48**, 471–88; (1960b). II. The source of inoculum. *Ann. appl. Biol.*, **48**, 489–517

Hirst, J. M., Stedman, O. J., Lacey, J. and Hide, G. A. (1965). The epidemiology of *Phytophthora infestans*. IV. Spraying trials, 1959 to 1963, and the infection of tubers. *Ann. appl. Biol.*, **55**, 373–95

Ivanoff, S. S. and Keitt, G. W. (1941). Relations of nectar concentration to growth of *Erwinia amylovora* and fireblight infection of apple and pear blossoms. *J. agric. Res.*, **62**, 733–43

Jones, A. L. and Parker, K. G. (1963). Fireblight blossom infection control on pear with streptomycin, as influenced by adjuvant addition, and with some common fungicides. *Pl. Dis. Reptr*, **47**, 1074–8

Keitt, G. W. and Ivanoff, S. S. (1941). Transmission of fireblight by bees and its relation to nectar concentration of apple and pear blossoms. *J. agric. Res.*, **62**, 745–53

Large, E. C. (1940). *The Advance of the Fungi*, pp. 13–43. Jonathan Cape, London.

Large, E. C. (1952a). Trials of substitutes for sulphuric acid for potato haulm killing. *Pl. Path.*, **1**, 2–9

Large, E. C. (1952b). The interpretation of progress curves for potato blight and other plant diseases. *Pl. Path.*, **1**, 109–17

Lewis, S. and Goodman, R. N. (1965). Mode of penetration of fireblight bacteria in apple leaf and stem tissue. *Phytopathology*, **55**, 719–23

Melhus, I. E. (1915). Germination and infection with the fungus of the late blight of potato. *Res. Bull. Wis. agric. Exp. Stn.*, No. 37, 64 pp.

Moon, H. H., Wilson, R. A. and Magness, J. R. (1957). Evaluation of some pear varieties and selections for transmitting blight resistance, fruit quality, and fruit size. *Proc. Am. Soc. hort. Sci.*, **70**, 70–3 (*Rev. appl. Mycol.*, **37**, 360)

Murphy, P. A. (1927). The production of the resting-spores of *Phytophthora infestans* on potato tubers. *Sci. Proc. R. Dublin Soc. N.S.*, **18**, 407–12

Naoumova, N. A. (1939). (The infection of potatoes by *Phytophthora infestans* de Bary. from diseased tubers.) *Bull. Pl. Prot. Leningr.*, 1939, 94–102 (*Rev. appl. Mycol.*, **19**, 426)

Parker, K. G. (1936). Fireblight: overwintering, dissemination and control of the pathogene. *Mem. Cornell agric. Exp. Stn.*, No. 193, 42 pp.

Parker, K. G., Fisher, E. G. and Mills, W. D. (1956). Fireblight on pome fruits and its control. *Ext. Bull. Cornell agric. Exp. Stn.*, No. 966, 23 pp.

Parker, K. G., Luepschen, N. S. and Fisher, E. G. (1961). Tree nutrition and fireblight development. *Phytopathology*, **51**, 557–60

Pierstorff, A. L. and Lamb, H. (1934). The honey bee in relation to the overwintering and primary spread of the fireblight organism. *Phytopathology*, **24**, 1347–57

Rosen, H. R. (1929). The life history of the fireblight pathogen, *Bacillus amylovorus* as related to the means of overwintering and dissemination. *Bull. Ark. agric. Exp. Stn.*, No. 244, 96 pp.

Rosen, H. R. (1933). Further studies on the overwintering and dissemination of the fireblight pathogen. *Bull. Ark. agric. Exp. Stn.*, No. 283, 102 pp.

Rosen, H. R. (1936). Mode of penetration and of progressive invasion of fireblight bacteria into apple and pear blossoms. *Bull. Ark. agric. Exp. Stn.*, No. 331, 68 pp.

Rosen, H. R. and Groves, A. B. (1928). Studies on fireblight: host range. *J. agric. Res.*, **37**, 493–505

Smith, L. P. (1956). Potato blight forecasting by 90 percent humidity criteria. *Pl. Path.*, **5**, 83–7

Statutory Instruments, 1966, No. 162. *Pests. Destructive Insects and Pests. The Fireblight Disease (Amendment) Order*, 1966. H.M.S.O., London.

Thomas, H. E. and Parker, K. G. (1933). Fireblight of pear and apple. *Bull. Cornell agric. Exp. Stn.*, No. 557, 24 pp.

Tullis, E. C. (1929). Studies on the overwintering and modes of infection of the fireblight organism. *Tech. Bull. Mich. (St. Coll.) agric. Exp. Stn.*, No. 97, 32 pp.

Van Everdingen, E. (1926). Het verband tusschen de weergesteldheid en de aardappelziekte (*Phytophthora infestans*). *Tijdschr. PlZiekt.*, **32**, 129–40 (*Rev. appl. Mycol.*, **5**, 627)

Woodham-Smith, G. (1963). *The Great Hunger, Ireland*, 1845–9, 510 pp. Hamish Hamilton, London.

CHAPTER 10

Anthracnose

The term anthracnose literally means 'like coal' and was first used by Fabre and Dunal in 1853 to describe a disease of grapes in which a blackening of the tissues was a striking feature. They coined this word to avoid using 'charbon' which was the current term for cereal smut. The pathogen of the grape disease was later described as *Sphaceloma ampelinum*, an imperfect fungus of the Melanconiales, which still later was found to be an ascomycete and was renamed *Elsinoe ampelina*. In 1887, an American, F. L. Scribner, extended the use of 'anthracnose' to a disease of blackberries also caused by a species of *Elsinoe* (*E. veneta*) and then to the disease of *Phaseolus* bean caused by *Colletotrichum lindemuthianum*. The term is now used for other diseases in an etiological sense, that is for diseases caused by fungi with *Sphaceloma*, *Colletotrichum* and *Gloeosporium* conidial states. Some of these diseases are also called 'scab', and it has been suggested that these terms should be used in a symptomatic sense, 'anthracnose' for diseases with necrotic and hypoplastic symptoms typically seen in the restricted lesions of bean anthracnose and 'scab' for hyperplastic symptoms, e.g. raised, scab-like pustules seen in citrus scab (Jenkins, 1933). The main objection is that both types of symptoms occur with one disease, and 'anthracnose' is still mainly used for diseases induced by certain species of *Colletotrichum* and *Gloeosporium*, and a few *Sphaceloma* species closely related to them.

A feature of these fungi is that their conidia are borne on acervuli, which are erumpent, cushion-like masses of conidiophores (Figure 10.1). The conidia are hyaline, 1-celled and ovoid to oblong. The distinction between *Gloeosporium* and *Colletotrichum* is that whereas the latter has large sterile hairs or setae in the acervulus, *Gloeosporium* does not. This is a very unsatisfactory criterion because many *Colletotrichum* spp. either produce setae rarely or only under certain conditions (Frost, 1964) and as a result the nomenclature is confused. The distinction between these two genera and *Sphaceloma* is also unsatisfactory. In *Sphaceloma* the conidiophores arise from a stroma whereas in *Gloeosporium* and *Colletotrichum* they do not but in natural infections gradations between stromatic and non-stromatic types are not uncommon. As indicated certain anthracnose fungi have an ascomycetous perfect state. Some examples are:

Conidial state	Ascomycete state
Sphaceloma ampelinum	*Elsinoe ampelina*
Gloeosporium venetum	*Elsinoe veneta*
Colletotrichum gloeosporoides	
Colletotrichum coffeanum	*Glomerella cingulata*
Gloeosporium limetticola	

The general features of anthracnose diseases are best illustrated by considering in some detail four specific examples:

Bean anthracnose

This disease causes considerable damage to *Phaseolus* beans in the U.S.A. and is becoming increasingly important in Britain. Barrus (1911, 1918) showed that there were two races of *C. lindemuthianum* on beans which he designated α and β, and this was the first time that pathogenic races had been demonstrated in a non-obligate parasite. Subsequently Burkholder (1923) described a third (γ) race and Andrus and Wade (1942) a fourth race (δ). Some workers have made further subdivisions; Schreiber (1932) differentiated

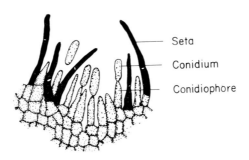

Seta

Conidium

Conidiophore

FIGURE 10.1 Acervulus of *Colletotrichum lindemuthianum*. From C. J. Alexopoulos, 1962, *Introductory Mycology*, John Wiley.

thirty-four races by their reactions on fifty-seven bean varieties but these nevertheless could be grouped into the more widely accepted α, β and γ types then known.

Anthracnose lesions occur on all above ground parts of the bean but are particularly conspicuous on the pods. On these the lesions, when fully developed, are black with a surrounding reddish margin. During wet weather the pinkish spore masses ooze from acervuli in the centre of these lesions. On leaves lesions are typically found on or near the veins on the lower surface (Figure 10.2). Pod infection frequently leads to infection of the seeds and this is one of the chief methods by which the fungus survives from one season to the next. Another is on crop debris (Barrus, 1921).

Infection of the leaves, stems and pods is briefly as follows. Given suitable conditions, a spore of *C. lindemuthianum* germinates in about 8–9 hours and forms an appressorium in close contact with the host surface. From this appressorium a thin penetration tube passes through the cuticle into an epidermal cell where it enlarges into a thick hypha (Dey, 1919). At first the fungus invades the parenchymatous tissue slowly, penetrating the cell walls by thin tubes which suggests that it does so by mechanical pressure. When a few cells have been colonized in this way, secondary hyphae are formed which penetrate cells in all directions and at this stage the cell walls appear to offer little resistance to the pathogen (Figure 10.3). Then hyphal branches aggregate beneath the epidermis and numerous conidiophores are produced from them. Finally the epidermis is ruptured and the spores, which are embedded in a gelatinous matrix, ooze out. With the formation of the acervuli, spread of the mycelium within the tissues usually stops and the underlying host tissue collapses (Leach, 1923).

The severity of the disease is influenced by three factors. Age of the host tissue is most important: infection occurs only on young tissue. Although some susceptible tissue is always present during the growth of the crop, generally if plants get past the seedling stage without heavy infection they are less likely to be severely attacked until perhaps the early stages of pod development when there is another phase of marked susceptibility.

Temperature and moisture are also important. Infection is optimal at 17°; below 13° there is little infection and none above 27° (Lauritzen, 1919). Moisture appears to be essential for spore formation and particularly for spore germination. Spore dispersal is largely by rain splash and the disease is most severe when heavy rains cause partial watersoaking of the young tissues.

(a)

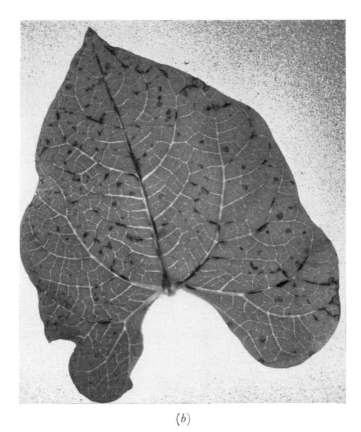

(b)

FIGURE 10.2 Bean anthracnose. (a) on the pods. (b) on the lower leaf surface. Photographs courtesy R. A. Skipp.

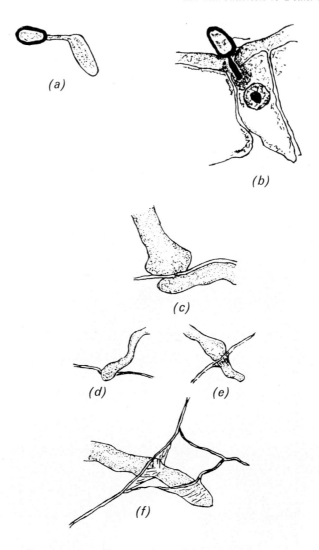

FIGURE 10.3 Penetration of *Colletotrichum lindemuthianum* into bean. (*a*) spore germination,
× 1050. (*b*) penetration of cuticle, × 1500.
(*c*) penetration of cell wall by primary mycelium
× 1000. (*d*), (*e*) and (*f*) penetration of cell wall
by secondary mycelium, × 1000. (*a*) and (*b*)
redrawn from Dey, 1919, *Ann. Bot.*, **33**, 305–12;
(*c*)–(*f*) redrawn from Leach, 1923, *Tech. Bull.
Minn. agric. Exp. Stn*, no. 14.

Since many of the primary infections arise from infected seed, the production of disease-free seed is of first importance in control. In the U.S.A., plants for this purpose are grown in some of the southern states where conditions are normally too dry and too warm for disease development. Sorting, and discarding infected seed is generally not practicable even on white-skinned varieties where incipient infections are more readily distinguished, and seed treatments have given variable results mainly because the mycelium is frequently deep-seated. Spraying beans in the field is seldom profitable except on crops grown for seed and with low levels of infection. As much control as by spraying can usually be obtained by not picking beans during wet weather which facilitates the distribution of inoculum at a time most favourable for infection.

Considerable progress has been made in the U.S.A. and Germany towards breeding for resistance. Resistance in the varieties obtained is based on a hypersensitive reaction of the host tissue which results in a small necrotic fleck on which the fungus cannot sporulate. However, this work is complicated by the number of pathogenic races of *C. lindemuthianum*.

Anthracnose of raspberry and loganberry

Bean anthracnose is an example of this type of disease on a herbaceous annual where carry-over of the causal fungus on the seed is of special significance With perennial crops anthracnose fungi frequently overwinter on the host This is so with raspberry anthracnose caused by *E. veneta*.

The disease is most conspicuous on the canes and is often called 'cane spot' (Harris, 1931). As with *C lindemuthianum* and beans it is the young tissue which is attacked and infection of the canes occurs most readily in, the early stages of the first year's growth The fungus may also gain entry via wounds caused by the raspberry cane midge, *Thomasiniana theobaldi* (Labruyere and Engels, 1963). Once an infection has been established the fungal mycelium renews its activities as host growth recommences in the following season, and produces fresh conidial inoculum from which new infections arise. Alternatively the ascospore stage develops in late summer of the first year and ascospores are ejected in the spring of the next. Once the raspberry canes have borne fruit the fungal mycelium appears to die out, but before this, splitting of the canes often occurs as the healthy parts increase in size while those invaded by the fungus do not. This induces cork formation and a small canker develops (Burkholder, 1917; L. K. Jones, 1924). The disease is controlled

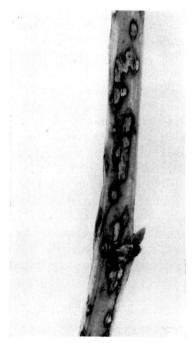

FIGURE 10.4 Anthracnose of
raspberry (cane spot). Photograph copyright East Malling
Research Station.

mainly by removing badly infected canes during winter and
spraying with Bordeaux mixture, lime sulphur or thiram when the
buds are not more than 12 mm long and again just before the
blossoms appear.

Coffee anthracnose (coffee berry disease)
   The above two examples are diseases of temperate crops but
anthracnose diseases generally are most troublesome in tropical
regions where periods of heavy rain provide ideal conditions for
spore dispersal and often result in temporary water soaking of
young tissues which facilitates infection. Coffee anthracnose, caused
by a form of *C. coffeanum* is one such disease which has become
increasingly important in Africa, notably in Kenya (Rayner, 1952;
Nutman and Roberts, 1960*a*). This is commonly called coffee berry
disease because of its devastating effects on the immature fruit.

The source of inoculum is an interesting variation of the stem invasion seen with *E. veneta* and raspberry. Although the production of spores on berries appears more spectacular, 70%–80% of the inoculum is produced on the bearing wood. The fungus colonizes the tissue external to the cork layer in those portions of the stem between the young shoot-tip and the mature wood. Berries borne on this part of the stem become severely infected and, by cutting and examining successive internodes along a fruiting branch Nutman and Roberts (1961) showed that this was related to an increased spore production in this area (Figure 10.5). They calculated that for an average bearing bush the area of such maturing wood available for conidial production was approximately 9730 cm² compared with approximately 270 cm² of diseased fruit. Indeed, successful spraying for the control of this disease depends much more on the

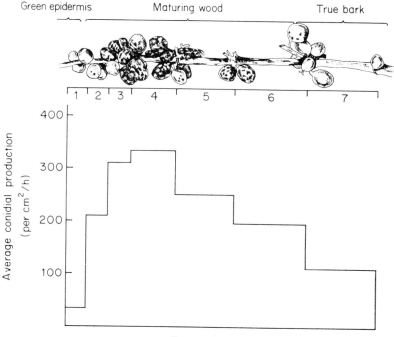

FIGURE 10.5 Coffee berry disease. Distribution of healthy and diseased berries along a fruiting branch of *Coffea arabica* in relation to conidial production from the maturing wood. Adapted from Nutman and Roberts, 1961, *Trans. Br. mycol. Soc.*, **44**, 511–21

reduction of inoculum produced on the stems than on protection of the berries. The perithecial state (*G. cingulata*) has recently been reported to occur occasionally and ascospores may be important in initiating infections in some areas (Hocking and others, 1967).

Temperature and moisture influence the severity of coffee berry disease in a manner similar to bean anthracnose. Lesion production by conidia on berries is most readily obtained at 22°; at temperatures below 15° and above 28° infection is almost negligible. Further, at humidities less than 100% very few spores germinate to form appressoria. With information of this type Nutman and Roberts (1960*b*) attempted to explain the limitation, at that time, of severe outbreaks of the disease in Kenya to areas of altitude 1,677 m or above. They were able to show from meterological data that there were many more days in the year suitable for infection in an area of altitude 1,981 m where the disease was consistently severe than in an area of altitude 1,646 m where the disease was of rare or local occurrence. Since these investigations, however, coffee berry disease has spread to areas of lower altitude that were formerly not much affected (Nutman and Roberts, 1965). This may be the result of abnormally high rainfalls in these areas but possibly temperature and moisture are less limiting than was formerly supposed.

Spraying with fungicides is at present the only control method widely practised and there are many aspects of this which require investigation. The elimination of inoculum from bearing wood requires a fungicide with an eradicant action, and in field trials phenylmercurial compounds were particularly effective. Unfortunately, these fungicides not only induced a zinc deficiency in the coffee bush (Bock and others, 1958) but coffee beans derived from sprayed bushes were found to contain mercury (Pickard and Martin, 1958). Attempts are now made to protect the berries by spraying with copper fungicides (Firman, 1965).

Anthracnose (**withertip**) of lime (*Citrus aurantifolia*)

This disease is also of some importance in the tropics and sub-tropics. It caused severe losses in the West Indies in the 1920's (Nowell, 1923) and has been troublesome since, both there and in southern Florida, and more recently in the island of Zanzibar (Wheeler, 1963*a*). The causal fungus is *G. limetticola* and like others of this group, it only infects young tissues.

The disease is most spectacular on the young shoots. When severe the entire shoot is killed leaving only a withered tip from which the common name for the disease is derived. When less severe, symptoms

(b)

(a)

FIGURE 10.6 Withertip disease of lime. (a) death of the young, terminal shoots, (b) a less severe attack, leaf spotting and leaf distortion.

range from leaf spotting to distortion of the leaf blade and loss of individual leaves on the shoot (Figure 10.6). Young flower clusters become infected and drop; so do the young fruits until they are about 12 mm in diameter when they no longer appear susceptible. Fruits which escape severe infection frequently develop prominent scabby areas and split due to uneven growth.

Withered shoots and leaf lesions are the main sources of inoculum but the action of the disease on the lime is such that there is often a continuous supply of young growth on which the fungus is maintained. Normally limes, in common with other citrus, produce a number of distinct 'flushes' of new growth and flowers, the occurrence of which is regulated to a certain extent by climatic factors. Where shoots are killed by *G. limetticola* buds develop which would otherwise have remained dormant and individual flushes tend to lose their identity. No commercial variety of lime has yet been produced which is resistant to withertip and most attempts to control the disease have been by spraying. Phenylmercuric fungicides were effective in Zanzibar without the serious side-effects found on coffee (Wheeler, 1963*b*; Wheeler and others, 1963). In the West Indies trees are sprayed with Bordeaux mixture or other proprietary copper-fungicides.

General comments

Anthracnose diseases form a small group in which the causal fungi are morphologically similar and behave similarly as pathogens. These fungi produce spores in very large numbers in sticky masses which are dispersed by rain, they require at least high humidities for infection and are most destructive when there is some water-soaking of the host tissue. In these respects they are not unlike some of the bacterial plant pathogens. Limitation of the term 'anthracnose' to diseases caused by particular, related fungi puts this group on a level with the mildews, rusts and smuts but there are not the same distinctive fungal lesions. Neither are the symptoms produced exclusive to the group. A severe attack of *G. limetticola* on young lime shoots is essentially 'blight', the raised pustules on the fruit 'scab' and leaf lesions of *C. lindemuthianum* on beans are typical leaf-spots.

REFERENCES

Andrus, C. F. and Wade, B. L. (1942). The factorial interpretation of anthracnose resistance in beans. *Tech. Bull. U.S. Dep. Agric.*, No. 810, 24 pp.

Barrus, M. F. (1911). Variation of varieties of beans in their susceptibility to anthracnose. *Phytopathology*, **1**, 190–5

Barrus, M. F. (1918). Varietal susceptibility of beans to strains of *Colletotrichum lindemuthianum* (Sacc. and Magn.) B. and C. *Phytopathology*, **8**, 589–614

Barrus, M. F. (1921). Bean anthracnose. *Mem. Cornell agric. Exp. Stn.*, No. 42, 101–215

Bock, K. R., Robinson, J. B. D. and Chamberlain, G. T. (1958). Zinc deficiency induced by mercury in *Coffea arabica*. *Nature, Lond.*, **182**, 1607

Burkholder, W. H. (1917). The anthracnose disease of the raspberry and related plants. *Bull. Cornell agric. Exp. Stn.*, No. 395, 155–83

Burkholder, W. H. (1923). The gamma strain of *Colletotrichum lindemuthianum* (Sacc. and Magn.) B. and C. *Phytopathology*, **13**, 316–23

Dey, P. K. (1919). Studies in the physiology of parasitism. V. Infection by *Colletotrichum lindemuthianum*. *Ann. Bot.*, **33**, 305–12

Firman, I. D. (1965). A review of leaf rust and coffee berry disease control in Kenya. *Trop. Agric., Trin.*, **42**, 111–9

Frost, R. R. (1964). Seta formation in *Colletotrichum* spp. *Nature, Lond.*, **201**, 730–1

Harris, R. V. (1931). Raspberry cane spot: its diagnosis and control. *J. Pomol.*, **9**, 73–99

Hocking, D., Johanns, J. C. and Vermeulen, H. (1967). Ascospore production, discharge and infection by *Glomerella cingulata* causing coffee berry disease. *Nature, Lond.*, **214**, 1144–5

Jenkins, A. E. (1933). Application of the terms 'anthracnose' and 'scab' to plant diseases caused by *Sphaceloma* and *Gloeosporium*. *Phytopathology*, **23**, 389–95

Jones, L. K. (1924). Anthracnose of cane fruits and its control on black raspberries in Wisconsin. *Res. Bull. Wis. agric. Exp. Stn.*, No. 59, 26 pp.

Labruyere, R. E. and Engels, G. M. M. T. (1963). Over schimmels als oorzaak van de stengelziekten van de Framboos en hun samenhang met het optreden van de frambozeschorsgalmug. *Netherl. J. Plant Path.*, **69**, 222–34, 235–57. (*Rev. appl. Mycol.*, **43**, 519)

Lauritzen, J. I. (1919). The relation of temperature and humidity to infection by certain fungi. *Phytopathology*, **9**, 7–35

Leach, J. G. (1923). The parasitism of *Colletotrichum lindemuthianum*. *Tech. Bull. Minn. agric. Exp. Stn.*, No. 14, 41 pp.

Nowell, W. (1923). *Diseases of Crop Plants in the Lesser Antilles*, pp. 207–9. West India Committee, London.

Nutman, F. J. and Roberts, F. M. (1960a). Investigations on a disease of
    Coffea arabica caused by a form of *Colletotrichum coffeanum* Noack. I.
    Some factors affecting infection by the pathogen. *Trans. Br. mycol. Soc.*,
    43, 489–505; (1960b). II. Some factors affecting germination and
    infection, and their relation to disease distribution. *Trans. Br. mycol.
    Soc.*, **43**, 643–59; (1961). III. The relation between infection of bearing
    wood and disease incidence. *Trans. Br. mycol. Soc.*, **44**, 511–21
Nutman, F. J. and Roberts, F. M. (1965). Coffee berry disease now.
    Kenya Coff., **30**, 147–9
Pickard, J. A. and Martin, J. T. (1958). Spray application problems.
    XLVI. Mercury residues on coffee leaves and berries in relation to the
    control of berry disease. *Rep. agric. hort. Res. Stn. Univ. Bristol*, 1958,
    88–93
Rayner, R. W. (1952). Coffee berry disease—a survey of investigations
    carried out up to 1950. *E. Afr. agric. J.*, **17**, 130–58
Schreiber, F. (1932). Resistenzzuchtung bei *Phaseolus vulgaris*. *Phytopath.
    Z.*, **4**, 415–54 (*Rev. appl. Mycol.*, **11**, 618)
Wheeler, B. E. J. (1963a). Studies on *Gloeosporium limetticola* causing
    withertip disease of limes in Zanzibar. *Trans. Br. mycol. Soc.*, **46**, 193–200
Wheeler, B. E. J. (1963b). Withertip disease of limes (*Citrus aurantifolia*)
    in Zanzibar. I. Field trials with fungicides. *Ann. appl. Biol.*, **51**, 237–51
Wheeler, B. E. J., Pickard, J. A. and Martin, J. T. (1963). Withertip
    disease of limes (*Citrus aurantifolia*) in Zanzibar. II. Mercury residues
    on leaves and fruits. *Ann. appl. Biol.*, **51**, 403–10

CHAPTER 11

Leaf spots

'Blight' implies sudden and extensive damage to leaves, but in many leaf diseases the area of necrosis is limited and the main symptom is simply a spot of varying size and shape. Leaf spots can be caused by unfavourable water relationships or temperatures, by mineral deficiencies or excesses and by insects. They are also caused by viruses, but in diseases of economic importance induced by these pathogens leaf spots *per se* are seldom the most prominent symptom. They are usually accompanied by other, visually more striking features, such as colour changes and leaf patterns. The latter include the so-called 'ring spots', in which many small, necrotic flecks appear in roughly concentric rings; a feature which is often an indication of a nematode-transmitted virus (p. 273). Diseases in which leaf spots are the principal symptom are most commonly caused by bacteria and fungi, and only these two groups will be considered here.

BACTERIAL LEAF SPOTS

Angular leaf spot of cotton

The disease of cotton induced by *Xanthomonas malvacearum* is outstanding in this group and is of considerable importance in the Sudan and southern states of America (Stapp, 1966). It has several names: angular leaf spot of cotton, blackarm and boll rot, and these refer to particular phases. The disease syndrome is often called 'bacterial blight of cotton' and this serves as a reminder that, under suitable conditions, leaf spots can be extremely destructive and then merit the term 'blight'.

The small angular leaf spots (Figure 11.1) result from the infection of the parenchyma in an area limited by vascular tissue. On young and expanding leaves infection is often restricted to tissue on either side of the main vein and may extend back to the petiole. Lesions on the stem are black and sunken and can extend for several inches and may eventually girdle the branch (blackarm phase). Capsules or bolls are frequently attacked at the base. Young bolls may be killed and drop, while on older capsules dark-green spots develop which later turn black. Infection of the boll can lead to seed infection by the bacteria entering the micropyle, or the seed surface may become contaminated. The latter appears to be more common (Wickens, 1953).

Seedlings which develop from infected or contaminated seed are frequently diseased but the extent of the infection depends on a number of factors of which soil temperature and moisture, and possibly soil type are most important (Stoughton, 1930, 1933).

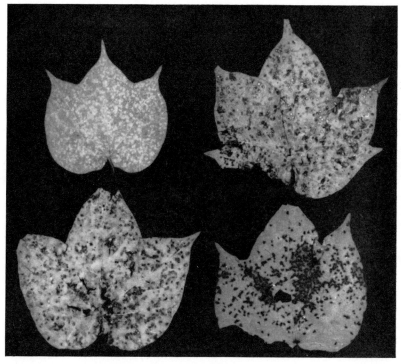

FIGURE 11.1   Angular leaf spot of cotton.   Photograph courtesy
F. T. Last.

Infection is most severe when the soil temperature at sowing is about 20° and remains at this for 2–3 days after, and when soil moisture approaches saturation. Seedling infection appears to be worse on some soils than others even under similar experimental conditions. Primary lesions on the seedlings provide inoculum for leaf infection. Two factors influence the initiation of such infection, stomatal opening and water content. Weindling (1948) showed that expanded leaves sprayed with bacterial suspensions became infected only when the stomata were open and severely when the tissues were watersoaked. Maximum leaf infection occurs at 35°–36° and 85% RH with a rapid fall-off as either temperature or humidity drops (Stoughton, 1931, 1932).

Stem lesions usually arise from the extension of the leaf lesions down the petiole to the stem cortex but internodal lesions have been observed occasionally suggesting that direct infection of the stem can occur. Wickens (1953) also reported a vascular type of infection in which the bacteria apparently moved from infected cotyledonary leaves, down the vascular system into the stem, and subsequently into the stem cortex where lesions developed. Other workers, however, could find no bacteria in the xylem elements but only in the parenchyma surrounding the xylem.

Bacteria carried in rain drops from the leaf and stem lesions infect the base of the capsule. Possibly the tissues at this point are particularly susceptible but growth of the capsule may also facilitate entry. At corolla drop, the calyx forms a cup around the base of the young boll in which water carrying *X. malvacearum* can lodge. As the boll grows it becomes pressed against the calyx thereby providing an ideal incubation chamber for bacterial growth and infection (Wickens, 1953).

If infected and contaminated seed were the only source of inoculum, angular leaf spot might be more readily controlled than it is, but *X. malvacearum* can also survive from one season to the next on volunteer plants and on infected plant debris. The latter has received much attention. Most evidence suggests that the bacterium can survive in dry trash for a considerable time but under wet conditions soon loses its viability. In experiments in the Sudan, Massey (1931, 1934) obtained virulent cultures of *X. malvacearum* from dry trash over a 5 month period but none was obtained after 72 hours from trash placed in moist Gezira soil or water from the Blue Nile. Similarly, flooding land 2 to 4 days before sowing greatly reduced the efficiency of trash as a source of inoculum. Massey considered that *X. malvacearum* was eliminated in these instances by the action of bacteriophages. There is some divergence of opinion as to the importance of trash under natural conditions. Survival of the bacterium in trash varies in different regions and this seems to result from climatic differences in the areas involved. Survival depends largely on the amount and intensity of rainfall during the closed season and to a certain extent on the soil type. The bacterium is more rapidly eliminated from trash lying on heavy, poorly drained soils than on free-draining, sandy soils (Arnold and Arnold, 1961).

Apart from removing volunteer plants and debris, the control of angular leaf spot is based on seed treatment and resistant varieties. Different seed treatments are used in the different cotton-growing regions: delinting with sulphuric acid in the U.S.A. and Rhodesia, steeping in 1% formalin in the U.S.S.R. and dusting with mercurial compounds in the Sudan.

Breeding for resistance has been carried out principally in the U.S.A. and in the Sudan. There are useful summaries of some aspects of this work by Knight and Hutchinson (1950), Wickens (1953) and Innes (1961, 1964), and reviews of the variability of *X. malvacearum* by Brinkerhoff (1963) and Hayward (1964).

Wildfire and angular leaf spot of tobacco

Angular leaf spot of cotton has deservedly received much attention, so have similar diseases of tobacco: wildfire caused by *Pseudomonas tabaci* and angular leaf spot caused by *Pseudomonas angulata* (Valleau and others, 1943; Lucas, 1965).

The first symptoms of wildfire are pale, greenish-yellow spots on the leaves and are usually first seen in the seedbeds. These spots enlarge to about 10–20 mm in diameter and a small, reddish-brown area of dead tissue appears in the centre of each so that the leaf lesion is typically a necrotic spot with a distinct halo. Young seedlings can become so heavily infected that they wither and collapse. Symptoms on mature leaves are similar (Figure 11.2) and the small lesions frequently coalesce to form large, necrotic areas. With favourable conditions disease rapidly spreads from the lower leaves to the top of the plant and even seed pods are affected. The severity of the disease depends on the weather and the type of tobacco. The bacterium is dispersed in rain drops and infects the leaf via the stomata, and as in angular leaf spot of cotton, infection is more readily established when leaves are partially watersoaked (Clayton, 1936; Diachun and others, 1942). Thin-leaved varieties of tobacco are more susceptible than thick-leaved varieties, again probably because they are more readily watersoaked (Heggestad,

FIGURE 11.2 Tobacco wildfire. Symptoms on a
mature leaf. From J. C. F. Hopkins, 1956.
Tobacco Diseases, by permission of the Commonwealth Mycological Institute.

1945) and this is possibly one reason why the disease has been most
troublesome in the U.S.A., and also caused heavy losses in Rhodesia
during the 1920's when these varieties were planted (Hopkins, 1956).

Ps. tabaci survives from one season to the next on seeds which have
become contaminated via capsule infection and in infected tobacco
debris, and therefore seed treatment and general field hygiene are
necessary for control. All the evidence indicates that the bacteria
are on the seed coat only and that penetration of the micropyle, as
in cotton, does not occur. Seed treatment is thus simplified and
immersion for 15 minutes in silver nitrate or mercuric chloride is
equally effective. One complication is that *Ps. tabaci* can live in
association with the roots of various weeds, and crop plants such

as wheat and barley (Valleau and others, 1944) so that once land has supported a crop of infected tobacco, the bacteria can remain viable for a long time, and indeed this source is considered by some to be much more important than infected seed. Some rotation is thus advisable but soybean should not be planted since *Ps. tabaci* can infect this through the pustules caused by another bacterium, *Xanthomonas phaseoli* var. *sojense*, and cause a serious wildfire type of disease (Graham, 1953). In seedbeds where wildfire has occurred some leguminous cover crop should be planted and disked in the year before sowing with tobacco, and the soil then drenched with Bordeaux mixture some time before sowing. Outbreaks of wildfire in the seedbeds can be limited by spraying. Heggestad and Clayton (1954) obtained good control with streptomycin (200–400 ppm) applied at a rate of 54.8 l/100m² seedbed. Cole (1960), however, found that while streptomycin initially gave some control, strains of *Ps. tabaci* developed which were resistant to the antibiotic, so it was of little practical value. Varieties of tobacco resistant to wildfire have been developed in the U.S.A.

Ps. tabaci and *Ps. angulata* appear to be closely related. *Ps. tabaci* produces a water-soluble and heat-stable substance in culture which induces lesions with chlorotic haloes on leaves of various plants including tobacco in the absence of the bacteria; *Ps. angulata* does not. In alkaline solution this toxin breaks down to a material named tabtoxinine, which is a structural analogue of the amino acid methionine and adversely affects the metabolism of this substance in tobacco cells (Braun, 1955). Ageing cultures of *Ps. tabaci* lose their ability to produce toxin and then resemble those of *Ps. angulata*.

The leaf symptoms of *Ps. angulata* are those of *Ps. tabaci* without the chlorotic halo. The necrotic area usually involves all the parenchyma between the vascular tissue so that an angular lesion results. Like wildfire, the disease is first found in the seedbeds but perhaps because the lesions lack the chlorotic haloes, small outbreaks are frequently missed. In the field the spots tend to enlarge and are thus more readily noticed. On thick leaves, especially of fire-cured varieties, lesions often coalesce to form large blotches with concentric rings, a symptom so different from the small, angular lesions that it was formerly considered a separate disease and called 'blackfire'. A further disease symptom occurs in prolonged periods of wet weather. Diffuse yellow areas appear on the leaves and black spots develop within them. The spots coalesce to give an irregular black blotch and the affected part of the leaf then soon disintegrates.

The control of angular leaf spot is essentially similar to that for wildfire but generally field spraying has been found more effective in limiting outbreaks than it is with wildfire.

Angular leaf spot of cucumber

Another disease worthy of mention is angular leaf spot of cucumber caused by *Pseudomonas lacrymans*. The pathogen gets its name from the conspicuous droplets which exude from the lesions. The disease is of some importance in the U.S.A. and is occasionally found in Britain. All parts above the ground may be attacked but spoilage of the developing fruit is commercially of most significance. Apart from direct losses in this way the bacteria can penetrate cracks in the fruit and contaminate the seed (Carsner, 1918; Wiles and Walker, 1951). Seed treatment is then necessary and this is usually a 5–10 minute soak in 1% mercuric chloride (Gilbert and Gardner, 1918). Spread of the disease within the crop can be checked by application of 1% Bordeaux mixture containing 0.5% resin soap (Hellmers, 1951).

FUNGAL LEAF SPOTS

There are so many fungi that cause leaf spots that a comprehensive account of them and the diseases would be a major work. The identification of these fungi is one of the plant pathologist's first tasks when dealing with this type of disease and it is little or no comfort that the majority are either Ascomycetes or Fungi Imperfecti. The Fungi Imperfecti are perhaps most difficult because they comprise a vast number of often ill-defined species for which no better taxonomic disposition can be made. For this reason examples of leaf spots will be chosen with particular reference to these fungi.

There are three main divisions within the Fungi Imperfecti:

1. Melanconiales—in which the conidia and conidiophores are borne in acervuli.

2. Sphaeropsidales—in which they arise within pycnidia.

3. Moniliales—in which there is no special fruiting structure although conidiophores are aggregated in some species.

Gloeosporium, Colletotrichum and *Sphaceloma* are the most important genera of the Melanconiales as far as plant pathogens are concerned, and these were considered in the previous chapter.

G

Pycnidial Fungi

Within the Sphaeropsidales the most important pathogens of crop plants are to be found in the following groups and genera:

(a) conidia hyaline, 1-celled, generally globose-oblong: *Phomopsis*, *Phoma*, *Phyllosticta*. Often these are associated more with stem cankers and rots than with leaf spots. Examples are *Phomopsis pseudotsugae* on conifers, *Phoma lingam* on brassicas, *P. solanicola*, *P. foveata* and *P. tuberosa* on potato, and *Phyllosticta mali* on apples.

(b) conidia hyaline, 2-celled: *Ascochyta*, e.g. *Ascochyta pisi* on peas.

(c) conidia dark, 2-celled: *Diplodia*, *Botryodiplodia*. These fungi are often associated more with fruit rots rather than leaf spots, e.g. *Botryodiplodia theobromae* on cacao.

(d) conidia hyaline, filiform: *Septoria*, e.g. *Septoria chrysanthemella* on chrysanthemum.

Of the diseases caused by these fungi those of celery and peas are particularly important and will serve as examples for the group.

Septoria leaf spot of celery

This is the most serious disease of celery in Britain and is also of considerable importance in the U.S.A. and other areas of the world where this crop is grown. It causes severe injury to the leaves and unsightly blemishes on the blanched leaf-petioles which reduce their market value (Figure 11.3). For a long time it was thought that there were two fungi involved in the disease, *Septoria apiigraveolentis* causing a small leaf spot, and *Septoria apii* causing a much rarer, large leaf spot (Cochran, 1932). It now seems clear that no distinction can be made morphologically or pathogenically between the supposed two fungi and the celery leaf spot fungus should be called *Septoria apiicola* (Gabrielson and Grogan, 1964).

Infected seed is the principal source of inoculum. When such seed is soaked pycnidia of the fungus can be seen in the seed coat and spores from these pycnidia infect the seedling leaves at germination. Mycelium of *S. apiicola* can be found within the pericarp and testa but its role in initiating infections is doubtful. There is also some evidence that the fungus can survive in leaf debris for several months but generally this is an unimportant source of inoculum compared with infected seed. Sheridan (1966) also showed that *S. apiicola* on wild celery (*Apium graveolens*) could infect cultivated varieties but as this host does not occur in the main celery growing areas in Britain it is not likely to be important as a source of inoculum.

FIGURE 11.3 *Septoria* leaf spot of celery.
From Sheridan, 1964, *Septoria blight of celery*. Ph.D. thesis University of London.

Once the fungus is established on the seedling, disease development depends on the prevailing weather. Generally, the disease is most severe when dry, dull days are followed by cool, misty nights. Such conditions are unfavourable for the growth of celery and the leaves remain moist for long periods, which is ideal for infection.

The best way to avoid severe outbreaks is to plant clean seed. Plants for seed production are usually sprayed at intervals from the seedling stage to ensure that they remain uninfected but this is both laborious and costly. Alternatively, seed is treated to eradicate the fungus. Two methods used are (a) a formaldehyde dip, in which the seeds are steeped for 3 hours in a solution of 1 part 40% formalin to 300 water and (b) a hot water treatment in which bagged seed is immersed at 50° for 25 minutes. Provided it is carefully carried out, and within a year of harvesting the seed, the hot-water treatment is more satsifactory (Bant and Storey, 1952); formaldehyde often injures the seed and results in poor germination. The fungus has also been successfully eliminated by soaking disease seed for 24 hours in a 0.2% suspension of thiram at 30° and this appears a promising control method (Maude, 1964).

Ascochyta leaf spot of peas

Etiologically, *Ascochyta* leaf spot of peas is more complicated since this can be caused by three similar but distinct species (Sattar, 1933). They are *Ascochyta pinodella*, *A. pisi* and *Mycosphaerella pinodes* (conidial state *Ascochyta pinodes*). In addition to leaf and stem spotting all three species can cause a foot rot but *A. pisi* is least active in producing this symptom. Certain differences have been recorded between the diseases caused by the three fungi (Jones, 1927) but these are unlikely to be significant except to the practised observer in one locality. Generally each *Ascochyta* spp. cannot be distinguished by symptoms but they are readily separated by spore size and appearance in culture (Hare and Walker, 1944), viz.

	M. pinodes	*A. pinodella*	*A. pisi*
Colour	light to dark	brown to greenish black	straw to red
Pycnidiospores	$4.5 \times 12.3\mu$	$3.7 \times 8.0\mu$	$4.2 \times 17.2\mu$

Like *S. apiicola* these organisms are seed-borne. In an examination of pea seeds at the Division of Botany and Plant Pathology Laboratory in Ottawa between 1939 and 1950, 51% of 5,000 samples were found to be infected with *Ascochyta* spp., of which the most common was *A. pisi* (Skolko and others, 1954); seed examinations from 1953 to 1964 indicate that *M. pinodes* is now more common (Wallen and others, 1967). In a similar survey at the Plant Pathology Laboratory, Harpenden, between 1925 and 1943, 23% of the samples examined had appreciable *Ascochyta* infection (Western, 1945). The amount of seed infection within a crop is not necessarily related to the degree of leaf and stem spotting. Pod infection seems to depend on the weather at the time of seed maturation. Heavily diseased plants often produce comparatively healthy seed while at other times badly diseased seed is produced from plants with little leaf and stem infection (Skolko and others, 1954). One danger is that apparently normal pea seeds from pods bearing lesions are often internally infected. Maude (1966) demonstrated this for *M. pinodes:* when seeds were sown in sterile grit almost all the seedlings showed disease lesions at or below soil level 4–6 weeks after sowing. Because of this deep-seated mycelium control by seed-dressings has been difficult but soaking seed in a 0.2% thiram suspension, as for celery and *S. apiicola*, appears promising (Maude, 1966).

The destruction of pea vines at the end of the season is also important particularly in regions where *M. pinodes* is prevalent. Perithecia either remain viable on the debris or new perithecia and pycnidia develop within it. Ascospore discharge is associated with rain but as little as 0.18 mm is effective and peak liberation from mature perithecia occurs within 30 minutes of wetting (Carter and Moller, 1961). When infected straw is buried in soil of high moisture content and at a temperature 28°–33° there is a rapid reduction in its ability to produce ascospores when subsequently unearthed. Apart from ploughing-in crop residues, there is the possibility of preventing ascospore discharge from pea stubble by the application of a chemical. Carter (1959) demonstrated this with an oil–water emulsion of pentachlorophenol, but there are technical difficulties in obtaining complete coverage with the fungicide which may make field control impracticable.

Others (*Moniliales*)

Within the Moniliales genera are differentiated on colour and morphology of the conidia and conidiophores. Of the 462 genera in Barnett's *Illustrated Genera of Imperfect Fungi* (1962) five are of special plant pathological interest.

Botrytis

Pathogenically *Botrytis* spp. fall into two groups, the aggregate species *Botrytis cinerea* which attacks a wide range of plants, and species morphologically distinct from *B. cinerea* which are relatively specialized in their parasitism (Wood, 1962). Not all cause discrete leaf spots. *B. cinerea* also causes rotting of strawberry and raspberry fruits (Jarvis, 1962), grey mould of lettuce (Smieton and Brown, 1940) and die back of gooseberry (Brooks and Bartlett, 1910); *Botrytis allii*, *Botrytis byssoidea* and *Botrytis squamosa* cause neck rots of onion (Walker, 1926) and *Botrytis tulipae*, tulip fire (Anon, 1965).

Amongst the leaf spot diseases, chocolate spot of broad bean (*Vicia faba*) is most interesting. This was once attributed to bacteria but is now known to be caused by *Botrytis fabae* and *B. cinerea*. From an agricultural viewpoint *B. fabae* is the more important since it can result in extensive damage to the crop. In Britain the disease appears in a mild form every year but in certain seasons becomes epiphytotic and results in substantial crop losses. Two types of the disease are thus distinguished, a 'non-aggressive' form in which the leaf lesions remain small (Figure 11.4) and an 'aggressive' form in which the spots enlarge, coalesce and involve the whole leaf so that the plants appear blighted. In artificial inoculations with *B. fabae* aggressive lesions are most readily obtained on older leaves with high concentrations of spores (Deverall and Wood, 1961) and in the field the rapid build-up of the disease is also associated with senescent leaves (Leach, 1955), or any conditions unfavourable to the host growth and which induce premature senescence, such as lack of phosphate (Glasscock, Ware and Pizer, 1944), or waterlogged soil (Ogilvie and Munro, 1947). While in these situations death of leaves may result initially from the activities of *B. fabae*, dead or moribund tissue is readily colonized by *B. cinerea* and it can grow from this into

FIGURE 11.4 Chocolate spot of broad bean; the non-aggressive form. Photograph by H. Devitt.

adjacent healthy tissue so aggravating the disease. Epiphytotics of chocolate spot are associated with heavy rainfall during April, May, June and July. Water is essential for spore germination and infection, and factors which help to maintain a watery film on the foliage for several days (e.g. high humidity with little or no wind), plus a temperature between 15° and 20° provide the optimum conditions for the 'aggressive' phase (Wilson, 1937; Hogg, 1956).

While spraying trials on a small scale have given good results the spasmodic occurrence of the 'aggressive' form of the disease makes it difficult to develop economic spray programmes, and it is only recently that an increase in acreage of field beans in Britain has aroused some interest in field control.

Cladosporium

One species, *Cladosporium herbarum*, is very common on semi-moribund material and frequently causes blackening of the ears of cereals where these contain little or no grain as a result of root infection (Bennett, 1928). A morphologically similar species, *Cladosporium cladosporioides* f.sp. *pisicola* causes a leaf spot and scab-like pustules on the pods of peas (Snyder, 1934) but is comparatively unimportant. Two other species cause diseases of economic significance on glasshouse crops. They are *Cladosporium cucumerinum* (gummosis of cucumbers) and *Cladosporium fulvum* (leaf mould of tomatoes).

Tomato leaf mould is the more important. In South Australia it is estimated that a third of the potential yield of glasshouse crops may be lost annually (Rogers, 1962). Chlorotic patches develop on the upper surfaces of leaves and the corresponding areas on the under surfaces become covered with a greyish mass of conidiophores which later turns brown. Many conidia are produced in a warm and moist atmosphere and they readily give rise to secondary infections. The spores are very resistant to drying and low temperature and are thus able to survive between crops in small bits of leaf debris and on bricks and woodwork (Small, 1930a). Temperature and humidity largely determine disease severity. The optimum conditions for the various stages of leaf mould are 22° and a relative humidity over 95%. At 10°–15° severe infection occurs under humid conditions but the disease develops more slowly. At humidities below 80% disease development is also retarded, especially at lower temperatures (Small, 1930b; Guba, 1938). Humid conditions at night appear particularly important possibly because light retards germ-tube growth.

Successful control is achieved by cultural practices and good glasshouse management, and by the use of chemicals and resistant varieties (Guba, 1939). Tomato debris should be removed and burnt at the end of the growing season. Fumigation of the house by burning sulphur or washing down with formaldehyde are two methods which have been suggested for eradicating spores lodged on wood and brick work. Good ventilation is essential during the development of the crop to reduce humidity. Proper spacing and pruning, and watering in the mornings and on bright days as far as possible, help in this respect.

Many fungicides give satisfactory control if spraying is properly carried out and repeated a sufficient number of times. Colloidal copper with a white oil emulsion is preferred because it leaves no visible deposit on the fruit (Beaumont, 1954). The most effective material in severe outbreaks is tank-mixed zineb (nabam plus zinc sulphate); it tends to scorch the foliage but this can be avoided by spraying only during dull periods (Wiggell, 1958; Rogers, 1962). A number of resistant tomato varieties have also been developed, one of the earliest of which was 'Vetomold', but this and others have subsequently succumbed to the disease owing to the appearance of new races of the pathogen (Williams, 1943; Bailey, 1950; Day, 1954). By 1964, ten races of *C. fulvum* were known (Bailey and Kerr, 1964).

Alternaria

Fungi belonging to this genus are commonly found on leaf spots and necrotic tissue. Their identification is not easy because of the variation within individual species (Neergaard, 1945). This is particularly true of the *Alternaria tenuis* group which occurs on a wide range of senescent and moribund tissue. Other species are more pathogenic but again disease severity is associated with crop maturation. An example is *Alternaria solani* on potato and tomato (Rowell, 1953). The disease is often called 'early blight' to distinguish it from 'late blight' caused by *Phytophthora infestans* but in many areas this is a misnomer as it often appears late in the season. Another disease name, 'target spot', refers to the concentric rings in the leaf lesions and this occurs fairly commonly in *Alternaria* leaf spots. The leaves of severely infected potato and tomato plants drop prematurely and yields are decreased. *A. solani* lives for at least a year on old vines and may also persist on other perennial solanaceous hosts. Spores from these sources infect tomato and potato either by direct penetration of the cuticle or through stomata (Rands, 1917). There appear to be several physiological races of the fungus which differ in their ability to form lesions (Henning and Alexander, 1959) and may also differ in their responses to the environment. Pound (1951), found that leaf infection by two isolates was markedly lower at 13° and 17° compared with that at 21° or 25°; with two other isolates there was considerable infection at all four temperatures. With all isolates disease development was greater at 16° than at 28° when relatively dilute inocula were used but with concentrated inocula defoliation was equally severe at both temperatures. The nutritional status of the host is also important. Pot experiments indicate that plants grown under a medium–high nitrogen and potassium, plus low phosphate regime are most susceptible (Thomas, 1948). Frequent rains or dew are necessary for sporulation on the lesions but spores are mainly wind dispersed and the maximum concentration of spores in the air are observed daily during the driest and windiest hours (Rotem, 1964).

Leaf spot or brown spot of tobacco caused by *Alternaria longipes* has many similar features. This disease has been important in Central Africa for some time and has become so in North America in recent years (Lucas, 1965). Large, necrotic lesions with yellow haloes develop on the leaves, and are often surrounded by numerous, smaller, satellite lesions (Figure 11.5). When these leaves are cured, they tend to disintegrate and are of little value. Few lesions are found during the early part of the season and while *A. longipes* may become established on young leaves, lesion extension and leaf destruction is associated with the ripening of the crop. Dry, sunny periods are most favourable for spore dispersal but these must be preceded by periods of high humidity which are necessary for spore production. Application of fertilizers high in nitrogen but low in phosphate and potassium appear to predispose tobacco plants to infection (Wheeler, 1958). Tobacco debris is the principal source of inoculum and some control can be achieved by attention to field sanitation, and to fertilization of the crop.

Alternaria brassicae and *Alternaria brassicicola* are two other species frequently encountered (Rangel, 1945; Wiltshire, 1947). They are associated with dark leaf spot of brassicas and can sometimes be troublesome on cabbage and cauliflower plants grown for seed. Lesions on the inflorescences cause the pods to rupture prematurely and much seed is lost. These fungi are seed-borne and some mycelium is deep seated. They can be eliminated by immersing seed for 18 minutes at 50° (Schimmer, 1953).

FIGURE 11.5. *Alternaria* leaf
spot of tobacco, showing the
necrotic lesions and sur-
rounding chlorotic zones.

Cercospora

Several leaf spot diseases of major economic importance are
caused by species of *Cercospora* (Chupp, 1954). In parts of Europe
and the U.S.A. *Cercospora apii* is frequently destructive on celery
(Chupp and Sherf, 1960), and *Cercospora beticola* similarly on beet
(Hull, 1960), but the most important pathogenic species occur in
the tropics. One of them, *Cercospora nicotianae*, causes 'frog-eye' of
tobacco. The disease gets its name from the appearance of the
lesion, which when fully developed consists of a small, blanched
area surrounded by a brown necrotic zone. Numerous lesions may
develop on leaves in the field and seriously reduce their market
value, but there is a second phase which is equally if not more

important. Numerous brown spots often appear on leaves when they are cured although they had comparatively few visible lesions at harvesting. This is called 'barn spot' and results from the development of incipient lesions during the early stages of curing. It can largely be avoided by starting the curing process at 38° in a saturated atmosphere (Stephen, 1955).

The fungus survives on small pieces of leaf debris and unless precautions are taken, initiates the disease in the seedbeds and from there it is distributed in the field at planting. Regular spraying of the seedbeds with Bordeaux mixture, proprietary coppers or zineb is thus advisable (Hopkins, 1956; Lucas, 1965).

Two species cause leaf spots on groundnut (*Arachis hypogea*): they are *Cercospora arachidicola* and *Cercospora personata* (Woodruff, 1933). The ascospore states have been found in the U.S.A. and described as *Mycosphaerella arachidicola* and *Mycosphaerella berkeleyii* respectively (Jenkins, 1938) but so far only the conidial form has been found in Central Africa where these leaf spots are particularly important, so perithecia are not an essential feature of the disease cycle.

C. personata is potentially the more destructive species, it produces more conidia and causes more rapid defoliation, but it tends to develop later in the season so that early maturing cultivars though they are highly susceptible may escape severe infection. Both fungi enter the host mainly through stomata but direct penetration through the epidermal cells has been reported. Sequentially branched, early cultivars are more susceptible than alternatively branched cultivars, possibly because they have a greater proportion of stomata of penetrable size (Hemingway, 1955; Gibbons, 1966). Although attempts have been made to control the disease with fungicides most methods rely on the destruction of crop debris and volunteer plants which harbour the pathogen, and on crop rotation (Hemingway, 1954). Efforts are also being made to breed resistant varieties but this is complicated by the occurrence of the two distinct, yet closely associated pathogens.

The *Cercospora* leaf spot which has probably received most attention in recent years is that of bananas (Calpouzos, 1955; Wardlaw, 1961; Leach, 1962). The fungus (*Cercospora musae*) was first described from Java in 1902 by Zimmerman but it was not until 1913 that the disease became important, and then in the Sigatoka valley of Fiji. It is now frequently called 'Sigatoka disease' or 'Sigatoka leaf spot'. From Fiji it spread to Australia and Ceylon and in 1933 to the Caribbean where it caused widespread damage. It has since spread to every important area of bananas except the Canary Islands

(Stover, 1962). The perfect state, *Mycosphaerella musicola*, was described by Leach in 1941.

In most places both conidia and ascospores are important in initiating infections. Infection occurs extensively through the stomata on the unfurling heart leaf and on leaves just opened. Old leaves can be infected but only after periods of drought when the antibiotic effect of surface moulds on germination of the pathogen is much reduced and then lesion development is restricted (McGahan and Fulton, 1965). Both conidia and ascospores produce spots of the same type but the distribution of spots on the leaf differs (Stover and Fulton, 1966). The conidia are dispersed in rain splash and when carried onto the spiral folds of the unfurling leaf give rise to line spotting. The ascospores are wind dispersed after ejection from perithecia, and tend to drift upwards to the undersurfaces of the youngest open leaves and cause tip spotting (Figure 11.6).

Conidia are produced only when the leaf surface is wet or the relative humidity is 98% or higher, but they can remain viable for at least a month and one lesion can produce as many as thirteen successive crops of spores so the potential inoculum is considerable. The conidia germinate only in a film of water and then slowly. It takes at least 24 hours even under the most favourable conditions before a short germ-tube, three cells long, is produced. Partially germinated conidia appear able to withstand the drier field conditions throughout the day and continue development during the nights when leaves are moist with dew. Several consecutive evenings may therefore be necessary for germination to reach a point when penetration can occur. Perithecia are produced in mature spots and particularly in diseased trash leaves on the ground. In contrast to conidia, ascospores germinate within 4–5 hours under favourable conditions and may infect a leaf during the course of one or two evenings.

A long incubation period follows penetration whether ascospores or conidia are involved. It varies from 24 days with dense, to 4 months with sparse spore inocula. The first symptom is a yellowing of a few cells around a stoma. This yellow area progressively enlarges and then the tissues within its centre dry out and die. A fully developed spot is slightly sunken and grey, with a well-defined narrow, black rim. Extensive areas of the leaf are killed when spotting is heavy but the development of the fungus is limited within the lesion and the amount of damage is determined by the number of spores initiating infections rather than the encroachment of the pathogen on the healthy tissue from a few loci. The overall

(a)   (b)

FIGURE 11.6 Banana leaf spot (Sigatoka disease). (a) conidial infection: line spotting, (b) ascospore infection: tip spotting. From R. Leach, 1946, *Banana Leaf Spot*, Government Printer, Kingston.

result of leaf spot is that the number of fruit clusters (hands) and the size of individual fruits (fingers) are much reduced.

Control is by the use of fungicides and mineral oil. Bordeaux was first used and this was applied in the conventional manner. Then Guyot in 1952 (see Wardlaw, 1961) tried the effect of incorporating fungicides in a mineral oil with the object of increasing coverage and retention. He found that oil alone, applied in droplets less than 50µ so as to form a light fog, markedly decreased disease severity. Since then a number of similar oils have been widely used to control this disease. They are usually of light viscosity with unsulphonatable mineral residue (UR) above 90%, and are applied either from the ground by motorized knapsack sprayers or from the air by helicopters or fixed-wing aircraft (Cuille, 1965).

The mode of action of the oil is still not clear. It does not prevent conidial germination on the leaf surface but does stop the growth of the fungus after it has become established on the leaf, particularly if applied before symptom development is beyond the yellow streak stage. The rates of transpiration and photosynthesis are reduced in leaves sprayed with oil and this may be significant because the same processes are similarly affected in shaded leaves which also appear relatively resistant to infection (Calpouzos and Corke, 1963; Corke and Jordan, 1963).

Helminthosporium

Species of *Helminthosporium* cause a number of important leaf spots of Graminae (Sprague, 1950; Dickson, 1956). Many of them that do so attack the host at the seedling stage and some were mentioned in Chapter 2. The fungi often continue their development on plants which are not killed and these, therefore, provide inoculum for the infection of the maturing crop. This occurs in the leaf stripe of barley caused by *Helminthosporium gramineum* (perfect state: *Pyrenophora graminea*). Some workers suggested that once the young seedling was invaded the fungus became distributed within the tissue as in loose smut or bunt of wheat (p. 137) but N. J. G. Smith (1929) found that each leaf was infected by 'externally applied' mycelium. The fungus initially penetrates the coleoptile and grows through it to the inner surface while the first leaf is still in contact with it. Penetration of the outer surface of the first leaf or its sheathing base occurs before or soon after its emergence, and then the fungus grows through the sheathing base of the first leaf and infects the second leaf in contact with it. Successive leaves are similarly penetrated and eventually the young ear through its adjacent, protective sheath.

In leaf stripe of oats caused by *Helminthosporium avenae* (perfect state: *Pyrenophora avenae*) there is not this continuity. The first few leaves may be badly attacked, but often the fourth leaf is only slightly affected and the remaining leaves appear healthy until earing when lesions appear not only on these, but on leaves of plants which were not infected as seedlings. There is little or no conidial production by *H. avenae* during the disease-free period and it may be that fungal activity is depressed by some host factor at this time (Grainger, 1954). Although there is continued mycelial development with *H. gramineum* conidial production also appears to be synchronized with the heading, blossoming and early stages of grain development.

In both diseases the pathogens are seed-borne and treating seed with organomercurial dusts has proved an effective control method. It may not continue to do so, for recently it has been shown that in Scotland *H. avenae* has developed resistance to the present formulations (Noble and others, 1966).

Two other helminthosporia of note which attack barley are *Helminthosporium teres* (perfect state: *Pyrenophora teres*) and *Helminthosporium sativum* (perfect state: *Cochliobolus sativus*). The latter also attacks wheat and a wide range of grasses. *H. teres* causes reticulate lesions which develop first at or near the tip, a symptom from which the disease name 'net blotch' is derived. The spots caused by *H. sativum* vary in shape and size but are usually uniformly dark-brown and coalesce to give blotches covering large areas of the leaf and is sometimes called 'spot blotch' (Drechsler, 1923). Both fungi are seed-borne, and *H. sativum* characteristically causes a blackening of the embryo end of the grain in wheat and barley. They also persist in crop residues. Control is by seed treatment with organomercurials, sanitation and crop rotation.

Certain oat varieties are attacked by *Helminthosporium victoriae* (perfect state: *Cochliobolus victoriae*, Nelson, 1960). This species was described by Meehan and Murphy (1946) from rust-resistant lines developed from the variety Victoria, and is severe only on oats with this parentage. The fungus is seed-borne and also persists in crop residues, and the disease is characteristically a seedling blight and culm necrosis. The linkage between rust-resistance and susceptibility to *H. victoriae* of the particular oat variety is not the only interesting aspect of this disease. It is one of the few diseases in which the effects on the susceptible host can be attributed to the production of a specific material by the pathogen. Extensive studies of this 'vivo-toxin' and its effects have been carried out, and these are reviewed by Pringle and Scheffer (1964). One practical use of the toxin is in the screening of new oat varieties for resistance to the *Helmintho-sporium* blight; applications of toxin to the seedlings replace the traditional method of inoculation with *H. victoriae* (Luke and others, 1960).

Helminthosporium oryzae (perfect state: *Cochliobolus miyabeanus*) is another important species which causes a leaf spot of rice. On susceptible varieties lesion development is often so extensive that the leaves dry out before the plants mature, or lesions below the panicle result either in broken heads or little grain. The fungus becomes established in the grain coat but seed treatment, while it reduces the seedling blight phase is seldom sufficient on its own. Extensive development of mycelium and conidia occurs on crop residues and it is even difficult to cope with this by sanitation and crop rotation (Watts-Padwick, 1950).

Finally, there are three diseases of maize each associated with a *Helminthosporium* sp. (Jennings and Ullstrup, 1957; Ullstrup, 1966), which should be mentioned. They are (Figure 11.7):

Northern leaf blight   *Helminthosporium turcicum* (perfect state: *Tri-chometasphaeria turcica*)

Southern leaf spot   *Helminthosporium maydis* (perfect state: *Coch-liobolus heterostrophus*)

Leaf spot   *Helminthosporium carbonum* (perfect state: *Cochliobolus carbonum*)

H. turcicum is widely distributed. It causes large, irregular to elliptical leaf lesions which may result in the death of the entire leaf blade, particularly in regions where moderate temperatures and frequent dew prevail. Penetration of the leaf surface and lesion development have been described in detail by Hilu and Hooker, (1964). The fungus enters through the epidermal cells and then advances slowly in the chlorenchyma tissue resulting in small, interveinal lesions. It also, however, enters the vascular tissue and although the cells outside the lesion appear normal most of the xylem and tracheids contain hyphae. Lesions enlarge greatly when these hyphae grow out from the xylem into the surrounding healthy tissue.

H. maydis is also widely distributed but chiefly in warmer areas. The leaf lesions are smaller than those caused by *H. turcicum* and frequently zonated. *H. carbonum* is particularly common in the eastern half of the U.S.A. There are two races of the fungus; race 1 causes similar lesions to *H. maydis*. It is generally a more virile

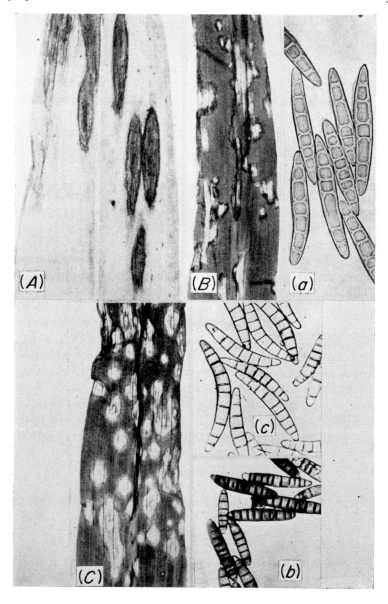

FIGURE 11.7 *Helminthosporium* leaf spots of maize, and conidia of the species involved, *(A,a) H. turcicum, (B,b) H. carbonum, (C,c) H. maydis.* From J. G. Dickson, 1956, *Diseases of Field Crops,* McGraw-Hill. Photograph by A. J. Ullstrup.

pathogen but of negligible importance because few of the inbred lines of maize are susceptible. *H. carbonum* sometimes grows over the kernels giving the ear a charred appearance and it is the only species on maize which is seed-borne. Infected crop residues are, however, the chief source of inoculum for this and the other two species, and the diseases are controlled largely by sanitation, rotation and the use of resistant hybrids.

Factors Limiting the Development of Leaf Lesions

The limited necrosis which is the essential feature of a leaf spot suggests that there are factors restricting the growth of the pathogen. In many hosts this may simply be a particular tissue which, for a variety of reasons, the pathogen is unable to colonize. This tissue may be already present; for example, *Xanthomonas malvacearum* colonizes the parenchyma cells of cotton (Thiers and Blank, 1951) and initially the veins of the leaf limit its progress, so that an angular lesion results. The vascular bundles similarly interfere with the lateral spread of *Pseudomonas lachrymans* in cucumber (Williams and Keen, 1967) and *Helminthosporium oryzae* in rice (Tullis, 1935). In other instances, structures are formed in response either to the pathogen or to the wounding which it has caused (Akai, 1959). In beet infected by *Cercospora beticola* a band of tissue develops around the leaf lesions and restricts the fungus (Figure 11.8). Cunningham (1928) used the term 'cicatrice' for this healing tissue and it appears to be a common reaction in species of *Beta*, *Pyrus*, and *Prunus* both to pathogens and to wounding. Sometimes, the diseased tissue falls away when the cicatrice is formed, giving a shot hole as in cherry leaves invaded by *Pseudomonas mors-prunorum*. The process has been described in detail by Samuel (1927) for almond (*Prunus amygdalus*) and the fungus *Stigmina carpophila*. Cells in the healthy mesophyll adjacent to the killed tissue enlarge and occlude the intercellular spaces. Some cells bordering the lesion then become lignified, others near the healthy tissue become meristematic. If there is abundant moisture at this stage and it is a young leaf, abscission occurs by the breaking of the epidermis on both surfaces and the dissolution of the middle lamellae between the two layers of cells immediately outside the lignified zone. The infected disk of tissue then drops away.

In other leaf spot diseases, indeed in the majority, there is no evidence of the physical barriers described. Possibly in these instances there are chemical changes within the infected tissues which are

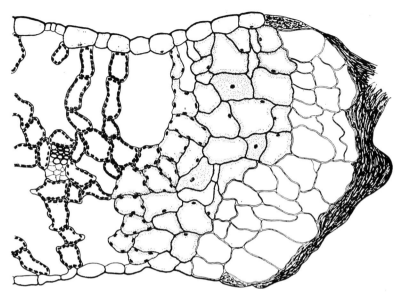

FIGURE 11.8 Cross-section through the edge of a lesion of *Cercospora beticola* on beet. From Cunningham, 1928, *Phytopathology*, **18**, 717–51

inimical to the pathogen (Allen, 1959). The nature of these chemical changes has been the subject of many investigations. One idea is that certain inhibitory substances are formed or activated only when the pathogen comes into contact with the host cells. These substances have been designated 'phytoalexins' (from the greek Phyton–plant, and alexin—warding-off compound), by Müller and his coworkers (Müller, 1961; Cruickshank, 1963, 1966). A broad interpretation of this hypothesis could include normal plant metabolites, such as chlorogenic acid, whose concentration increases when the tissues are infected, but interest centres more on chemical substances which develop in infected tissue and are not normal metabolites. A few have been isolated already and their structure determined. How they might limit the expansion of a leaf lesion has been indicated by Cruickshank and Perrin (1963). They have shown that a phytoalexin (called pisatin) is formed in varying amounts when a number of fungi, pathogens and non-pathogens, come into contact with pea tissue. With *Ascochyta pisi* high concentrations are formed, but only low amounts with *Septoria pisi*, although both fungi are sensitive to pisatin. Significantly the lesions of *A. pisi* are restricted to a small necrotic spot, those of *S. pisi* are of the spreading type. A similar situation exists in the behaviour of *Botrytis cinerea* and *Botrytis fabae* on bean leaves. The lesion of *B. cinerea* is restricted, but not that of *B. fabae*, and Purkayastha and Deverall (1965) have produced evidence that this results from differences in the amounts of inhibitors formed when leaves are infected by these two *Botrytis* species.

A more detailed examination of this subject is beyond the scope of this book. Lesion restriction is obviously only one aspect of the wider problem of disease resistance in plants and this is discussed fully by Wood (1967).

REFERENCES

Akai, S. (1959). Histology of defense in plants. In *Plant Pathology: an advanced treatise* (Ed. J. G. Horsfall and A. E. Dimond), **1**, 391–434. Academic Press, New York.

Allen, P. J. (1959). Physiology and biochemistry of defense. In *Plant Pathology: an advanced treatise* (Ed. J. G. Horsfall and A. E. Dimond), **1**, 435–67. Academic Press, New York.

Anonymous (1965). Tulip fire. *Adv. Leafl. Minist. Agric. Fish.*, No. 536, 7 pp.

Arnold, M. H. and Arnold, K. M. (1961). Bacterial blight of cotton. Trash-borne infection. *Emp. Cott. Grow. Rev.*, **38**, 258–70

Bailey, D. L. (1950). Studies in racial trends and constancy in *Cladosporium fulvum* Cooke. *Can. J. Res. C*, **28**, 535–65

Bailey, D. L. and Kerr, E. A. (1964). *Cladosporium fulvum* race 10 and resistance to it in tomato. *Can. J. Bot.*, **42**, 1555–8

Bant, J. H. and Storey, L. F. (1952). Hot-water treatment of celery seed in Lancashire. *Pl. Path.*, **1**, 81–3

Barnett, H. L. (1962). *Illustrated Genera of Imperfect Fungi.* 225 pp. Burgess Publishing Co., Minneapolis.

Beaumont, A. (1954). Tomato leaf mould: spraying trials in Lancashire and Yorkshire, 1949–52. *Pl. Path.*, **3**, 21–5

Bennett, F. T. (1928). On *Cladosporium herbarum*: the question of its parasitism, and its relation to 'thinning out' and 'dwarf ears' in wheat. *Ann. appl. Biol.*, **15**, 191–212.

Braun, A. C. (1955). A study of the mode of action of the wildfire toxin. *Phytopathology*, **45**, 659–64

Brinkerhoff, L. A. (1963). Variability of *Xanthomonas malvacearum*, the cotton bacterial blight pathogen. *Tech. Bull. Okla. agric. Exp. Stn.*, No. T-98, 95 pp.

Brooks, F. T. and Bartlett, A. W. (1910). Two diseases of gooseberry bushes. *Annls mycol.*, **8**, 167–85

Calpouzos, L. (1955). *Studies on the Sigatoka Disease of Bananas and its Fungus Pathogen*, 70 pp. Atkins Garden and Research Lab. Cienfuegos, Cuba.

Calpouzos, L. and Corke, A. T. K. (1963). Variable resistance to Sigatoka leaf spot of bananas. *Rep. agric. hort. Res. Stn. Univ. Bristol*, 1962, 106–10

Carsner, E. (1918). Angular leaf spot of cucumber: dissemination, overwintering, and control. *J. agric. Res.*, **15**, 201–20

Carter, M. V. (1959). Chemical destruction of mature perithecia of *Mycosphaerella pinodes*. *Nature, Lond.*, **183**, 162–3

Carter, M. V. and Moller, W. J. (1961). Factors affecting the survival and dissemination of *Mycosphaerella pinodes* (Berk. and Brox.) Vestergr. in South Australian irrigated pea fields. *Aust. J. agric. Res.*, **12**, 878–88

Chupp, C. (1954). *A Monograph of Cercospora*, 667 pp. Ithaca, New York.

Chupp, C. and Sherf, A. F. (1960). *Vegetable Diseases and their Control*. pp. 203–5. Ronald Press Co., New York.

Clayton, E. E. (1936). Water soaking of leaves in relation to development of the wildfire disease of tobacco. *J. agric. Res.*, **52**, 239–69

Cochran, L. C. (1932). A study of two *Septoria* leaf spots of celery. *Phytopathology*, **22**, 791–812

Cole, J. S. (1960). Field spray trials against wildfire and angular leaf spot of tobacco in Rhodesia. *Ann. appl. Biol.*, **48**, 291–8

Corke, A. T. K. and Jordan, V. W. L. (1963). Experiments on the effects of oil treatment on banana leaves. *Rep. agric. hort. Res. Stn. Univ. Bristol*, 1962, 115–123

Cruickshank, I. A. M. (1963). Phytoalexins. *A. Rev. Phytopathol.*, **1**, 351–74

Cruickshank, I. A. M. (1966). Defence mechanisms in plants. *Wld Rev. Pest. Control*, **5**, 161–73

Cruickshank, I. A. M. and Perrin, D. R. (1963). Studies on phytoalexins. VI. Pisatin: the effect of some factors on its formation in *Pisum sativum* L., and the significance of pisatin in disease resistance. *Aust. J. biol. Sci.*, **16**, 111–28

Cuille, M. (1965). Aerial treatment against *Cercospora musae* in bananas. *PANS*, **11**, 281–8

Cunningham, H. S. (1928). A study of the histologic changes induced in leaves by certain leaf-spotting fungi. *Phytopathology*, **18**, 717–51

Day, P. R. (1954). Physiologic specialization of *Cladosporium fulvum* in England and Wales. *Pl. Path.*, **3**, 35–9

Deverall, B. J. and Wood, R. K. S. (1961). Infection of bean plants (*Vicia faba* L.) with *Botrytis cinerea* and *B. fabae*. *Ann. appl. Biol.*, **49**, 461–72

Diachun, S., Valleau, W. D. and Johnson, E. M. (1942). Relation of moisture to invasion of tobacco leaves by *Bacterium tabacum* and *Bacterium angulatum*. *Phytopathology*, **32**, 379–87

Dickson, J. G. (1956). *Diseases of Field Crops*, 517 pp. McGraw Hill, New York.

Drechsler, C. (1923). Some graminicolous species of *Helminthosporium*. *J. agric. Res.*, **24**, 641–740

Gabrielson, R. L. and Grogan, R. G. (1964). The celery late blight organism *Septoria apiicola*. *Phytopathology*, **54**, 1251–7

Gibbons, R. W. (1966). *Mycosphaerella* leaf spots of groundnuts. *FAO Plant Prot. Bull.*, **14**, 25–30

Gilbert, W. W. and Gardner, M. W. (1918). Seed treatment control and overwintering of cucumber angular leaf spot. *Phytopathology*, **18**, 229–33

Glasscock, H. H., Ware, W. M. and Pizer, N. H. (1944). Influence of certain soil factors on chocolate spot of beans. *Ann. appl. Biol.*, **31**, 97–9

Graham, J. H. (1953). Cultural and epiphytotic relationships of three bacterial pathogens of soybeans. *Phytopathology*, **43**, 193–4

Grainger, J. (1954). Spore production by *Helminthosporium avenae*. *Trans. Br. mycol. Soc.*, **37**, 412–9

Guba, E. F. (1938). Tomato leaf mold as influenced by environment. *Bull. Mass. agric. Exp. Stn.*, No. 350, 24 pp.

Guba, E. F. (1939). Control of tomato leaf mold in greenhouses. *Bull. Mass. agric. Exp. Stn.*, No. 361, 36 pp.

Hare, W. W. and Walker, J. C. (1944). Ascochyta diseases of canning pea. *Res. Bull. Wis. agric. Exp. Stn.*, No. 150, 31 pp.

Hayward, A. C. (1964). Result of a survey of *Xanthomonas malvacearum* on cotton. *Emp. Cott. Grow. Rev.*, **41**, 280–4

Heggestad, H. E. (1945). Varietal variation and inheritance studies on natural water-soaking in tobacco. *Phytopathology*, **35**, 754–70

Heggestad, H. E. and Clayton, E. E. (1954). Control of tobacco wildfire with streptomycin sulfate. *Pl. Dis. Reptr*, **38**, 661–5

Hellmers, E. (1951). Angular leaf spot of cucumbers [*Pseudomonas lacrymans* (Smith and Bryan) Carsner] in Denmark. *Trans. Dan. Acad. tech. Sci.*, 1950, No. 9, 28 pp.

Hemingway, J. S. (1954). *Cercospora* leafspots of groundnuts in Tanganyika. *E. Afr. agric. J.*, **19**, 263–71

Hemingway, J. S. (1955). The prevalence of two species of *Cercospora* on groundnuts. *Trans. Br. mycol. Soc.*, **38**, 243–6

Henning, R. G. and Alexander, L. J. (1959). Evidence of existence of physiological races of *Alternaria solani*. *Pl. Dis. Reptr*, **43**, 298–308

Hilu, H. M. and Hooker, A. L. (1964). Host–pathogen relationship of *Helminthosporium turcicum* in resistant and susceptible corn seedlings. *Phytopathology*, **54**, 570–5

Hogg, W. H. (1956). Weather and the incidence of chocolate spot of beans. *N.A.A.S. q. Rev.*, **32**, 87–92

Hopkins, J. C. F. (1956). *Tobacco Diseases, with special reference to Africa*, pp. 62–72, 84–93. Commonwealth Mycological Institute, Kew.

Hull, R. (1960). *Sugar Beet Diseases*, p. 34. H.M.S.O., London.

Innes, N. L. (1961). Bacterial blight of cotton. A survey of inoculation techniques, grading scales and sources of resistance. *Emp. Cott. Grow. Rev.*, **38**, 271–8

Innes, N. L. (1964). Sudan strains of cotton resistant to bacterial blight. *Emp. Cott. Grow. Rev.*, **41**, 285–91

Jarvis, W. R. (1962). The infection of strawberry and raspberry fruits by *Botrytis cinerea* Fr. *Ann. appl. Biol.*, **50**, 569–75

Jenkins, W. A. (1938). Two fungi causing leaf spot of peanut. *J. agric. Res.*, **56**, 317–32

Jennings, P. R. and Ullstrup, A. J. (1957). A histological study of three *Helminthosporium* leaf blights of corn. *Phytopathology*, **47**, 707–14

Jones, L. K. (1927). Studies of the nature and control of blight, leaf and pod spot, and foot rot of peas caused by species of *Ascochyta*. *Bull. N.Y. St. agric. Exp. Stn.*, No. 547, 46 pp.

Knight, R. L. and Hutchinson, J. B. (1950). The evolution of blackarm resistance in cotton. *J. Genet.*, **50**, 36–58

Leach, R. (1941). Banana leaf spot *Mycosphaerella musicola*, the perfect stage of *Cercospora musae* Zimm. *Trop. Agric.*, *Trin.*, **18**, 91–5

Leach, R. (1955). Recent observations on the *Botrytis* infection of beans. *Trans. Br. mycol. Soc.*, **38**, 171

Leach, R. (1962). Banana leaf spot. *Outl. Agric.*, **3**, 203–8

Lucas, G. B. (1965). *Diseases of Tobacco*, pp. 359–79 (brown spot), pp. 380–7 (frog-eye), pp. 494–520 (wildfire and angular leaf spot). Scarecrow Press, New York.

Luke, H. H., Wheeler, H. E. and Wallace, A. T. (1960). Victoria-type resistance to crown rust separated from susceptibility to *Helminthosporium* blight in oats. *Phytopathology*, **50**, 205–9

Massey, R. E. (1931). Studies on blackarm disease of cotton. II. *Emp. Cott. Grow. Rev.*, **8**, 187–213; (1934) III. *Emp. Cott. Grow. Rev.*, **11**, 188–93

Maude, R. B. (1964). Studies on *Septoria* on celery seed. *Ann. appl. Biol.*, **54**, 313–26

Maude, R. B. (1966). Pea seed infection by *Mycosphaerella pinodes* and *Ascochyta pisi* and its control by seed soaks in thiram and captan suspensions. *Ann. appl. Biol.*, **57**, 193–200

McGahan, M. W. and Fulton, R. H. (1965). Leaf spot of banana caused by *Mycosphaerella musicola*: a comparative anatomical study of juvenile and adult leaves in relation to lesion morphology. *Phytopathology*, **55**, 1179–82

Meehan, F. and Murphy, H. C. (1946). A new *Helminthosporium* blight of oats. *Science, N.Y.*, **104**, 413–4

Müller, K. O. (1961). The phytoalexin concept and its methodological significance. *Recent Advances in Botany*, **1**, 396–400

Neergaard, F. (1945). *Danish species of Alternaria and Stemphylium; taxonomy, parasitism, economic significance*, 560 pp. Oxford University Press.

Nelson, R. R. (1960). *Cochliobolus victoriae*, the perfect state of *Helminthosporium victoriae*. *Phytopathology*, **50**, 774–5

Noble, M., MacGarvie, Q. D., Hams, A. F. and Leafe, E. L. (1966). Resistance to mercury of *Pyrenophora avenae* in Scottish seed oats. *Pl. Path.*, **15**, 23–8

Ogilvie, L. and Munro, M. (1947). Chocolate spot of field beans in the Southwest. *Rep. agric. hort. Res. Stn. Univ. Bristol*, 1946, 95–100

Pound, G. S. (1951). Effect of air temperature on incidence and development of the early blight disease of tomato. *Phytopathology*, **41**, 127–35

Pringle, R. B. and Scheffer, R. P. (1964). Host-specific plant toxins. *A. Rev. Phytopathol.*, **2**, 133–56

Purkayastha, R. P. and Deverall, B. J. (1965). The detection of antifungal substances before and after infection of beans (*Vicia faba* L.) by *Botrytis* spp. *Ann. appl. Biol.*, **56**, 269–77

Rands, R. D. (1917). Early blight of potato and related plants. *Res. Bull. Wis. agric. Exp. Stn.*, No. 42, 48 pp.

Rangel, J. F. (1945). Two *Alternaria* diseases of cruciferous plants. *Phytopathology*, **35**, 1002–7

Rogers, I. S. (1962). Nabam/zinc sulphate sprays control leaf mould in glasshouse tomatoes. *J. agric. S. Aust.*, **65**, 458–60

Rotem, J. (1964). The effect of weather on dispersal of *Alternaria* spores in a semi-arid region of Israel. *Phytopathology*, **54**, 628–32

Rowell, J. B. (1953). Leaf blight of tomato and potato plants—factors affecting the degree of injury incited by *Alternaria dauci* f. *solani*. *Bull. Rhode Isl. agric. Exp. Stn.*, No. 320, 29 pp.

Samuel, G. (1927). On the shot-hole disease caused by *Clasterosporium carpophilum* and on the shot-hole effect. *Ann. Bot., Lond.*, **41**, 375–404

Sattar, A. (1933). A comparative study of the fungi associated with blight diseases of certain cultivated leguminous plants. *Trans. Br. mycol. Soc.*, **18**, 276–301

Schimmer, F. C. (1933). *Alternaria brassicicola* on summer cauliflower seed. *Pl. Path.*, **2**, 16–7

Sheridan, J. E. (1966). Celery leaf spot: sources of inoculum. *Ann. appl. Biol.*, **57**, 75–81

Skolko, A. J., Groves, J. W. and Wallen, V. R. (1954). *Ascochyta* diseases of peas in Canada—with special reference to seed transmission. *Can. J. agric. Sci.*, **34**, 417–27

Small, T. (1930*a*). Tomato leaf mould. *Rep. exp. Res. Stn., Cheshunt*, 1929, 43–51

Small, T. (1930*b*). The relation of atmospheric temperature and humidity to tomato leaf mould (*Cladosporium fulvum*). *Ann. appl. Biol.*, **17**, 71–80

Smieton, M. J. and Brown, W. (1940). *Botrytis* disease of lettuce, its relation to damping-off and mildew, and its control by pentachloronitrobenzene dust. *Ann. appl. Biol.*, **27**, 489–501

Smith, N. J. G. (1929). Observations of the *Helminthosporium* diseases of cereals in Britain. I. The behaviour of *Helminthosporium gramineum* in a common barley disease. *Ann. appl. Biol.*, **16**, 236–60

Snyder, W. C. (1934). A leaf, stem, and pod spot of pea caused by a species of *Cladosporium*. *Phytopathology*, **24**, 890–905

Sprague, R. (1950). *Diseases of Cereals and Grasses in North America*, 538 pp. Ronald Press, New York.

Stapp, C. (1966). *Xanthomonas malvacearum*, der Erreger der Baumwoll-bakteriose. *Zentbl. Bakt. ParasitKde* Abt 2, **120**, 509–42

Stephen, R. C. (1955). Frog-eye and barn spot. *Bull. Tob. Res. Bd Rhod. and Nyasald*, No. 4, 36 pp.

Stoughton, R. H. (1930). The influence of environmental conditions on the development of the angular leaf spot disease of cotton. II. The influence of soil temperature on primary and secondary infection of seedlings. *Ann. appl. Biol.*, **17**, 493–503; (1931). III. The influence of air temperature on infection. *Ann. appl. Biol.*, **18**, 524–34; (1932). IV. The influence of atmospheric humidity on infection. *Ann. appl. Biol.*, **19**, 370–7; (1933). V. The influence of alternating and varying conditions on infection. *Ann. appl. Biol.*, **20**, 590–611

Stover, R. H. (1962). Intercontinental spread of banana leaf spot. (*Mycosphaerella musicola* Leach.). *Trop. Agric., Trin.*, **39**, 327–38

Stover, R. H. and Fulton, R. H. (1966). Leaf spot of bananas caused by *Mycosphaerella musicola*: the relation of infection sites to leaf development and spore type. *Trop. Agric., Trin.*, **43**, 117–29

Thiers, H. D. and Blank, L. M. (1951). A histological study of bacterial blight of cotton. *Phytopathology*, **42**, 499–510

Thomas, H. R. (1948). Effect of nitrogen, phosphorus and potassium on susceptibility of tomatoes to *Alternaria solani*. *J. agric. Res.*, **76**, 289–306

Tullis, E. C. (1935). Histological studies of rice leaves infected with *Helminthosporium oryzae*. *J. agric. Res.*, **50**, 81–90

Ullstrup, A. J. (1966). Corn diseases in the United States and their control. *Agric. Handbk U.S. Dep. Agric. Res. Serv.*, No. 199, 44 pp.

Valleau, W. D., Johnson, E. M. and Diachun, S. (1943). Angular leaf spot and wildfire of tobacco. *Bull. Ky agric. Exp. Stn.*, No. 454, 60 pp.

Valleau, W. D., Johnson, E. M. and Diachun, S. (1944). Root infection of crop plants and weeds by tobacco leaf spot bacteria. *Phytopathology*, **34**, 163–74

Walker, J. C. (1926). *Botrytis* neck rots of onions. *J. agric. Res.*, **33**, 893–928

Wallen, V. R., Cuddy, T. F. and Grainger, P. N. (1967). Epidemiology and control of *Ascochyta pinodes* on field peas in Canada. *Can. J. Pl. Sci.*, **47**, 395–403

Wardlaw, C. W. (1961). *Banana Diseases including Plantains and Abaca*, pp. 314–79. Longmans, Green, London.

Watts Padwick, G. (1950). *Manual of Rice Diseases*, pp. 21–34, Commonwealth Mycological Institute, Kew.

Weindling, R. (1948). Bacterial blight of cotton under conditions of artificial inoculation. *Tech. Bull. U.S. Dep. Agric.*, No. 956.

Western, J. H. (1945). Seed-borne fungi. *Nature, Lond.*, **155**, 36–7

Wheeler, B. E. J. (1958). Investigations on *Alternaria* leaf spot of flue-cured tobacco in Nyasaland. *Misc. Pap. Commonw. mycol. Inst.*, No. 15, 32 pp.

Wickens, G. M. (1953). Bacterial blight of cotton. *Emp. Cott. Grow. Rev.*, **30**, 81–103

Wiggell, D. (1958). Tomato leaf mould: spraying trials in Lancashire and Yorkshire 1953–56. *Pl. Path.*, **7**, 26–9

Wiles, A. B. and Walker, J. C. (1951). The relation of *Pseudomonas lachrymans* to cucumber fruits and seeds. *Phytopathology*, **41**, 1059–64

Williams, P. H. (1943). Tomato leaf mould (*Cladosporium fulvum*). *Rep. exp. Res. Stn., Cheshunt*, 1942, 30.

Williams, P. H. and Keen, N. T. (1967). Histology of infection by *Pseudomonas lachrymans*. *Phytopathology*, **57**, 254–6

Wilson, A. R. (1937). The chocolate spot disease of beans (*Vicia faba* L.) caused by *Botrytis cinerea* Pers. *Ann. appl. Biol.*, **24**, 258–88

Wiltshire, S. P. (1947). Species of *Alternaria* on Brassicae. *Mycol. Pap.*, No. 20, 15 pp.

Wood, R. K. S. (1962). The biology and control of diseases caused by *Botrytis* spp. *Proc. Br. Insecticide and Fungicide Conf.*, 1961, **2**, 309–314

Wood, R. K. S. (1967). *Physiological Plant Pathology*, 570 pp. Blackwell Scientific Publications, Oxford.

Woodruff, N. C. (1933). Two leaf spots of the peanut (*Arachis hypogea* L.). *Phytopathology*, **23**, 627–40

Chapter 12

Leaf curl, witches' broom and club root

The last three chapters have all been concerned with diseases in which varying amounts of the leaf and stem tissues are killed. The diseases considered in this and the two chapters which follow are those in which the pathogens induce abnormal growth (Braun, 1959). This can result from an increase both in size (hypertrophy) and number (hyperplasia) of cells within a particular tissue. This chapter is specifically concerned with diseases in which growth changes alter the form and size of the leaf, stem or root.

LEAF CURL

In leaves an increase in cells either side of the mid-rib and a stimulation in growth of the palisade cells and, to a lesser extent, of cells of the spongy parenchyma results in a puckering and curling commonly called leaf curl.

Peach leaf curl
One of the most spectacular diseases of this type occurs on peach (Matuyama and Misawa, 1961) and is caused by the fungus, *Taphrina deformans*. Leaves show symptoms at or soon after emergence. Either a part, or the entire leaf blade thickens and curls (Figure 12.1), the chlorophyll soon disappears and red or purple tints develop within the affected area. Later this appears to be covered by a greyish bloom due to the sporulation of the fungus.

FIGURE 12.1   Peach leaf curl.

Leaves drop prematurely, often so much so that dormant buds are stimulated and further new leaves emerge. These in turn may also become infected but frequently are not, so that the tree appears to recover. Repeated losses of leaves in successive seasons greatly reduce the vigour of the tree and its cropping capacity. Blossoms and young fruit can be attacked and these normally drop too, but occasionally some infected fruit matures and on these there are prominent warty outgrowths with reddish tints, though less well developed than on leaves (Pierce, 1900).

The fungus is not an obligate parasite but generally forms a mycelium only in the host; in culture it usually produces cells by budding (Martin, 1925), though it may form some mycelium on media rich in carbohydrates, peptones, and B vitamins (Caporali, 1959). It is generally considered to be a primitive Ascomycete, with affinities to certain yeasts. The asci can be clearly seen in sections of diseased leaves (Figure 12.2); they are not enclosed but form an exposed layer on the leaf surface, hence the old name for the genus, *Exoascus.* There are initially eight ascospores but these produce secondary spores (conidia) by budding so that many spores may eventually be formed from one ascus.

The exact sequence of events in the disease cycle, and therefore the methods most suitable for control, were for some time matters of dispute which centred on the ability or not of the mycelium to perennate in twigs. Present opinion is that this rarely, if ever, hap-

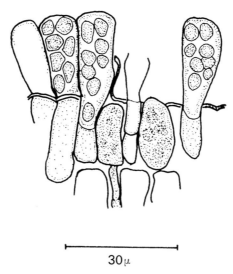

FIGURE 12.2 Peach leaf curl. T. S.
of peach leaf with curl showing
asci and ascospores of *Taphrina
deformans*.

pens. It is generally thought that ascospores or conidia lodge on the
surface of the trees then, in spring as the buds open these spores
germinate and infect any young leaves with which they come in
contact. It is assumed that ascospores and bud conidia can produce
secondary spores whenever suitable conditions prevail so that a
considerable inoculum is built up. During unfavourable conditions
such as hot, dry summers or very cold winters, conidia may become
thick-walled and there is evidence that they then remain viable
for two years or more. This feature together with budding may
partly explain severe outbreaks of leaf curl following seasons of light
infection.

Environmental conditions also markedly affect disease severity.
Rain is essential for infection and the disease is generally most
severe when there is cold, wet weather at bud burst. Under such
conditions leaf development is slow and there is a longer period
favourable for infection (Fitzpatrick, 1934; Mix, 1935).

Disease control is largely aimed at removing inoculum during
the dormant period and/or protecting the opening buds. Field
experiments have shown that one thorough application of a fungi-

cide in the autumn or 3–4 weeks before bud burst is effective. Lime sulphur and Bordeaux, and more recently ziram, ferbam, thiram and captan have been used for this purpose (Burgaud, 1956; English, 1958).

Leaf curl of cotton and tobacco

Other diseases of this type result from virus infection: two examples are the leaf-curl diseases of cotton and tobacco. These have much in common, in particular the causal virus of each is transmitted by a whitefly, *Bemisia tabaci*.

In cotton the leaf symptoms vary; there may be curling of the leaf margins, local or irregular vein thickening resulting in a crinkled appearance and in a severe form, foliar outgrowths (enations), or there may be chlorotic spots and streaks especially along the main veins. The symptoms depend partly on the age of the plant when infection occurs. Cotton leaves with curl are abnormally dark green and thick. The palisade parenchyma beneath the upper epidermis is converted to a mass of rectangular cells with large intercellular spaces and this spongy tissue is also found under the lower epidermis and particularly beneath the larger vascular bundles. There is often considerable meristemmatic activity in the stems of severely infected plants giving rise to extrastclar vascular bundles (Tarr, 1951, 1964; Massey and Andrews, 1932).

The symptoms of tobacco leaf curl also vary and are essentially similar in range to those of cotton (Figure 12.3), but they arise from slightly different histological changes. Diseased tobacco leaves have more layers of densely aggregated spongy-parenchyma cells and fewer intercellular spaces than healthy leaves. There is an increase in the primary phloem, the pericycle is enlarged, new wood vessels are formed, and leaf dorsiventrality is lost by the substitution of palisade for spongy parenchyma (Kerling, 1933).

With both diseases the amount of damage varies. If young plants are infected they fail to develop much and yield very little. With plants infected late in the season, the top leaves alone may curl and there is little loss of crop. When cotton leaf curl first appeared in the Sudan Gezira it often became widespread on plants 7–8 weeks after sowing and resulted in heavy losses. With the introduction of control measures it does not now appear generally until 10 weeks or more after sowing and losses are small. With cotton there are indications that severe leaf curl inhibits fertilisation; experiments in Nigeria showed that the disease significantly reduced weight of seed cotton and the number of seeds per boll (Lewin, 1927).

FIGURE 12.3 Tobacco leaf curl. Photograph by H. H. Storey, from Hopkins,
1956, *Tobacco Diseases*, Commonwealth
Mycological Institute, Kew.

Both cotton leaf curl virus and tobacco leaf curl virus are bud
and graft transmittable but neither is transmitted through the seed
or by sap inoculation. In the field both viruses are transmitted
exclusively by infective whiteflies which insert their stylets into the
phloem tissues (Pollard, 1955). The immobile larval stages pick up
the viruses by feeding on infected plants and then retain them as
adults but they are not transmitted through the eggs. When either
cotton and tobacco leaf curl virus has been introduced into a plant
there is an incubation period before symptoms appear, on average
this is 11–19 days for cotton and 12–33 days for tobacco. The flies
or their larvae need to feed for a certain time before acquiring
the viruses and there is then a further (latent) period before they

are able to transmit them. With cotton the leaf curl virus is acquired after about 3 hours feeding and the latent period is about 30 minutes (Kirkpatrick, 1932). A single insect is an efficient vector of both viruses. The adults are unable to fly more than a few metres in a single flight but they can be carried several miles by wind.

In considering the initiation of these diseases in new crops both the source of inoculum and persistence of the insect vector must be taken into account. By far the most important source of inoculum for both viruses is ratoon growth from a previous crop, i.e. secondary growth from infected plants or stumps of plants which have been left in old cotton or tobacco fields. Alternative hosts of the viruses can also serve as inoculum sources though these are generally less important. *Hibiscus esculentus* and *Malvaviscus arborens* are minor sources of cotton leaf curl virus in the Sudan and possibly *Rhynchosia minima* for tobacco leaf curl virus in Puerto Rico (Bird, 1962). The whiteflies survive on a variety of cultivated plants and weeds, most of which are not hosts for the respective viruses. In the Sudan they spend the dry season mainly on beans, *Phaseolus vulgaris* and *Dolichos lablab*. Then with the onset of rains they migrate and breed on certain weeds, e.g. *Ipomoea cordofana* and on ratoon cotton. The severity of disease development depends largely on the amount of the inoculum source and its distance from the new crops and also proximity to large populations of whitefly.

Control of leaf curl in cotton and tobacco relies mainly on the elimination of ratoon growth and on the use of resistant varieties. Although some direct control of the insect vector has been attempted (Tarr, 1964) it is seldom satisfactory and may even be harmful because insecticides also kill the natural predators which help to keep the whitefly population in check.

In these two diseases it is the virus which causes leaf curl and the insect is merely the vector. There are many instances, however, in which curling of leaves may be caused solely by insects feeding on them. This is particularly so with aphid attack and should always be borne in mind when investigating leaf-curl diseases. This type of leaf malformation is also caused by certain hormone weedkillers such as 2,4–D (2,4-dichlorophenoxyacetic acid).

WITCHES' BROOM

In peach leaf curl the affected leaves eventually fall and although there may be other indications such as lack of vigour and dead twigs, little or no hypertrophied tissue remains. Other species of

Taphrina, e.g. *Taphrina cerasi* on cherry, stimulate shoot production by the host: the result is a dense cluster of twigs called a witches' broom, which persists for many years. Similar malformations are caused on a variety of hosts by insects or mites, viruses, and parasitic flowering plants such as dwarf mistletoes (Bos, 1957; 1963). While of interest few of these diseases are of economic significance. Two exceptions are dwarf mistletoe of ponderosa pine (*Pinus ponderosa*) and witches' broom of cacao caused by the basidiomycete fungus *Marasmius perniciosus*.

Dwarf mistletoe of Ponderosa pine

Mistletoes have aroused man's curiosity for centuries mainly because of their unusual growth habit, and many papers have been written on them: these are reviewed by Gill and Hawksworth (1961). The mistletoe family (Loranthaceae) contains some 1300 species disposed in about thirty-six genera. All species are parasitic on the stems and branches of trees and shrubs but most of them are only of academic interest because they do little damage to their hosts. Within the genus *Arceuthobium*, however, there are some notable exceptions. In the U.S.A. these dwarf mistletoes, as they are called, are amongst the most important pathogens of the western coniferous forests, and the damage they cause is rated second only to that induced by various heart rots (Hawksworth, 1961). Surveys in California, for example, showed that 30% of the white fir (*Abies concolor*) and 40% of the red fir (*Abies magnifica*) were infected by the dwarf mistletoe *Arceuthobium campylopodum* f. *abietinum* (Scharpf and Parmeter, 1967).

The appropriation of nutrients by the dwarf mistletoes results in a decline in the overall growth of their hosts, particularly in the vigour of the crown of the tree; the effective photosynthetic area is gradually diminished and the tree frequently dies as a result of this. The presence of the characteristic growth of the parasite clearly establishes the cause of the disease in most instances but on many hosts the most conspicuous symptom is the formation of witches' brooms, though these are not induced by all *Arceuthobium* spp. and in some infections by broom-inducing mistletoes broom formation is inhibited.

The brooms induced by *Arceuthobium vaginatum* f. *cryptopodium* on ponderosa pine are most spectacular, and of three kinds (Figure 12.4). The most common or typical broom is approximately spherical in outline with characteristically tapered branches that may extend to give a broom diameter of some 3·6 m or more. In young stands of

H

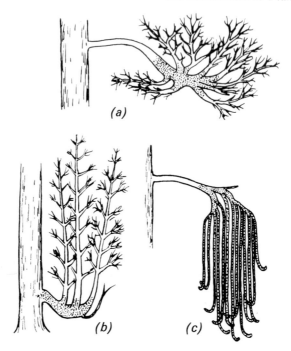

FIGURE 12.4 Three types of brooms
associated with dwarf mistletoe on
ponderosa pine. (*a*) typical broom,
(*b*) volunteer leader broom, (*c*) weeping
broom. The stippling indicates the
areas invaded by the parasite. From
Hawksworth, 1961, *Tech. Bull. U.S.
Dep. Agric.*, No. 1246; courtesy U.S.
Forest Service.

Pinus ponderosa 'volunteer leader brooms' in which the branches
of the broom stand erect are also common. The third type, the
weeping broom, in which the branches bend downwards is comparatively rare. In this last type the growth of the mistletoe within
the host is systemic in the sense that it keeps pace with the growth
of the host's branches; in the other two, growth of the parasite is
restricted to the centre or base of the broom.

The range of this particular dwarf mistletoe extends from Guate-
mala to North Colorado, and Hawksworth (1961) estimates that in
Arizona and New Mexico some 36% of the ponderosa pine stands

are affected and that the losses caused by the reduction in growth of these trees is equivalent to approximately 150 million board feet of timber annually.

Once established the parasite extends within the stem of the host and it produces new shoots progressively farther away from the original infection as its old shoots die. It is dioecious and also perennial (Figure 12.5), the female shoots producing successive crops of flowers. Fruits mature during a 3-week period from the end of July to the beginning of August. Each fruit contains a single seed which is forcibly ejected to some 5·2 m by a mechanism which is still not fully understood. The seeds are coated with a mucilagious substance called viscin which enables them to adhere to the needles or branches on which they alight. Most of them become trapped on the needles but are then washed by rain to the branches and infection is initiated only on branches. The seeds germinate within a month and produce a hypocotyl which grows along the host surface until its food supply is exhausted or until it reaches some obstacle such as the base of a needle. In the latter instance the tip of the hypocotyl swells to form a structure called a holdfast from which the parasite grows into the host cortex. So far as is known, the intrusion of the parasite into the host is by mechanical pressure; there is no evidence of death of host cells in advance of the penetrating structure or haustorium. The mistletoe then develops extensively in the host cortex with extensions (sinkers) into the xylem.

The control of dwarf mistletoe in ponderosa pine forests at present relies on the removal of infected trees, those of marketable size first, followed some 3–5 years later by the remainder that are infected. Pruning of the mistletoe growth is of limited value because in time the parasite produces new growth and also an infected tree often has many latent infections. It is also an expensive operation. Chemical treatment of the mistletoe has so far not proved practical. Many herbicides will kill the shoots of the parasite without excessively damaging the host but as with pruning resprouting of the mistletoe soon occurs.

Witches' Broom of cacao

A review by Baker and Holliday (1957) provides the basis for this account. The disease was first reported from Surinam at the close of the 19th Century and resulted in heavy losses both there and in Guyana in the 1920's. It is apparently indigenous to tropical South America in an area which encompasses the Amazon and Orinoco basins, and it has spread north to include some of the

(b)

(a)

FIGURE 12.5 Shoots of dwarf mistletoe (*Arceuthobium vaginatum* f. *cryptopodium*) on Ponderosa pine. (a) a female plant showing the fruits about 3 months before maturity, (b) a male plant showing the flowers at time of pollination. U.S. Forest Service photograph, courtesy Hawksworth, 1961. *Tech. Bull. U.S. Dept. Agric.*, no. 1246.

Caribbean islands where cacao is grown. The causal fungus, *Maras-mius perniciosus*, is an obligate parasite and infects only the com-mercially important *Theobroma cacao* and a few other *Theobroma* spp.

As the disease name implies, on various aerial parts of the trees there is excessive lateral branching and aggregations of short and swollen shoots or brooms are produced. Pods can also be infected and become carrot shaped or variously distorted (Figure 12.6), the symptoms depending on the stage of development at the time of infection. Beans within these pods remain small and are of no value. Sometimes only a portion of the pod is affected and then the infec-tion is usually visible as a localized necrotic area of unusual hard-ness, but this may be associated with extensive internal necrosis. The overall effect of the disease on yield can be disastrous with almost total loss of the marketable crop.

In considering the disease cycle we may conveniently start with the production of sporophores. They are formed on dead brooms and rarely on dead pods, either singly or in groups. Since the fungus is homothallic all dead brooms are potentially capable of bearing sporophores but generally only 70% do so and this can be modified by weather. Showery weather is most favourable; fewer sporophores are formed under dry conditions or excessive rain. Basidiospores are discharged mainly at night and are carried by air currents throughout the plantations. Germination can start less than an hour after discharge and be complete 4 hours later if the spore alights on a suitable infection court and the relative humidity is above 90%. Under less humid conditions the basidiospores do not remain viable for long and for practical purposes after 48 hours are considered to be ineffective as inoculum. Only young host tissue is penetrated and even then stomatal entry appears to be more common than direct penetration of the cuticle. Symptoms do not usually appear until some 6 weeks after penetration, sometimes even longer, then shoots begin to swell and branch abnormally. On flower cushions the first indication is usually that one flower fails to fall and its pedicel becomes slightly thickened. Then several weeks later the cushion starts to produce diseased flowers, pods or hypertrophied shoots. The fungus is intercellular within the host and is largely confined to the hypertrophied tissue but does extend slightly into the healthy part of the shoot. Some 5–6 weeks after they are fully formed the brooms turn brown and are then con-sidered to be dead. Sporophore formation starts on average some 5–6 months later and can continue for 2 years though fewer sporo-phores are produced in the second year.

(a)

(b)

FIGURE 12.6 Witches' broom of cacao. (a) lateral broom (b)
infected pods, showing distortion and internal necrosis. Infections
occurred at positions marked X. From Baker and Holliday, 1957.
Phytopathol. Pap. no. 2. Crown copyright.

In a new area, spread of the disease is initially most rapid in the vegetative canopy; pods and flower cushions are affected later. In an epiphytotic the trees may be covered with so many brooms that hardly a single, healthy green shoot can be seen. The optimum climate for such a high disease incidence is an evenly-distributed annual rainfall of 177–229 mm, giving night humidities at saturation point over long periods, with minimum night temperatures not below 16°. Disease severity also depends on the amount of inoculum initially present and there is a strong positive correlation between the number of sporophores and the number of brooms which appear some 5 weeks later.

It is essential for disease control that numerous sporophores must not be allowed to develop. As a general rule brooms should be removed every 3–4 months; this is the minimum time in which a newly formed green broom develops to a sporophore-producing state. Local conditions modify this, and in a dry season removing brooms once a year may be adequate. Because the mycelium extends slightly beyond the brooms they are cut off with some 100–150 mm of apparently healthy stem: infected flower cushions are cut off flush with the bark. Diseased pods are most conveniently removed at normal harvesting. With comparatively light outbreaks of witches' broom these eradicative measures give good control. With more severe outbreaks they are effective only if the brooms are removed strictly at the recommended times over large areas, e.g. 120 ha, and the trees concerned are not of a highly susceptible variety. There have been attempts to control the disease with protectant fungicides and to link this with control of pod-infecting fungi such as *Phytophthora palmivora* (causing black pod) or *Botryodiplodia theobromae* (causing brown pod) but so far with disappointing results. A number of *Theobroma* spp. from the Amazon area show marked resistance to witches' broom and it is possible that a commercially acceptable variety will eventually be derived from them.

The importance of this disease lies not only in its effects on cacao production in the Caribbean area but in its potential danger to the more extensive cacao-producing areas of West Africa, particularly in view of the limited control methods at present available.

CLUB ROOT

In the majority of root diseases rotting of the tissues is the principal feature (see Chapter 3), but there are a few in which the main symptom is an abnormal development of the root. Rotting occurs only in the later stages of the disease and then often as a result of invasion by other organisms. The most important is the 'club-root' or 'finger and toe' disease of crucifers.

Club root of crucifers

This is caused by *Plasmodiophora brassicae*, a primitive fungus of the order Plasmodiophorales, which has no filamentous hyphae but only naked masses of protoplasm from which various structures including resting spores are derived.

The disease was first studied by Woronin in 1878. The characteristic symptom is the club-like swelling of infected roots (Figure 12.7); the entire root system may be so affected or just a few roots. If these swellings are cut they show a marbled or mottled appearance and this distinguishes them from crown gall (p. 228), and from certain insect galls such as those caused by the turnip gall weevil. The shoot symptoms reflect the interference to water and nutrient uptake by the roots. Growth is checked and there is yellowing and some wilting of the foliage in the later stages of the disease.

Colhoun (1958) has summarized our present knowledge of club root and the following is based mainly on his review. Infection can occur during any stage of growth of the host provided there are young root hairs full of protoplasm. These become invaded and the amoeba-like bodies of the fungus (myxamoebae) can be seen in the root-hair cells 4–7 days after initial infection. There follows a sequence of events in which the myxamoebae divide into a number of protoplasts (zoosporangia), which further segment into motile bodies. There is disagreement as to the nature and function of these stages but in some form the fungus migrates from the root hairs to the cortical cells and by growth and nuclear division forms a multinucleate plasmodium. In the early stages there is close contact between plasmodium and host cytoplasm and it is difficult to distinguish them. Once a cell has become infected it is stimulated to divide and this initiates the swellings which form the main disease symptom. When the cambial cells of the root are infected, the development of club roots is rapid. Finally, plasmodia within the cells divide into a mass of spherical spores (Figure 12.8). When the host tissue decays, the spores are liberated into the soil where they can remain viable for periods up to 7–8 years, and provide inoculum for the infection of further susceptible crops. These spores on germination give rise to a single zoospore which is initially motile but subsequently becomes amoeboid, and apparently in this form infects root hairs.

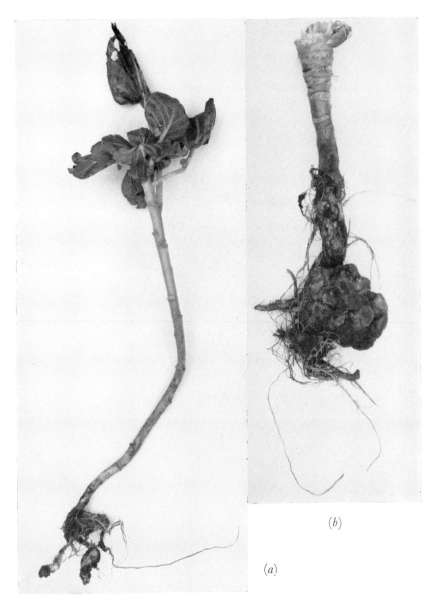

(b)

(a)

FIGURE 12.7   Club-root of cabbage. (a) 'clubs' on a young transplant, (b) much malformed root of an old plant.

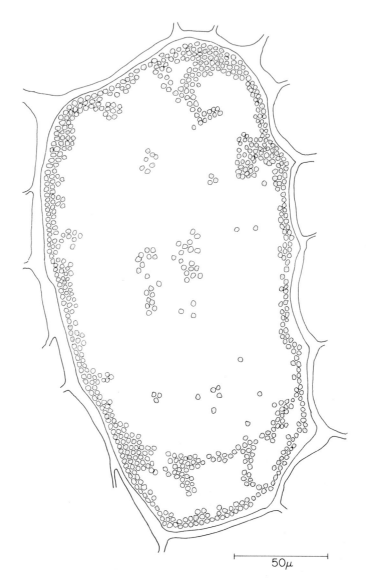

50μ

FIGURE 12.8 Hypertrophied cell from a cabbage root showing resting spores of *Plasmodiophora brassicae*. (Most of the spores in the centre of the cell have been lost in cutting the section).

The large number of resting spores produced by *P. brassicae* and their longevity in soil makes the control of club root difficult and this situation is further complicated by the many cultivated and wild hosts of this fungus. Many aspects of control are detailed by Colhoun (1958); in practice reduction in disease incidence is achieved by good husbandry, soil treatment and growing resistant varieties of cultivated plants. Liming of the soil is one of the oldest control practices, and various forms of lime and other materials containing calcium have been tried. Although the results have varied in efficiency liming remains one of the standard treatments. How it controls club root is still not entirely clear. Some workers consider that germination of the resting-spores is inhibited by the reduction in soil acidity and this has certainly been demonstrated in several experiments. Others, however, maintain that the resting spores are killed by liming.

Other soil treatments involve the use of fungicides in seed boxes, seedbeds or at transplanting. Materials containing mercury, either in inorganic form such as mercuric and mercurous chloride or organically combined, copper compounds, dilute formalin, and chlorinated nitrobenzenes have proved to be of some value in this respect. These are used as drenches, or applied as dusts and mixed with the soil.

Crop rotations are of limited value since there needs to be such long periods between susceptible crops and cruciferous weeds must also be eliminated. Some experiments suggest, however, that certain crops in a rotation may have some more positive effect in reducing the population of resting spores, and those of MacFarlane (1952), in which he showed that certain plants such as rye grass (*Lolium perenne*) stimulated spore germination without themselves serving as hosts of *P. brassicae*, suggest that some could be used as catch crops.

REFERENCES

Baker, R. E. D. and Holliday, P. (1957). Witches' broom disease of cacao (*Marasmius perniciosus* Stahel). *Phytopathol. Pap.*, No. 2, 42 pp.

Bird, J. (1962). A whitefly transmitted mosaic of *Rhynchosia minima* DC, and its relation to tobacco leaf curl and other virus diseases of plants in Puerto Rico. *Phytopathology*, **52**, 286

Bos, L. (1957). Heksenbezemverschijn-selen een pathologischmorfologisch onderzoek. *Meded. LandbHoogesch. Wageningen*, **57**, 1–79 (English summary).

Bos, L. (1963). Heksembezems en Laksenbezengroei bij houtige gewassen. *Meded. Inst. plziek-tenk. Onderz.*, **355**, 162–74 (English summary).

Braun, A. C. (1959). Growth is affected. In *Plant Pathology: an advanced treatise* (Ed. J. G. Horsfall and A. E. Dimond), **1**, 189–248. Academic Press, New York.

Burgaud, L. (1956). Les fongicides organiques de synthese dans la lutte contre la cloque du Pecher (*Taphrina deformans* Tul.) *Phytiat.-Phytopharm.*, **5**, 17–20 [*Rev. appl. Mycol.*, **36**, 105]

Caporali, L. (1959). Contribution a l'etude du comportement de *Taphrina deformans* (Berk.) Tul. en culture in vitro. *C.r.hebd. Seanc. Acad. Sci.*, *Paris*, **249**, 441–443 [*Rev. appl. Mycol.*, **38**, 756]

Colhoun, J. (1958). Club root disease of crucifers caused by *Plasmodiophora brassicae* Woron. *Phytopathol. Pap*, No. 3, 108 pp.

English, H. (1958). Fall applications of ziram and ferbam effectively control peach leaf curl in California. *Pl. Dis. Reptr*, **42**, 384–7

Fitzpatrick, R. E. (1934). The life history and parasitism of *Taphrina deformans*. *Scient. Agric.*, **14**, 305–26

Gill, L. S. and Hawksworth, F. S. (1961). The Mistletoes: a literature review. *Tech. Bull. U.S. Dep. Agric.*, No. 1242, 87 pp.

Hawksworth, F. S. (1961). Dwarf mistletoe of ponderosa pine in the southwest. *Tech. Bull. U.S. Dep. Agric.*, No. 1246, 112 pp.

Kerling, L. C. P. (1933). The anatomy of the 'Kroepoek-diseased' leaf of *Nicotiana tabacum* and of *Zinnia elegans*. *Phytopathology*, **23**, 175–90

Kirkpatrick, T. W. (1932). Further studies on leaf curl of cotton in the Sudan. *Bull. ent. Res.*, **22**, 323–63

Lewin, C. J. (1927). On the incidence of leaf curl of cotton in southern Nigeria. *Bull. agric. Dep. Nigeria*, No. 6, 70–7

MacFarlane, I. (1952). Factors affecting the survival of *Plasmodiophora brassicae* Wor. in the soil and its assessment by a host test. *Ann. appl. Biol.*, **39**, 239–56

Martin, E. M. (1925). Cultural and morphological studies of some species of *Taphrina*. *Phytopathology*, **15**, 67–76

Massey, R. E. and Andrews, F. W. (1932). The leaf curl disease of cotton in the Sudan. *Emp. Cott. Grow. Rev.*, **7**, 32–45

Matuyama, N. and Misawa, T. (1961). Anatomical studies on the leaf curl of peach caused by *Taphrina deformans* Tul. *Tohoku J. agric. Res.*, **12**, 317–25

Mix, A. J. (1935). The life history of *Taphrina deformans*. *Phytopathology*, **25**, 41–66

Pierce, N. B. (1900). Peach leaf curl: its nature and treatment. *Bull. Div. Veg. Physiol. Path. U.S. Dep. Agric.*, No. 20, 204 pp.

Pollard, D. G. (1955). Feeding habits of the cotton whitefly, *Bemisia tabaci* Genn. (Homoptera: Aleyrodidae). *Ann. appl. Biol.*, **43**, 664–71

Scharpf, R. F. and Parmeter, J. R., Jr. (1967). The biology and pathology of dwarf mistletoe, *Arceuthobium campylopodum* f. *abietinum*, parasitizing true firs (*Abies* spp.) in California. *Tech. Bull. U.S. Dep. Agric.*, No. 1362, 42 pp.

Tarr, S. A. J. (1951). *Leaf Curl Disease of Cotton*, 55 pp. Commonwealth Mycological Institute, Kew.

Tarr, S. A. J. (1964). Virus Diseases of Cotton, *Misc. Publs Commonw. mycol. Inst.*, No. 18, 23 pp.

Chapter 13

Galls

In leaf curl, witches' broom and club root the leaves, shoots and roots, respectively, grow abnormally as a result of infection by individual pathogens, yet basically these organs retain some semblence of their normal form. In other diseases, pathogens induce localized swellings or outgrowths which although they themselves might have a characteristic shape are quite unlike any organ of the normal plant. These outgrowths are called galls, and they can be caused by the independent action of bacteria, fungi, nematodes, and insects; by bacteria and viruses when introduced into the plant by particular insect vectors, and by the combined action of bacteria and nematodes.

Crown gall

This is probably the most intensively studied gall disease. It is caused by the bacterium *Agrobacterium tumefaciens* and affects plants belonging to at least 142 genera, including many of economic importance. The galls vary considerably in size and texture. They are generally much smaller on roots than on the crown or collar; on herbaceous stems they are usually soft but are always hard on woody stems (Figure 13.1). The gall tissue itself is a confused mass of parenchyma and vascular elements. The bacteria are found mainly towards the outside of the galls and are more readily isolated from scrapings of the peripheral tissues; there are relatively few bacteria deeper in the gall (E. F. Smith and others, 1911, 1912; E. F. Smith, 1920).

A. tumefaciens was first shown to be the causal agent of crown gall by E. F. Smith and Townsend (1907) and was subsequently isolated

FIGURE 13.1 Crown gall on an apple rootstock. Photograph copyright East Malling Research Station, from Wormald, 1955, *Diseases of Fruits and Hops*, Crosby Lockwood.

from galls on a number of different plants by various investigators and its pathogenicity established in these instances. Within these isolates there are a number of physiologic races which differ in their host ranges and biochemical activities (Wormald, 1945).

There is evidence that *A. tumefaciens* can exist in soil for considerable periods (Patel, 1928). Investigations on crown gall of raspberry showed that the bacterium could overwinter in fallow soil and in non-sterile soil in the nursery, and that pathogenic isolates could be obtained from these soils over fourteen months (Banfield, 1934).

Infection occurs only through a wound, and indeed wounding appears essential for gall formation (Rack, 1953). Once within the tissues the bacterium has the ability to alter the normal growth-control mechanism of the host cells permanently after a short period of contact, normally about 4–5 days. Then abnormal growth can continue independently of the bacteria. In some hosts such as sunflower, secondary galls develop at sites some distance from the primary inoculations and under experimental conditions they have been obtained free from bacteria. When portions of the bacteria-free galls are transferred to sterile culture media they continue to grow and healthy plants inoculated with small pieces of this sterile tumour tissue develop typical galls. The nature of the changes which convert a healthy plant cell into one over which the host has little control is still not understood, but the apparent similarity between this and cancerous growth in mammals makes it of more than plant pathological interest. Reviews by Braun (1962) and Wood (1967) summarize present information on the physiology of gall formation.

At one time crown gall was considered to be a very serious disease but with many hosts there is no certain evidence of adverse effects. This is particularly true of fruit trees where even large galls appear to have little effect on the bearing and growth (Riker and others, 1959). Crown galls may, however, cause losses in nursery stock (Melhus and Maney, 1921; Siegler and Bowman, 1940) and adversely affect growth in vines, hops and roses under glass (Dowson, 1957).

Various methods of control have been advocated depending on the host affected. Careful inspection of fruit-tree nursery stock is particularly important. Most infections in the nursery appear to result from the grafting process and can be greatly reduced by budding (Anderson, 1956). Attempts have been made to eradicate galls *in situ* from orchard trees. Ark (1941) successfully treated galls on almond by painting them with sodium dinitrocresol in methyl alcohol and extending the application about 25 mm beyond the gall outlines. There have been similar experiments with antibiotics such as penicillin and streptomycin but the practical value of these methods is doubtful (Hampton, 1948; Klemmer and others, 1955; Deep, 1958). There have also been attempts to eradicate *A. tumefaciens* from soil with fumigants (Dickey, 1962). There are varieties of particular fruit crops which are highly resistant to *A. tumefaciens* and these are often used as rootstocks thus avoiding the development of large crown galls, e.g. East Malling rootstock XVI for apples (Harris and Pearse, 1938).

Root knot

Nematodes cause galls also, of varying types, on roots and shoots (Krusberg, 1963). Species of *Meloidogyne* particularly attack roots and are known as 'root knot' nematodes from the small swellings which result (Figure 13.2). Some nine species and subspecies are recognized, each associated with a type host but capable of infecting a wide range of plants (Chitwood and Oetifa, 1952). Infection appears to follow a similar pattern in the nematode-host combinations which have been thoroughly investigated. The nematode larva penetrates the epidermis near the root tip killing some cells in the process. It migrates intercellularly in the cortex and eventually reaches the edge of the vascular cylinder. Some 24 hours after

FIGURE 13.2 Tobacco root knot. Photograph courtesy J. Shepherd, Tobacco Research Board of Rhodesia.

penetration changes occur in cells adjacent to the larva. Cells near its head divide rapidly and then those immediately surrounding its mouth enlarge. Cell walls next to the hypertrophied cells dissolve so that large multinucleate units with dense protoplasm are formed, called 'giant cells' (Dropkin and Nelson, 1960). Cell division and enlargement continues in the tissues immediately surrounding the giant cells and this, plus nematode growth, causes the root to swell and produce a 'root knot'. The size of the gall appears to depend not only on the host and species of nematode but also on the number of larvae which penetrate in any particular part. Experiments with *Meloidogyne incognita* var. *acrita* on tomato and cucumber suggest that the response of the root to the nematode is a local one and is related to the amount of stimulation provided by each nematode (Dropkin, 1954). Moreover, giant cell development and the growth of the root knot depends on a continuous stimulus from the nematode. Once this is removed the cytoplasm of the giant cell breaks down (Bird, 1962).

Adult female nematodes inside the gall deposit their eggs within a gelatinous matrix in the cortex and this tissue is often ruptured. The eggs may hatch in the root and the larvae establish themselves in adjacent tissue, or they may hatch at or near the root surface and the larvae migrate and enter new roots (Christie, 1936). Root diffusates appear to stimulate hatching of the eggs (Viglierchio and Lownsberry, 1960), and there is also evidence that *Meloidogyne* larvae are attracted to roots of host plants. Experiments with sterile tomato and *M. incognita* root cultures showed that larvae were strongly attracted to the root tips even when separated from them by cellophane (Peacock, 1959). Once the root is penetrated it becomes even more attractive and many larvae enter through the wound made by the first larva.

Nematode development is affected considerably by soil temperature and moisture, aeration and by host nutrition (Wallace, 1963). In the tropics *Meloidogyne* spp. undergo many life cyles in one year; in temperate climates there are generally fewer cycles and the nematodes survive the winter months as eggs or by infecting roots of weed hosts. The distance travelled by larvae in soil probably only amounts to about a metre per year and the nematodes are generally distributed over fields by the action of farm machinery and animals, by percolating rain water, and in plant material moved from one place to another. Field control of root knot through crop rotations is difficult because each *Meloidogyne* sp. has a wide host range and for some this has not been fully investigated; previous host records need to be reassessed as formerly all root knot nematodes were referred to one species, originally *Heterodera radicicola* and later *Heterodera marioni*. More than one *Meloidogyne* species in any locality is an additional complication, but in some areas satisfactory crop rotations have been evolved. On seedbed sites and other areas where the economics of the crop will permit it, soil fumigation with nematicides appears to be the most satisfactory control method but there is also an increasing interest in the development of root-knot resistant varieties (Thorne, 1961).

Insect galls

The galls produced by *A. tumefaciens* and *Meloidogyne* spp. respectively on their hosts vary in size but differ little in their general shape. Insect galls on the other hand show extreme diversity of form, and there are a great many insects which cause them (Leach, 1940; Carter, 1962). Most gall formers belong to one of five families: Cynipidae (cynipids) Cecidomyidae (gall midges), Aphididae (aphids), Psyllidae (Psyllids) and Eriophyidae (gall mites). Most cynipid galls are formed on species of oak, rose and various composites. Some midges are constantly associated with fungi in galls which are often called 'ambrosia galls', and in one group of mite galls there is an excessive production of abnormal leaf hairs (trichomes), so they are called 'felt galls'. Other mites infest buds causing them to swell but not unfold, a condition known as 'big bud', e.g. in blackcurrants (Mani, 1964).

Apparently the females of some gall-forming insects secrete an irritant at oviposition and this induces some enlargement of the plant tissues before the egg is hatched, but the presence of the developing larva is necessary for the completion of the typical gall. As Braun (1959) points out, the distinguishing feature of insect galls, particularly the highly developed cynipid galls, is their determinate growth. Although initially this may appear haphazard it eventually leads to an orderly arrangement of cells and cell layers, orientated to the developing insect. The outer tissues of epidermal cells, stone cells and fibres serve to protect the larva, while a layer of thin-walled cells with dense protoplasmic contents, serves as nutritive tissue as do the giant cells in root knot. The form of the gall and its position on the plant is characteristic of the insect which induces it and species can often be identified from these features (van Leuween, 1957). On one host, several insects often induce quite distinct galls (Figure 13.3). This suggests that a large number of highly specific chemical substances are elaborated by gall-forming

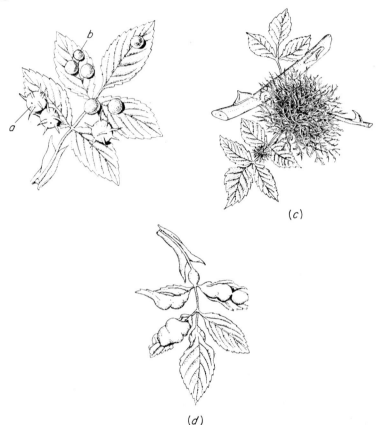

FIGURE 13.3 Insect galls on rose caused by (*a*) *Rhodites rosarum* (*b*) *Rhodites eglanteriae* (*c*) *Rhodites rosae* (*d*) *Rhodites spinosissimae.* From W. M. Docters van Leeuwen, 1957, *Gallenboek,* W. J. Thieme, Zutphen.

insects, each with its particular morphogenetic effect on the cells and tissues of the host, but so far little is known of the physiology of insect gall formation.

Injury to plants through insect galls is generally not great and apart from their removal from prized ornamentals few control measures are practised.

Olive knot

Gall formation is not always the result of a simple host–parasite combination. Even in some examples already discussed other parasites play an important part. Fungus and insect both appear essential for the development of ambrosial galls and the incidence of crown gall on raspberry is markedly increased by root-feeding arthropods which cause wounds necessary for gall formation by *A. tumefaciens* (Banfield, 1934). In olive knot there is a highly evloved association between the causal bacterium, *Pseudomonas savastanoi* and an insect vector, *Dacus oleae*. The main symptom of this disease is a knot or tubercle on young twigs and leaves, consisting mainly of cortical tissue, within which there are pockets containing the bacteria. In wet weather the bacteria ooze from the knots and are distributed by rain (Wilson, 1935). They can initiate infection through leaf scars soon after leaf fall, or through small wounds caused by hail or by the olive fly (*D. oleae*) at oviposition. The association between this insect and *P. savastanoi* was first investigated by Petri in Italy (Leach, 1940). The bacteria are found in the intestinal tract of the insect in all stages of development and the anatomy of the insect is such that at oviposition eggs are contaminated with bacteria, so that egg-laying involves also inoculation of the olive with *P. savastanoi*. Soon after oviposition the bacteria enter the egg and eventually become established in the larval gut. While *P. savastanoi* can initiate galls through leaf scars and hail wounds independently of the insect, the insect larva needs the bacterium for its further development. Without it, the larva cannot utilize the flesh of the olive, possibly because the tissues do not contain methionine and threonine, and Diptera, in which amino acid requirements have been determined, require these two to complete larval development. The bacteria may synthesize these amino acids and also facilitate larval growth by hydrolyzing plant proteins (Hagen, 1966).

Olive knot is of some importance in California and in the Mediterranean countries. The disease is controlled mainly by removing galls and by applying protective sprays. In California, applications of Bordeaux mixture are recommended early in November and, where there is considerable disease, again in December and March to prevent new infections.

Wound tumour virus

Certain viruses which cause galls are also introduced into their hosts by insects but in these instances the virus is totally dependent on the insect for its transmission. There are not a great many gall diseases of this type and few are of economic importance. Fiji disease of sugar cane is an exception. This was first reported from Fiji in 1910–11 and subsequently caused significant losses in Hawaii (Lyon, 1921). The virus is transmitted by leaf-hoppers and causes an abnormal proliferation of the phloem and adjacent tissues resulting in elongated swellings on the under surfaces of the leaves (Kunkel, 1924). Affected plants eventually die back. A similar disease was reported on maize in southeastern Queensland (Schindler, 1942) in which the veins of the young leaves rapidly become swollen from the tip of the sheath and the growth of the plant, especially of the cobs, is much retarded. This is called 'wallaby ear disease' and was shown to be transmitted by the jassid, *Cicadula bimaculata*. A club root of tobacco (Valleau, 1947), and woody galls on certain citrus (Wallace and Drake, 1960) are also possibly caused by insect-transmitted viruses.

None of the viruses associated with these diseases has been so intensively studied as wound tumour virus. This is of no economic importance but of considerable scientific interest. It was discovered in 1941 when plants of white clover developed a disease that had not previously been described, after a particular collection of leaf-hoppers had been allowed to feed on them (Black, 1952). In further tests with one hundred plant species the virus induced symptoms in forty-three of them, the most constant symptom being irregular enlargement of the veins and woody tumours on the roots (Figure 13.4). The most susceptible hosts were the cultivated sorrels (*Rumex acetosa*) and sweet clover (*Melilotus albu*). Three species of leaf-hopper (*Agalliopsis novella, Agallia constricta* and *Agallia quadripunctata*) are now known to transmit the virus and the disease can also be produced by grafting a piece of gall tissue, or an apparently symptomless scion from an infected plant on an appropriate host.

The virus multiplies both in its plant host and insect-vector. After leaf-hoppers have fed on an infected plant there is a latent period of 15 days or more before they can transmit the virus. They then remain infective and there appears to be some transfer of the virus via the egg to a small proportion (1%–2%) of the offspring of viruliferous females. As with crown gall, some wounding of the plant tissue is necessary for tumour formation and a high proportion of tumours start at the wounds made by the emerging lateral roots. The gall tissue induced by wound tumour virus can similarly be maintained in culture and is another useful system for studying the mechanism of gall formation.

'Cauliflower' of strawberries

In olive knot and the galls of wound tumour virus, insects act as vectors but, as far as is known, they do not themselves directly contribute to the disease syndrome. A more complex situation exists in

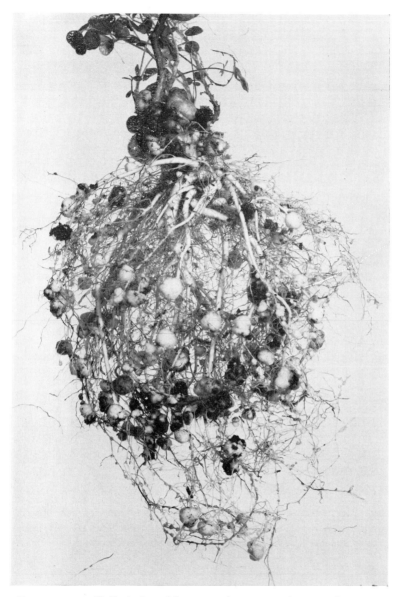

FIGURE 13.4 Galls induced by wound-tumour virus on the roots of sweet clover. Photograph courtesy L. M. Black, 1952, *Amer. J. Bot.*, **38**, 256–67.

the disease of strawberries in which proliferation of axillary buds reduces the crown to stunted fleshy rosettes superficially like the curd of a cauliflower. Two types of organism are constantly associated with the disease: nematodes, either *Aphelenchoides ritzema-bosi* or *Aphelenchoides fragariae*, and the bacterium *Corynebacterium fascians*. Neither inoculated separately on strawberries reproduces the disease. Nematodes induce alaminate leaves, usually a rosette of small, glabrous petioles, 5–10 mm, tapered to a point which represents an extremely reduced lamina. These leaves and the primary crown that bears them usually die, giving an 'open-centre' plant. Certain strains of *C. fascians* induce leafy galls, which are not known in field strawberries but occur on chrysanthemum and sweet pea. 'Cauliflower' appears to result from the combined action of nematode and bacterium on the strawberry. Pitcher and Crosse (1958) consider that the disease is predominantly bacterial in that strains of *C. fascians* initiate leafy galls which are then modified by the nematodes. The nematodes probably also act as vectors for the bacterium since by feeding they enable it to penetrate the crown tissues.

Cauliflower disease is not common but alaminate leaves and 'open-centre' plants are often found in fields infested with nematodes. *C. fascians* can be isolated from these plants but they appear to have no causal role and the symptoms can be related solely to nematode infection.

REFERENCES

Anderson, H. W. (1956). *Diseases of Fruit Crops*, p. 111 McGraw-Hill, New York.

Ark, P. A. (1941). Chemical eradication of crown gall on almond trees. *Phytopathology*, **31**, 956–7

Banfield, W. M. (1934). Life history of the crown gall organism in relation to its pathogenesis on the red raspberry. *J. agric. Res.*, **48**, 761–87

Bird, A. F. (1962). The inducement of giant cells by *Meloidogyne javanica*. *Nematologica*, **8**, 1–10

Black, L. M. (1952). Plant virus tumours. *Ann. N.Y. Acad. Sci.*, **54**, 1067–75

Braun, A. C. (1959). Growth is affected. In *Plant Pathology: an advanced treatise* (Ed. J. G. Horsefall and A. E. Dimond), **1**, 189–248. Academic Press, New York.

Braun, A. C. (1962). Tumor inception and development in the crown gall disease. *A. Rev. Pl. Physiol.*, **13**, 535–58

Carter, W. (1962). *Insects in relation to Plant Disease*, 705 pp. Interscience Publishers, (John Wiley), New York.

Chitwood, B. G. and Oteifa, B.A. (1952). Nematodes parasitic on plants. *A. Rev. Microbiol.*, **6**, 151–84

Christie, J. R. (1936). The development of root knot nematode galls. *Phytopathology*, **26**, 1–22

Deep, I. W. (1958). Crown gall chemotherapy with terramycin. *Pl. Dis. Reptr*, **42**, 1210–3

Dickey, R. S. (1962). Efficacy of five fumigants for the control of *Agrobacterium tumefaciens* at various depths in the soil. *Pl. Dis. Reptr*, **46**, 73–6

Dowson, W. J. (1957). *Plant Diseases due to Bacteria*, pp. 180–5. Cambridge University Press.

Dropkin, V. H. (1954). Infectivity and gall size in tomato and cucumber seedlings infected with *Meloidogne incognita* var. *acrita* (root knot nematode). *Phytopathology*, **44**, 43–9

Dropkin, V. H. and Nelson, P. (1960). The histopathology of root knot nematode infections in soybeans. *Phytopathology*, **50**, 442–7

Hagen, K. S. (1966). Dependence of the olive fly, *Dacus oleae*, larvae on symbiosis with *Pseudomonas savastanoi* for utilization of olive. *Nature, Lond.*, **209**, 423–4

Hampton, J. E. (1948). Cure of crown gall with antibiotics. *Phytopathology*, **38**, 11–2

Harris, R. V. and Pearse, H. L. (1938). The crown gall disease of nursery stocks. III. A progress report on experiments from 1929 to 1937 to determine the relative susceptibility of Malling apple stocks and including the production of galls by synthetic growth substances. *Rep. E. Malling Res. Stn.*, 1937, 187–93

Klemmer, H. W., Riker A. J., and Allen, O. N. (1955). Inhibition of crown gall by selected antibiotics. *Phytopathology*, **45**, 618–25

Krusberg, L. R. (1963). Host response to nematode infection. *A. Rev. Phytopathol.*, **1**, 219–40

Kunkel, L. O. (1924). Histological and cytological studies on the Fiji disease of sugar cane. *Bull. Hawaiian Sug. Plrs' Ass. Exp. Stn.* Bot. Ser. No. 3, 99–107

Leach, J. G. (1940). *Insect Transmission of Plant Diseases*, 615 pp. McGraw-Hill, New York.

Leuween, W. M. van (1957). *Gallenboek* 331 pp. W. J. Thieme and Cie, Zutphen.

Lyon, H. L. (1921). Three major cane diseases: mosaic, sereh and Fiji disease. *Bull. Hawaiian Sug. Plrs' Ass. Exp. Stn.*, Bot. ser. No. 3, 1–43

Mani, M. S. (1964). *Ecology of Plant Galls*, 434 pp. W. Junk, The Hague.

Melhus, I. W. and Maney, T. J. (1921). A study of the control of crown gall on apple grafts in the nursery. *Res. Bull. Iowa agric. Exp. Stn.*, No. 69, 169–72

Patel, M. K. (1928). A study of pathogenic and non-pathogenic strains of *Pseudomonas tumefaciens* Sm. and Town. *Phytopathology*, **18**, 331–43

Peacock, F. C.(1959). The development of a technique for studying the host/parasite relationship of the root knot nematode *Meloidogyne incognita* under controlled conditions. *Nematologica*, **4**, 43–55

Pitcher, R. S. and Crosse, J. E. (1958). Studies in the relationship of eelworms and bacteria to certain plant diseases. II. Further analysis of the strawberry cauliflower disease complex. *Nematologica*, **3**, 244–56

Rack, K. (1953). Untersuchungen uber die Bedeutung der Verwundung und die Rolle von Wuchstoffen beim bacteriellen Pflanzenkrebs. *Phytopath. Z.*, **21**, 1–44 [*Rev. appl. Mycol.* **33**, 470]

Riker, A. J., Berbee, J. G. and Smalley, E. B. (1959). Effects of crown gall and hairy root on the growth of apple trees. *Phytopathology*, **49**, 88–90

Schindler, A. J. (1942). Insect transmission of wallaby ear disease of maize. *J. Aust. Inst. agric. Sci.*, **8**, 35–7

Siegler, E. A. and Bowman, J. J. (1940). Crown gall of peach in the nursery. *Phytopathology*, 30, 417–26

Smith, E. F. (1920). *An Introduction to Bacterial Diseases of Plants*, pp. 413–72. W. B. Saunders, Philadelphia.

Smith, E. F., Brown, N. A., and Townsend, C. O. (1911). Crown-gall of plants: its cause and remedy. *Bull. Bur. Pl. Ind. U.S. Dep. Agric.*, No. 213, 215 pp.

Smith, E. F., Brown, N. A. and McCulloch, L. (1912). The structure and development of crown gall: a plant cancer. *Bull. Bur. Pl. Ind. U.S. Dep. Agric.* No. 255, 60 pp.

Smith, E. F. and Townsend, C. O. (1907). A plant tumor of bacterial origin. *Science*, N.S., **25**, 671–3

Thorne, G. (1961). *Principles of Nematology*, McGraw-Hill, New York.

Valleau, W. D. (1947). Club root of tobacco: a wood-tumorlike graft-transmitted disease. *Phytopathology*, **37**, 580

Viglierchio, D. R. and Lownsberry, B. F. 1960). The hatching response of *Meloidogyne* species to the emanations from the roots of germinating tomatoes. *Nematologica*, 5, 43–52

Wallace, H. R. (1963). *The Biology of Plant Parasitic Nematodes*, Edward Arnold, London.

Wallace, J. M. and Drake, R. J. (1960). Woody galls on citrus associated with vein-enation virus infection. *Pl. Dis. Reptr*, **44**, 580–4

Wilson, E. E. (1935). The olive knot disease: its inception, development and control. *Hilgardia*, **9**, 233–64

Wood, R. K. S. (1967). *Physiological Plant Pathology*, pp. 263–86. Blackwell Scientific Publications, Oxford.

Wormald, H. (1945). Physiologic races of the crown gall organism in Britain. *Trans. Br. mycol. Soc.*, **28**, 134–46

CHAPTER 14

Cankers and scab

The principal feature of galls is the localized, abnormal development of the host tissues. This occurs also in cankers but the tissues produced in these structures are seldom so disorganized. Instead there is an orderly development so that the area of necrosis caused by the pathogen becomes surrounded by successive layers of callus tissue. The formation of cork layers within the cortex, near the killed tissues, is part of this host response. In certain diseases of leaves, fruits and storage organs there is a basically similar host response and though the overall effect is less spectacular the formation of cork layers results in conspicuous, raised, scab-like pustules. The term 'scab' is often used to describe diseases in which lesions of this type predominate (Jenkins, 1933).

CANKERS

Cankers are mainly associated with forest or orchard trees, and though the term is sometimes used for similar lesions on herbaceous stems, e.g. bacterial canker of tomato caused by *Corynebacterium michiganense*, this section will be confined to cankers on woody stems.

Externally the initial spread of a canker lesion can be seen by a discolouration of the bark which then becomes blackened and sunken. The affected cortical and phloem tissues below the bark dry out, separate from the wood and then eventually crack and break away exposing the xylem. Successive folds of callus tissue are then laid down around this area of necrosis. The extent of the affected area is generally greater along the length of the stem than around the circumference and there is usually a marked swelling of the shoot in the cankered region (Figure 14.1). Though there is evidence that physical factors such as frost can initiate a canker and may even play a significant part in its further development, most canker diseases of importance are caused by fungi or bacteria and a few possibly by viruses (Bos, 1963).

Formation of a canker

One of the clearest accounts of canker formation is that of Hiley (1919) for larch, in which the fungus *Trichoscyphella willkommii* is now known to play a major part. Figure 14.2a shows diagrammatically a transverse section of a 3-year old stem in which a portion (X) of the cortex has been attacked and killed. The fungus has not reached the cambium but is sufficiently near to a section of it (AB) to induce it to produce abnormal wood, by the end of the first year of attack (Figure 14.2b). At this stage the fungus has extended tangentially in the cortex but the development of new phloem outside AB has prevented it reaching the cambium. During the winter the fungus extends further into the cortex and a section (CD) of the cambium is killed (Figure 14.2c): further sections (EC, DF) are stimulated to produce abnormal wood in the following year. During the next winter the fungus encroaches both on the tissues of the cortex and those bordering the dead cambium (CD). By the spring the canker has the structure depicted in Figure 14.2d, section CD has made no wood but sections of abnormal wood have formed around it (EC, DF) and the fungus has made further inroads into the tissues at CG and DH. Figure 14.2e shows the development of the canker after a further year's growth and it continues to enlarge in a similar manner.

Interactions of pathogen and host: apple canker

A canker lesion is essentially the result of a balance between the spread of the pathogen and reaction of the host. Details of these interactions have been obtained for a number of canker diseases and the following is based on investigations of (European) apple canker caused by *Nectria galligena* (Zeller, 1926; Crowdy, 1949).

The fungus is able to enter the host only through some type of wound, but if the wound is shallow it may be confined to the cortex and no canker result. For canker formation the wound must penetrate almost to the wood and then a small area of cambium is killed (as in Figure 14.2c). The fungus enters the current year's xylem via

FIGURE 14.1 Canker on stem of European larch, showing malformation, exudation of resin, and fruiting bodies of *Trichoscyphella wilkommii*. Photograph copyright Forestry Commission.

the medullary rays and grows up and down the vessels and tracheids, passing from cell to cell via the pits. There is, however, a marked host reaction to this invasion. Within the vessels movement of the fungus is impeded by gum formation and tyloses, and the formation of a wound callus restricts its lateral spread in tissue external to the xylem. The callus consists of two zones (Figure 14.3). In areas adjacent to the dead cambium a zone of wound wood is laid down (corresponding to the abnormal wood of Figure 14.2), consisting of thickened, isodiametric cells, which shades into normal xylem away from the active canker. This tissue readily produces gum which impedes further penetration by the fungus. Outside this zone a layer of parenchymatous tissue is formed and this reacts to infection in the same way as the normal phloem and cortex and is distinguishable from it only by the absence of fibre bundles. Movement of the

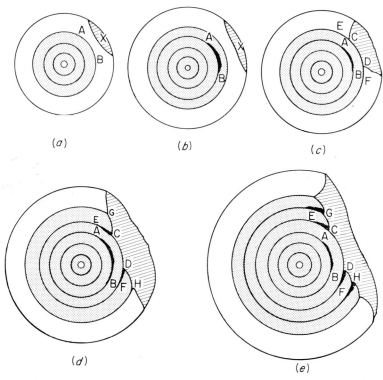

(*a*)   (*b*)   (*c*)

(*d*)   (*e*)

FIGURE 14.2 Stages in the formation of a canker. (see text for explanation). From Hiley, 1919, *The Fungal Diseases of the Common Larch*, by permission of the Clarendon Press.

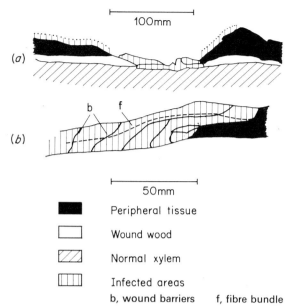

FIGURE 14.3 Apple canker. Longitudinal sections through
cankers on (*a*) Cox's Orange Pippin, (*b*) Worcester Permain.
From Crowdy, 1949, *Ann. appl. Biol.*, **36**, 483–95.

fungus within the wound and normal wood is slow mainly due to
gum formation. Its activities in the peripheral tissue are therefore
of the greatest significance. There, the fungus stimulates the formation of a cork-producing layer (phellogen) but seldom is its progress
halted for long. The reason for this appears to be that active re-
generation of tissue which could effectively seal off the canker is
confined in apple to a few months during the growing season
whereas the development of *N. galligena* is not so affected. The fungus
passes the cork barrier in two ways: 1, by direct penetration, which
is preceded by a build-up of mycelium in front of the barrier and is
thus considered to be mainly a pressure effect; 2, by growing in the
lumen of phloem fibre cells which themselves pass through the cork
barrier. When this occurs new phellogens are often laid down at the
limit of fungus penetration but these in turn are breached.

Entry of canker-inducing pathogens into the host

The ways in which canker-inducing pathogens enter their hosts
have received considerable attention. Generally they do so through
some kind of wound and for *N. galligena* the leaf scar is particularly

important (Wiltshire, 1921; Crowdy, 1952). The conidia are sucked into the exposed ends of the tracheids and are then conveniently sheltered from adverse environmental conditions. The scars do not remain susceptible for long, even one hour after leaf-fall they are infected much less readily. Leaf scar infections may develop immediately into cankers or be confined by suberized tissue or gum formation. In the latter instance the mycelium often spreads into healthy tissue in the spring via the growth cracks which develop at bud burst. Leaf scars are also important in the bacterial canker of cherry caused by *Pseudomonas mors-prunorum* (Crosse, 1956, 1957). Again the susceptibility of scars decreases with time after leaf-fall and there is evidence that this is related to factors which influence the numbers of bacteria penetrating the scars. Nevertheless the overall period of natural leaf scar infection in the field is a long one, starting possibly even in September and continuing through October.

A pruning cut is another common entry point for the pathogens. With *N. galligena* and apple it has been suggested that as the normal wound wood grows over the cut it forms a depression in which moisture is retained thus providing a particularly suitable environment for spore germination (Moore, 1934). Another possibility arises when the cut shoot is itself infected because mycelium may be left behind in the fibres of the exposed wood. As callus tissue grows over the cut, some of the covering parenchyma becomes crushed inside the callus pad; this then provides a favourable medium for the fungus and it grows out of the fibres (Crowdy, 1949).

Frost cracks and winter injury of young shoots are also suitable sites for infection (e.g. in larch canker), and serious cankers can result if the crotch of the tree is affected in this way. There may also be a certain amount of infection through injuries caused by insects and other fungi, for example *N. galligena* can establish itself in apple through the galls of the woolly aphid (Wiltshire, 1914) and through scab lesions caused by *Venturia inaequalis* (Wiltshire, 1922). Finally cankers may arise from the progression of the pathogen down a young shoot to a main stem. This occurs particularly in the fireblight disease of pears (p. 156).

Cankers as sources of inoculum

Cankers not only facilitate the overwintering of the pathogen (e.g. the 'hold-over' cankers in fireblight), but in many instances they also provide inoculum over a number of years. The conidia of *N. galligena* are produced usually on young cankers in pinkish-white cushions (sporodochia); they are dispersed mainly during wet periods in spring and autumn. The dark red perithecia are produced usually on older cankers; ascospore discharge occurs throughout the year but reaches a maximum in January and February and is least during the summer months (Munson, 1939). Similarly, on larch the apothecia of *T. willkommii* form around the cankers particularly during the winter months (Peace, 1962).

Eradication of cankers which are likely sources of inoculum is a control method common to many of these diseases. Some techniques have already been mentioned in connexion with fireblight and others are discussed in Chapter 19. It is comparatively easy to protect pruning cuts from invasion by painting them with fungicides but protection of the freshly exposed leaf scars is much more difficult, particularly when leaf fall occurs over a number of weeks. With apple, spraying at leaf fall can be of some value in checking sporulation of *N. galligena* on the cankers and thus reducing inoculum at a time of marked host susceptibility (Byrde and others, 1952).

SCAB

Range of scab diseases

As might be expected diseases called 'scab' vary widely both in etiology and epidemiology, and there are some to which the term is doubtfully applied. One is wheat scab, caused chiefly by *Gibberella zeae* (conidial state, *Fusarium graminearum*), and occasionally by certain other species of *Fusarium*. This disease is essentially an ear or head blight in which the glumes and developing grain are attacked. If affected plants produce any grain it is of poor quality and often bears an incrustation of fungal growth (Dickson, 1942). The use of the term 'scab' is here quite different to that envisaged in this chapter since there is no cork formation by the host giving a raised pustule. This apart, scab diseases fall into three groups:

1. A number of fungi cause prominent corky lesions on citrus fruits. *Elsinoe fawcetti* (citrus or sour orange scab), *Elsinoe australis* (sweet orange scab) and *Sphaceloma fawcetti* var. *scabiosa* (Tryon's scab of rough lemon) are some examples (Fawcett, 1936; Knorr and others, 1957). Although these are anthracnose fungi they produce scab-like pustules on leaves also, rather than the sunken lesions described in Chapter 10. Other anthracnose fungi e.g. *Gloeosporium limetticola* produce 'scab' lesions on the fruit only (Figure 14.4).

J

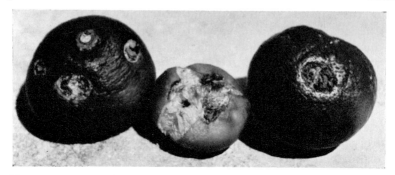

Figure 14.4 'Scab' lesions on lime fruits caused by *Gleosporium limetticola.*

2. A somewhat heterogeneous collection of diseases of storage organs and fruits: (i) Common scab of potatoes caused by *Streptomyces scabies* (Figure 14.5), and powdery or corky scab of potatoes caused by *Spongospora subterranea.* In both, unsightly pustules of the tubers reduce their market value and storage qualities. The pathogens are soil-borne and epidemologically these diseases have much in common with club root of crucifers described on p. 222 (Walker, 1952).

Figure 14.5 Common scab of potatoes. Photograph copyright Rothamsted Experimental Station.

(ii) Cucumber scab caused by *Cladosporium cucumerinum*. On leaves and stems the fungus results in a necrotic leaf spot (p. 189). On young fruits a viscous exudate is produced at the edge of the lesions and the disease is sometimes called 'gummosis' (Chupp and Sherf, 1960). (iii) Scab of gladiolus caused by the bacterium *Pseudomonas marginata*. The lesions occur on the corms, first as yellow, circular spots which later blacken; the host forms a barrier of cork and stone cells giving a prominent rim to the lesion (Figure 14.6). The scabbed areas exude a yellow, gummy substance containing the bacteria, and so the surrounding soil becomes contaminated. From this source the bacteria often infect the developing leaves causing a 'neck rot' phase of the disease (Stapp, 1961).

3. A small but very important group involving the leaves and fruits of pome and stone fruits. The diseases are all caused by species of *Venturia*, apple scab by *Venturia inaequalis*, pear scab by *Venturia pirina*, cherry scab by *Venturia cerasi* and peach scab by *Venturia carpophila* (Keitt, 1917; Fisher, 1961). There are many similarities in the behaviour of these fungi as pathogens, particularly in the way they invade their hosts. In terms of economic importance and effort to control it, apple scab is one of the most important plant diseases and it will be considered in detail.

Apple scab

On leaves, lesions are first visible on the upper surfaces as small areas, lighter in colour than the healthy leaf and lacking its natural lustre. As lesions develop they become velvety, olive brown to black and then finally lose their velvety appearance and appear as a dry

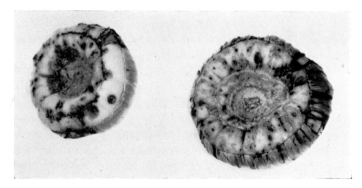

FIGURE 14.6 Gladiolus scab. Photograph courtesy J. L. Forsberg, Illinois Natural History Survey.

corky scab. Similar lesions occur on the fruit and they are most numerous around the blossom end since infection occurs mainly in the spring when the apples are still in an upright position. Growth is reduced in the affected area and cracks often appear around the lesion as the healthy part of the fruit enlarges (Figure 14.7).

The events which result in this type of lesion are briefly as follows. Under suitable conditions (which will be considered later) a spore of *V. inaequalis* germinates on the host surface and almost immediately the germ tube enters the cuticle. The fungus grows in the cuticle as bundles or strands of hyphae and, at a later stage, short brown conidiospores develop from this subcuticular mycelium. The cuticle is then ruptured by the increasing pressure of fungal growth (Wiltshire, 1915; Nusbaum and Keitt, 1938; Preece, 1963). Host cells show no evidence of injury until some time after the fungus penetrates the cuticle, indeed in some situations there may be an incubation period of 3–4 weeks. Then the epidermal cells become increasingly vacuolated, turn brown and collapse; a cork cambium is formed in cells beneath the dead tissue and, as a result, the fungal stroma is pushed up giving the typical scab lesion. This is particularly well-marked on fruit where there is a stimulation in growth of the pith cells as well as cork formation. Conidia are produced only in parts of the lesion where there is no necrosis. When the epidermal cell is killed the conidiophores stop sporulating, hence the gradual disappearance of the velvety covering of spores on the lesion.

Conidia are produced from spring until early autumn; then just before leaf fall the fungus, which until this time has been confined to the cuticle, grows into the leaf mesophyll and forms its perithecial primordia. The perithecia do not immediately mature but at some stage development is completed within the fallen leaves and by spring many perithecia contain asci with typical 2-celled ascospores (Figure 14.8). Perithecia are not the sole means of overwintering (Keitt and Jones, 1926); twig infection is not uncommon in some areas and mycelium is able to overwinter in these lesions and produce conidia in the following season. Mycelium may also overwinter within the bud-scales (McKay, 1938).

The relative importance of conidia from overwintered mycelium and ascospores in initiating infections in the spring is of particular interest. In some localities only ascospores appear to play a significant role in the epidemiology of the disease, for instance Hirst and others (1955) showed this was true in the Wisbech area of England. They found no conidial pustules on the twigs, and only a few bud scale infections; and no conidia were caught in spore traps during

(b)

(a)

FIGURE 14.7 Apple scab. Lesions on the leaf (a) and fruit (b). Photograph copyright East Malling Research Station.

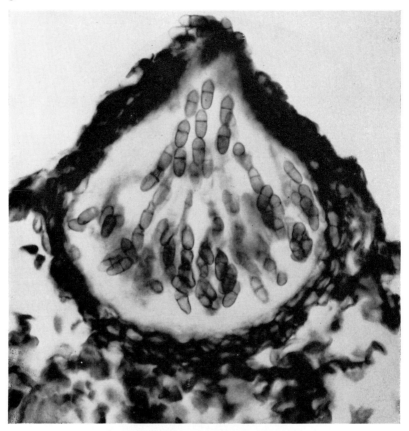

FIGURE 14.8 *Venturia inaequalis*. L. S. of a mature perithecium from an overwintered apple leaf. Photograph copyright East Malling Research Station.

early spring. Further, there appeared to be no relationship between the degree of leaf infection in the autumn and that on the same shoots in the following spring; twigs that had borne infected foliage in the autumn were not infected more than those that had been healthy, which suggested infection from uniformly distributed ascospores rather than conidia derived from local and undetected mycelium on twigs and bud scales. Spore trapping confirmed that spring outbreaks of scab were preceded by releases of ascospores.

These and further observations (Hirst and Stedman, 1961; 1962*a*) have provided interesting data on ascospore liberation. Dew released some ascospores, but few compared with rain. In laboratory tests the equivalent of 0.2 mm rain applied evenly with an atomizer released very many spores. In orchards some small daytime releases occurred in dry weather but these generally followed wetting at night by dew or rain. Most spores (75%) released by brief rains were liberated within 3 hours, and for rains of all durations, the comparable figure was 6 hours. In general, therefore, ascopore release is related to rainfall though other factors are also concerned.

Rain is also necessary for leaf infection by ascospores. How long the leaves remain wet following rain, and temperature, chiefly determine disease severity. Mills and La Plante (1954) have compiled a table for the benefit of fruit growers which indicates the relationship between these factors. Such information is valuable for timing spray applications. The relevant part of the Mills–La Plante table is that which shows the number of hours that the leaves need to remain wet, at different temperatures, to ensure a light scab infection, assuming of course, that ascospores are present, viz:

Mean temperature over period	$5.6°$	$7.2°$	$10°$	$11.7°$	$15°$	$15.6°$
Hours leaf wetness	30	20	14	11	10	$9\frac{1}{2}$

Each temperature/leaf wetness combination, (e.g. $10°/14$ hours) is now known as a 'Mills period', and these periods can be assessed from temperature data and those obtained by a 'surface-wetness recorder' (Hirst, 1957). In the same way that a 90% humidity criterion is often used instead of the original humidity requirements of Beaumont for potato blight forecasting (p. 153), so here by substituting humidities of 90% or above for surface wetness we get a corresponding Smith period. Observations over the period 1956–60 showed that, for England and Wales, both Mills and Smith periods were suitable for determining the main, widespread meteorological conditions favouring infection in the spring (Preece and Smith, 1961).

One of the main purposes of spraying for apple scab control is to prevent the early infections by ascospores which then give rise to large amounts of conidial inoculum. A number of fungicides are used, e.g. sulphur (either lime sulphur or wettable sulphur), captan, thiram, and organomercurials such as phenylmercury chloride, -acetate, -nitrate or more complex compounds like phenylmercurydimethyl dithiocarbamate (phelam). There are disadvantages with each. For instance some apple varieties are sulphur-shy, captan gives poor control of apple mildew so where this is important sulphur or dinocap must also be included, thiram is unsuitable for certain varieties, and so are the phenylmercurials. In addition, the phenylmercurials have a high mammalian toxicity. Many of the materials are used as protectants, the aim being to keep a continuous cover on the leaves, shoots and fruits as they develop. Timing of the spray applications is therefore most important. Spraying normally starts at budburst and then there is a choice of applying further sprays at 10–14 day intervals irrespective of shoot growth, or relating further applications to particular growth stages such as green cluster or green bud, pink bud, petal fall (80% of the petals dropped) and fruitlet (2–3 weeks after petal fall). Another type of spraying is based on the organomercurial compounds (e.g. see Moore and Bennett, 1967). They have a marked eradicant action and it is possible to obtain control if they are applied after infection has occurred. Again there is a choice of starting at bud burst and then spraying at 10-day intervals, or relating spraying to the occurrence of Mills or Smith periods, that is to periods favouring infection.

In recent years the possibility of controlling apple scab by destroying the overwintering perithecia has been re-examined. It is now realised that appreciable destruction occurs naturally through the activity of earthworms which bury much of the apple leaf-litter (Raw, 1962). In isolated orchards a considerable reduction in ascospore inoculum has been obtained with postharvest applications of phenylmercurials (Hutton, 1954) but how successful this would be in less isolated conditions is not clear. There are indications (Anon. 1967) that most ascospores are deposited less than 30 m from an inoculum source so there is hope that this method may be of more general application. Applying dinitro-orthocresol (in 1% petroleum) to the fallen leaves in spring is another possibility. The material is used to kill insect eggs on trees and it was first shown by American workers to be effective in reducing ascospores inoculum, and to give improved scab control particularly in years of high rainfall (Keitt and Palmiter, 1937; Palmiter, 1946). The method was not fully explored in Europe for a variety of reasons—that it was too expensive, it did not completely eradicate the ascospores, and that ascospores or conidia would still enter the orchards from untreated areas. The method was re-examined by Hirst and Stedman (1962b) in relation to the supply of ascospores. They found that the number of ascospores liberated within treated areas was reduced by at least 90%. A similar result was obtained by broadcasting nitrogenous fertilizers such as ammonium sulphate over the orchards floor, an effect which had been recorded earlier by Keitt and Palmiter (1937). This suggests a connexion with work reported by Burchill and others (1965). They sprayed scab-infected trees with dilute (2% and 5%) urea solutions, then collected the leaves and allowed them to overwinter in nylon-mesh envelopes. Observations were made at intervals on the state of the leaves and microbial activity within them, and finally in the spring on their ascospore productivity (Hutton and Burchill, 1965). Leaves sprayed with a 5% urea solution decomposed much more rapidly than unsprayed leaves and this was linked with a higher, initial nitrogen content and a much increased bacterial population per unit leaf area. Ascospore production of the sprayed leaves was only some 3% of the controls, apparently because perithecia failed to form in the treated leaves.

REFERENCES

Anonymous (1967). Diseases of pome fruit. *Rep. Dep. Agric. N.S.W.*, 1965–1966, p. 79
Bos, L. (1963). *Symptoms of Virus Diseases in Plants*, p. 65. Centre for Agricultural Publications and Documentation, Wageningen.
Burchill, R. T., Hutton, K. E., Crosse, J. E. and Garrett, C.M.E. (1965). Inhibition of the perfect stage of *Venturia inaequalis* (Cooke) Wint. by urea. *Nature, Lond.*, **205**, 520–1
Byrde, R. J. W., Crowdy, S. H. and Roach, F. A. (1952). Observations on apple canker. V. Eradicant spraying and canker control. *Ann. appl. Biol.*, **39**, 581–7
Chupp, C. and Sherf, A. F. (1960). *Vegetable Diseases and their Control*, pp. 306–9. Ronald Press, New York.
Crosse, J. E. (1956). Bacterial canker of stone fruits. II. Leaf scar infection of cherry. *J. hort. Sci.*, **31**, 212–24; (1957). III. Inoculum concentration and time of inoculation in relation to leaf-scar infection of cherry. *Ann. appl. Biol.*, **45**, 19–35
Crowdy, S. H. (1949). Observations on apple canker. III. The anatomy of the stem canker. *Ann. appl. Biol.*, **36**, 483–95; (1952). IV. The infection of leaf scars. *Ann. appl. Biol.*, **39**, 509–80
Dickson, J. G. (1942). Scab of wheat and barley and its control. *Fmrs' Bull. U.S. Dep. Agric.*, No. 1599, 22 pp.
Fawcett, H. S. (1936). *Citrus Diseases and their Control*, pp. 529–49. McGraw-Hill, New York.
Fisher, (1961). *Venturia carpophila* sp. nov., the ascigerous state of the apricot freckle fungus. *Trans. Br. mycol. Soc.*, **44**, 337–42
Hiley, W. E. (1919). *The Fungal Diseases of the Common Larch*, pp. 33–6. Clarendon Press, Oxford.
Hirst, J. M. (1957). A simplified surface-wetness recorder. *Pl. Path.*, **6**, 57–61

Hirst, J. M. and Stedman, O. J. (1961).The epidemiology of apple scab (*Venturia inaequalis*) (Cke.) Wint. I. Frequency of air-borne spores in orchards. *Ann. appl. Biol.*, **49**, 290–305; (1962a). II. Observations on the liberation of ascospores *Ann. appl. Biol.*, **50**, 525–50; (1962b). III. The supply of ascospores. **50**, 551–67

Hirst, J. M., Storey, I. F., Ward, W. C. and Wilcox, H. J. (1955). The origin of apple scab epidemics in the Wisbech area in 1953 and 1954. *Pl. Path.* **4**, 91–6

Hutton, K. E. (1954). Eradication of *Venturia inaequalis* (Cooke) Wint. *Nature, Lond.*, **174**, 1017

Hutton, K. E. and Burchill, R. T. (1965). The effect of some fungicides and herbicides on ascospore production of *Venturia inaequalis* (Cke.) Wint. *Ann. appl. Biol.*, **56**, 279–84

Jenkins, A. E. (1933). Application of the terms 'anthracnose' and 'scab' to plant diseases caused by *Sphaceloma* and *Gloeosporium*. *Phytopatholcgy*, **23**, 389-95

Keitt, G. W. (1917). Peach scab and its control. *Bull. Bur. Pl. Ind. U.S. Dept. Agric.*, No. 395, 66 pp.

Keitt, G. W. and Jones, L. K. (1926). Studies of the epidemiology and control of apple scab. *Res. Bull. Wis. agric. Exp. Stn.*, No. 73, 104 pp.

Keitt, G. W. and Palmiter, D. H. (1937). Potentialities of eradicant fungicides for combating apple scab and some other plant diseases. *J. agric. Res.*, **55**, 397–438

Knorr, L. C., Smit, R. F. and Bucharme, E. P. (1957). Handbook of citrus diseases in Florida. *Bull. Fla agric. Exp. Stn.*, No. 587, 157 pp.

McKay, R. (1938). Conidia from infected bud-scales and adjacent wood as a main source of primary infection with the apple scab fungus [*Venturia inaequalis* (Cooke) Wint.] *Scient. Proc. R. Dubl. Soc.*, N.S. **21**, 623–40

Mills, W. D. and La Plante, A. A. (1954). Diseases and insects in the orchards. *Ext. Bull. Cornell agric. Exp. Stn.*, No. 711, 20–2

Moore, M. H. (1934). Some field observations on apple canker (*Nectria galligena*). *Rep. E. Malling Res. Stn.*, 1933. 166–75

Moore, M. H. and Bennett, M. (1967). Routine versus postinfection sprays against apple scab on Cox's Orange Pippin. *J. hort. Sci.*, **42**, 367–76

Munson, R. G. (1939). Observations on apple canker. I. The discharge and germination of spore of *Nectria galligena* Bres. *Ann. appl. Biol.*, **26**, 440–57

Nusbaum, C. J. and Keitt, G. W. (1938). A cytological study of host–parasite relations of *Venturia inaequalis* on apple leaves. *J. agric. Res.*, **56**, 595–618

Palmiter, D. H. (1946). Ground treatments as an aid in apple scab control. *Bull. N.Y. St. agric. Exp. Stn.*, No. 714, 27 pp.

Peace, T. R. (1962). *Pathology of Trees and Shrubs*, pp. 319–26 Clarendon Press, Oxford.

Preece, T. F. (1963). Micro-exploration and mapping of apple scab infections. *Trans. Br. mycol. Soc.*, **46**, 523–9

Preece, T. F. and Smith, L. P. (1961). Apple scab infection weather in England and Wales, 1956–60. *Pl. Path.*, **10**, 43–51

Raw, R. (1962). Studies of earthworm populations in orchards. I. Leaf burial in apple orchards. *Ann. appl. Biol.*, **50**, 389–404

Stapp, C. (1961). *Bacterial Plant Pathogens*, pp. 178–81 (Transl. by A. Schoenfeld). Oxford University Press.

Walker, J. C. (1952). *Diseases of Vegetable Crops*, pp. 329–38. McGraw-Hill, New York.

Wiltshire, S. P. (1914). A note on the relation between woolly aphis and canker. *Rep. agric. hort. Res. Stn. Univ. Bristol*, 1914, 94

Wiltshire, S. P. (1915). Infection and immunity studies on the apple and pear scab fungi (*Venturia inaequalis* and *V. pirina*). *Ann. appl. Biol.*, **1**, 335–50

Wiltshire, S. P. (1921). Studies on the apple canker fungus. I. Leaf scar infection. *Ann. appl. Biol.*, **8**, 182–92; (1922). II. Canker infection of apple trees through scab wounds. *Ann. appl. Biol.*, **9**, 275–81

Zeller, S. M. (1926). European canker of pomaceous fruit trees. *Bull. Ore agric. Exp. Stn.*, No. 222, 52 pp.

Chapter 15

Mosaics and yellows

Colour changes in leaves occur with many diseases but in two groups, those caused by mineral deficiencies and by viruses, they are particularly common and sometimes of diagnostic value. The development of irregular, light and dark green blotches (mosaic or mottle) and yellowing of the leaf margins, tips or interveinal areas (yellows) are specially striking, and the appropriate term is often included in the common name of a specific disease in which one of these symptoms predominates, e.g. Tobacco mosaic, Tea yellows. That similar symptoms occur in diseases of vastly different etiology suggests at first sight that the host metabolism is affected in a similar way but there is at present no clear evidence that the effects of a virus on the cells of its host resemble those of a mineral deficiency. Yet there is some merit in considering the two groups under one general heading, because the field pathologist is left with these alternatives when he can find no visible pathogen in an obviously diseased plant.

MINERAL DEFICIENCIES

Two groups of mineral nutrients are distinguished in relation to plant growth, those required in substantial quantities (major elements) and those, equally essential, but required only in minute amounts (trace elements or micronutrients). The major elements are nitrogen, phosphorus, potassium, calcium, magnesium and sulphur, and the principal trace elements, iron, manganese, boron, copper, zinc and molybdenum (Wallace, 1961). The plant absorbs these nutrients from soil and there are a number of factors which influence this process. The elements must be present in certain forms, e.g. sulphur can only be absorbed by plants from sulphates and boron from borates. For this reason figures for particular elements obtained by chemical analysis of the soil are often meaningless because they do not indicate availability. On the other hand, elements present in forms that are not absorbed by plants may become available through microbial action, e.g. nitrogen in proteins by conversion to nitrate. Aeration of the soil and its pH are also important, and the relative amounts of the various elements which are absorbed. If, for example, large amounts of nitrogen are absorbed compared with potassium, then symptoms of potassium deficiency are likely to develop. Certain elements also influence the absorption of others; calcium slows down the absorption of potassium and *vice versa*.

It should be clearly understood that colour changes are not the only symptoms of mineral deficiencies. Stunting is also common, especially where nitrogen is deficient because this element is essential for plant proteins. Lack of other elements produces highly characteristic symptoms in particular crops, for instance manganese deficiency in peas causes an internal browning of the cotyledons known as 'marsh spot' (Piper, 1941) and molybdenum deficiency in cauliflower and broccoli causes a disease known as 'whiptail' because the leaf lamina fails to develop properly (Plant, 1951). Nor are all the colour changes of the yellows type. The leaves of cereals deficient in phosphorus become a dark, bluish-green and later develop a purple tint (Wallace, 1961, Plate 32), and those of sweet cherry deficient in magnesium develop purple, red and orange tints (Wallace, 1961, Plate 285).

To a large extent the type of colour change depends on the host, but yellowing of the foliage is generally most prevalent in deficiencies of elements that have an important role in chlorophyll production: nitrogen, magnesium, sulphur, iron and manganese. In few instances has a specific disease name been applied to the symptoms of these deficiencies in any particular crop. Tea yellows is an exception. This first became important in Malawi about 1920. The main symptoms are interveinal yellowing in the leaves, excessive defoliation and poor, stunted growth of new shoots. The disease was studied by Storey and Leach (1933), and after it was shown that the symptoms were not caused by *Botryodiplodia theobromae* (p. 184) as was currently thought, extensive fertilizer trials were carried out. These indicated that sulphur applied as such or as sulphate always produced a marked

improvement in diseased plots; in some instances there was an 85%
recovery of tea bushes. Analyses showed that chlorotic leaves, especially young ones, contained much less sulphur than healthy ones,
and water culture experiments confirmed that the disease was
caused by sulphur-deficiency.

Control of deficiency diseases is not always achieved by soil
application of the element which is lacking. Iron deficiency often
occurs in crops on calcareous soils because the pH and other soil
factors limit the availability of this element. In this situation control
is obtained with foliage sprays of iron chelates such as ethylenediamine tetra-acetic acid (E.D.T.A.), though care must be taken
as these can damage the leaves. With fruit trees an alternative
method is to introduce a solid compound, e.g. ferrous sulphate, into
the stem. Manganese deficiency is also best controlled by foliage
applications of manganese salts. Generally, lack of magnesium can
be corrected by soil applications of magnesian limestone or magnesium
sulphate, but foliage sprays are useful when acute deficiency symptoms appear in fruit crops and tomatoes, because the plants responds
more quickly to them.

Mosaics and Yellows Caused by Viruses

With these diseases the way in which the virus is transmitted is
all important since this largely determines disease spread and the
methods of control. The examples chosen are therefore grouped
on this basis.

Transmitted Mechanically

Many viruses causing mosaics and some causing yellows can
be transmitted by rubbing the leaves of a healthy plant with sap
expressed from an infected one, but mechanical transmission in the
field, for instance by handling an infected leaf and then a healthy
one, is comparatively rare. Ironically it is the chief method by which
tobacco mosaic virus is spread for this was the first plant virus to be
studied seriously and about which most is known.

Tobacco mosaic
The disease was serious in Holland about 1870 and was investigated
there by Mayer. He described the symptoms as 'mosaic' (Figure
15.1) and showed that the disease was infectious and transmissible

(b)

(a)

FIGURE 15.1 Tobacco mosaic. Photographs courtesy J. S. Cole, Tobacco Research Board of Rhodesia.

by injecting juice from a diseased leaf into the midrib of a healthy plant. The next important advance in knowledge was made in 1892 by Ivanowski who showed that the juice from a diseased plant retained its infectivity after passing through a bacteria-proof filter. He, nevertheless, still thought bacteria were involved and suggested that a toxin secreted by them could pass through the filter and thus make the filtrate infectious.

It was left to Beijerinck, who continued the study of the disease in Holland, to suggest, in 1898, that the cause was quite different from a bacterium; that it was some contagious entity capable of increasing in tobacco which he called a '*contagium vivum fluidum*' and later in his paper, a virus (*Phytopathological Classics No.* 7). Other investigations quickly followed, some of them attempting to show that tobacco mosaic was caused by enzymes or toxins, others that an organism was involved.

Attempts to isolate the virus began in the 1920's and these are summarized by Walker (1957) and by Bawden (1964). The credit goes to Stanley, who in 1935 first reported the isolation of a crystalline protein possessing the properties of tobacco mosaic virus (see Stanley, 1936). Bawden and Pirie (1937) subsequently showed that the virus was a nucleoprotein, containing nucleic acid of the ribose type. These discoveries intensified the controversy on the nature of viruses, some arguing that they were molecules, others calling them organisms. As Bawden (1964) points out, neither name was applicable and viruses could have been compared more reasonably with other components of plant cells also with the complex particles, which superficially at least behave like viruses, than with bacteria or comparatively simple molecules.

Other investigations were more concerned with the ability of the virus to induce disease. It soon became clear that tobacco mosaic virus infects a wide range of plants (Grant, 1934; Holmes 1938, 1946), that there are different strains of the virus (Jensen, 1937), and that symptoms vary with host and virus strain. Also symptom expression is much affected by temperature, light and the supply of nitrogen to the host.

Tobacco mosaic is one of the most persistent viruses known and this, plus the ease with which it is transmitted mechanically makes it difficult to control. Much cured tobacco contains the virus (Johnson, 1937) and workers who smoke and then handle tobacco in the field are thus likely to transmit the disease. It does not necessarily follow that smoking tobacco is an important source for all susceptible crops because there are different strains. Tests in Britain suggest that it is relatively unimportant for tomatoes under glass (Broadbent, 1962; Broadbent and Fletcher, 1966). The virus also persists in soil within plant debris and readily enters the roots, presumably through small injuries incurred while they are growing through the soil, and then usually moves into the shoot (Broadbent, 1965a). Carry-over of the virus on tobacco seed has not been unequivocally established but there is evidence that it may be carried in low concentrations on tomato seed and may be present within the testa and endosperm of a few of them. The number of plants that become infected from seed is likely to be small but they are important sources of inoculum for further spread of the disease when the crop is handled (Broadbent, 1965*b*). With tomatoes grown under glass, virus persisting on workers' clothing or on glasshouse structures may also occasionally be sources of inoculum (Broadbent and Fletcher, 1963).

Control of the disease is attempted in the first instance by avoiding infested soil in the seedbed or glasshouse and taking precautions in handling the crop. Methyl bromide, for example, helps to destroy the virus in tobacco seedbeds (Wiggs and Lucas, 1962). It is difficult to remove virus entirely from sap-engrained hands but Broadbent (1963) found that washing in a 3% solution of trisodium orthophosphate, and then soap and water was reasonably effective. Varieties resistant to mosaic are also being developed but even for tobacco there are still relatively few available (Lucas, 1965).

Although there are reports that tobacco mosaic virus can be transmitted by insects this apparently seldom happens in nature. In contrast most other viruses causing mosaics and yellows are transmitted under field conditions by insects and other animals while feeding and these are considered in relation to their vectors.

Transmitted by Aphids

Aphids exhibit a range of behaviour in transmitting different viruses. The two extremes of this range are:

1. The aphids acquire and transmit the virus within seconds or minutes, but soon lose their infectivity unless they feed again on a plant containing the virus.

2. The aphids often need several hours to acquire and transmit the virus, but then remain infective for many days even with no further access to a virus source.

The terms non-persistent (or mechanical) and persistent (or non-mechanical) have been applied, respectively, to viruses transmitted by aphids in these different ways. Because of the many intermediate types of behaviour, however, other criteria have been sought for the grouping of aphid-transmitted viruses. One is to relate them to the routes of virus tansport in the vector (Kennedy and others, 1962). Two groups are distinguished:

1. Stylet-borne (external) in which the virus is carried on the tips of the stylet and infectivity is lost through moults.

2. Circulative (internal) where the virus is ingested, eventually reaches the salivary gland, and is not lost in the moult. Some viruses of this type may also multiply in the aphid (propagative).

The stylet-borne group includes most viruses previously described as non-persistent or semi-persistent (see below), and the circulative group those described as persistent (Maramorosch, 1963).

Cucumber mosaic

This is caused by a stylet-borne or non-persistent virus Transmission is optimal when starved aphids feed for a short while (about 2 minutes) on infected plants, but infectivity is then usually lost within 5 minutes for aphids that are feeding. However, most aphids that can transmit the virus do so within the first minute of feeding on a healthy plant (Watson and Roberts, 1939; Bhargava, 1951). There are many strains of the virus, some associated with particular hosts, and differing in their host range and other properties. Cucumber, spinach, celery, tomato and tobacco are among the more important susceptible crops (Smith, 1957).

The disease on cucumbers first became important in the U.S.A. around 1920, though it was probably present during the preceding 20 years. Crops were most seriously affected in the trucking (vegetable) regions of the south, and in the Central States. Transmission in the field was shown to be effected by insects such as the melon aphid (*Aphis gossypii*),or mechanically during the thinning or training of plants and picking of the fruit (Doolittle, 1920).

In addition to a yellow mottling, the leaves of a diseased cucumber are wrinkled and sometimes distorted and curled. The older leaves die, leaving the basal portion of the stem bare, and in plants infected early the remaining leaves are small and bunched into a rosette-like cluster owing to a shortening of the petioles and stem internodes. Fruits are also mottled and often have dark green, wartlike outgrowths. Changes in the external appearance of leaves are associated with cellular changes. The palisade cells of yellow areas are shorter, the spongy parenchyma more compact, and the chloroplasts smaller than in healthy, green tissue.

Wild hosts have for some time been considered important in the overwintering of the virus, and as sources of virus for aphids which then move to nearby crops. Because aphids retain their infectivity only for short periods it should be possible to obtain some control of the disease by removing wild hosts near crops. Wellman (1937) successfully controlled mosaic of celery in Florida by this method, and Doolittle and Walker (1926) made similar claims for cucumber mosaic in Wisconsin. Faan and Johnson (1951), however, could find no relationship between virus infection in cucumber and the occurrence of wild hosts, and they considered eradication of doubtful value for disease control within this crop. Evidence from studies of other stylet-borne viruses support the separation of crops from virus-sources implicit in the eradication method. Beet mosaic virus, for instance, spreads much more in root crops grown near seed crops which are sources of both virus and aphids. Since 1950 this disease has almost disappeared in Britain largely as a result of measures taken to keep seedbeds from becoming virus infected, and by growing seedlings in areas away from root crops (Watson, 1967).

Cucumber mosaic is otherwise controlled mainly by the use of resistant varieties, and in glasshouses by excluding aphids with screens.

Barley yellow dwarf

This is caused by a circulative (persistent) virus which infects oats, barley, wheat, and perennial grasses in many of the cereal-growing areas of the world (Bruehl, 1961; Slykhius, 1967). The severity of the symptoms depends largely on the age of the plant at infection. Young barley is moderately to severely stunted and the leaves turn golden-yellow from the tips; with young oats there is also stunting plus a reddening of the leaves, and wheat at the seedling stage becomes chlorotic and severely dwarfed. Infection of older plants induces in barley and wheat a yellowing, and in oats a reddening of the upper leaves. The disease occurred in epiphytotic proportions on cereals in California in 1951 and its virus nature was demonstrated by transmission experiments with several grain-infesting aphids (Oswald and Houston, 1953*a*). At least ten aphid species are now known to be vectors (Kennedy and others, 1962) but *Rhopalosiphum padi*, *Macrosiphum* (*Sitobium*) *avenae* and *Rhopalosiphum maidis* are considered to be the main ones.

The vectors acquire and transmit the virus only after prolonged feeding. Watson and Mulligan (1960) found that a few *R. padi* acquired virus from infected leaves during feeds of 30 minutes, and equally a few viruliferous aphids were able to transmit virus during 15 minutes feeding on healthy seedlings, but the minimum total time taken both to acquire and transmit the virus was 10 hours and half the aphids needed 32 hours to do so. This, and other evidence, suggests that aphids do not transmit the virus for some time after acquiring it. This latent period may be about 5 days in some instances (Rochow, 1963). Once acquired, however, the virus persists in the aphid for relatively long periods, ranging from 6–21 days. Other factors influence transmission; for instance, there are different strains of the virus, possibly even different viruses, which cause barley yellow dwarf and some of them are transmitted well by one aphid but inefficiently or not at all by others (Rochow, 1959). Clones of an aphid species may also differ in their ability to transmit one virus strain; for example, Rochow and Eastop (1966) found that a clone of *R. padi* from New York rarely transmitted a strain of barley yellow dwarf virus but an aphid clone from Kansas regularly did so. Variations in transmission such as these involving vector specificity, mean that the most abundant aphid species is not necessarily the most important in spreading the virus.

Early infestations of aphids which result in early virus infection affect yields seriously (Figure 15.2), and some losses can be avoided by sowing at times which ensure that the young plants are not exposed to them. The success of this depends largely on the weather and the source of the virus and its aphid vector. In some northern areas of the U.S.A. aphids do not survive the winter and infection of spring-sown cereals is possibly by aphids migrating from crops

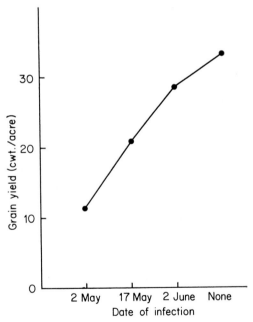

FIGURE 15.2 Relationship between yield of cereals and date of infection with barley yellow dwarf virus. Based on Watson and Mulligan, 1960, *Ann. appl. Biol.* **48**, 559–74.

sown earlier in the south. In other areas, e.g. California, aphids may survive on perennial grasses. In this instance the conditions which favour severe outbreaks of barley yellow dwarf are, 1. a warm but continuously wet winter, because this encourages growth of these wild hosts and reproduction of the aphid vector, yet delays sowing of the cereals and 2. a sudden, long dry period soon after the grain is seeded, because this encourages large flights of the aphids from the drying grasses into the fields of young grain (Oswald and Houston, 1953*b*). Other attempts to reduce losses from barley yellow dwarf are the incorporation of tolerance to the virus in new varieties, and the use of systemic organophosphorus insecticides to kill the aphid and prevent secondary spread of the virus (Rochow, 1961; H. C. Smith, 1963).

Beet yellows

In terms of persistence within their aphid vectors there are a few viruses which fall between the extremes illustrated by cucumber mosaic and barley yellow dwarf. The best known is beet yellows virus and for this Sylvester (1956) coined the term 'semi-persistent'; it is now thought that this probably belongs to the circulative group (Maramorosch, 1963). Aphids lose their infectivity with this virus within 24–36 hours and even if they do not acquire it as readily as cucumber mosaic virus there is no clear latent period. The proportion of aphids that transmit increases with time of feeding on both infected and healthy plants but the minimum total time is only some 15–30 minutes. The time spent on infected plants also influences the ability of aphids to transmit the virus successively to a number of plants, but does not make the aphids remain infective for much longer (Watson, 1940).

A yellowing of the tips of the middle-aged leaves is the first symptom of infection on sugar beet. These leaves then turn completely yellow, although the areas adjacent to the veins remain green for some time, and they also become thick and brittle. Eventually all the older leaves yellow and die leaving only the younger ones still green (Bennett, 1960; Hull, 1960). Before 1958 these symptoms were thought to be caused chiefly, if not solely by beet yellows virus. Then another, called beet mild yellows virus, was shown to cause similar symptoms (Russell, 1958), and it is thought that in Britain it is now responsible for much of the yellows in sugar beet. In contrast to beet yellows virus it persists in its aphid vector for 10 days (Russell, 1962). Of the two, beet yellows virus has the greater effect on root yield; it decreases both the leaf area and net assimilation rate of the plant (Watson and Watson, 1953). Losses from beet yellows are specially severe in years when plants are infected early. Crop losses in Britain for each of two such years, 1949 and 1957, were put at one million tons of roots worth about £6 million (Hull, 1961). No distinction was made in these estimates between the two viruses but the indications are that the greater part was due to beet yellows virus.

In Britain beet yellows virus overwinters in young beet (stecklings) planted for seed, in wild beet (*Beta maritima*) and in roots (especially mangels) stored in clamps for cattle feed. These may also be sources of the aphid vectors. Beet mild yellows possibly also overwinters in weeds such as *Stellaria media*, *Senecio vulgaris* and *Capsella bursa-pastoris* that survive in sheltered places.

In laboratory experiments the aphids *Myzus persicae* and *Aphis fabae* are equally efficient in transmitting beet yellows virus, but in the field disease incidence appears to be related only to the number of *M. persicae* (Figure 15.3). Its importance as a vector can be attributed to its activity; it often probes several times before settling on a leaf and then may move off again after a few hours to another plant. In contrast once *A. fabae* has settled on a beet leaf it seldom moves away (Watson, 1967). In mild winters *M. persicae* survives on cabbages, on sprouts from clamped roots, and on stecklings, often in large numbers depending on the autumn weather and incidence of predators; in severe winters it survives as eggs on the peach. Dry, warm and calm weather early in the year then favours aphid development and movement. Generally, severe aphid infestations and therefore severe outbreaks of virus yellows in beet, are associated with mild winters and dry, hot springs and summers (Hull, 1960).

Reducing aphid numbers and the amount of virus inoculum are essential for the control of beet yellows in root crops. Beet for seed production is now grown either in districts away from root crops, in beds sprayed regularly with systemic insecticides and inspected at intervals for disease, or under a cover crop such as a cereal; when the cereal is harvested the young beet is sprayed with an insecticide and allowed to grow on *in situ*. In Britain, growers are also advised to clear clamped roots by April or, alternatively, to prepare a clamp of closely topped roots for late use because the lack of leaves prevents them from becoming so heavily infested with aphids (Hull, 1961). Early planting of the root crop is sometimes beneficial, though not invariably so, and also less disease develops in crops with a high, uniform stand (Blencowe and Tinsley, 1951).

But apart from dealing with overwintering aphids and virus, control is based chiefly on spraying root crops with systemic insecticides so that aphids die after feeding on them and spread of the disease is then limited. Several countries now have schemes whereby growers are advised when to spray by a central organization (see Hull, 1968).

Transmitted by Whiteflies

The transmission of cotton and tobacco leaf curl by the whitefly, *Bemisia tabaci*, was described in Chapter 12, and they are the most

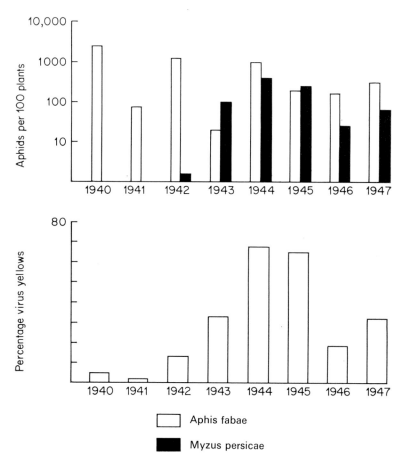

FIGURE 15.3 Relationship between the incidence of beet yellows virus in the field and its aphid vectors, *Aphis fabae* and *Myzus persicae*. From Watson and others, 1951, *Ann. appl. Biol.* **38**, 743–64.

important viruses carried by these insects. A few viruses causing mosaics of their hosts are also transmitted by whiteflies (Bawden, 1964).

Abutilon variegation

Historically, at least, *Abutilon* variegation is the most interesting. In the late 1800's a person called Thompson brought an apparently new species of *Abutilon* with attractive, variegated leaves from the West Indies to England (Figure 15.4) This was introduced into the horticultural trade as an ornamental under the name *Abutilon thompsonii*. It was then discovered that ordinary *Abutilon* became variegated when grafted with scions from *A. thompsonii*, and both Beijerinck and Baur thought that this 'infectious chlorosis' was caused by a virus though their concepts of a virus differed (Phytopathological Classics 7). The virus nature of *Abutilon* variegation was accepted on its transmission by grafting but no vector was found until 1946 when Orlando and Silberschmidt showed that in South America it could be transmitted by *Bemisia tabaci* both to *Abutilon striatum* var. *spurium* and to *Sida rhombifolia*, a species already known to become variegated like *Abutilon*. It is now clear that

FIGURE 15.4 Abutilon variegation. The leaf on the right came from a plant with the virus, the one on the left from a non-infected plant. Photograph by A. Ironside.

Thompson's 'new' species was no more than a diseased plant of *A. striatum*, but it is still valued in the northern hemisphere where insect transmission does not occur.

Transmitted by Mites

There is an increasing interest in the transmission of viruses by animals other than insects, and over the past 10–15 years six viruses causing mosaic diseases have been shown to be carried by eriophyid mites. Previously only one disease, currant reversion, was thought to be transmitted in this way.

Wheat streak mosaic

The cereal disease, wheat streak mosaic (Figure 15.5), is probably of most economic significance and its salient features have been ably reviewed by Slykhuis (1962, 1967). The disease was first described under the name 'yellow mosaic' from Nebraska and Kansas in the 1920's and was recognized as the cause of serious losses in the wheat crop. Transmission by the wheat curl mite, *Aceria tulipae* (Figure 15.6) was demonstrated by Slykhuis (1953) and so far this is the only known vector. When mites are reared on diseased plants all stages become infective except the eggs but acquisition of the virus directly by adult mites has not been demonstrated. Nymphs acquire the virus after feeding on diseased plants for 15–30 minutes, and mites transferred to a virus-immune host retain their infectivity for 9 days. It is not yet known whether the virus multiplies in the mite; an accumulation of virus particles has been found in the mid and hind intestine but these may have been ingested while feeding on infected wheat (Paliwal and Slykhuis, 1967).

The virus has been transmitted mechanically and by mites to barley, oats, and maize, and to a number of common grasses. Some perennial grass species may be sources of the virus but wheat is the most favourable host for both the virus and its vector, and is most important in the epidemiology of the disease. Winter wheat becomes infested with mites in the autumn and they and the virus thus overwinter. In spring and summer the mites multiply, and though their independent movement is limited, they are readily dispersed by wind and possibly also transported by insects to other plants, and particularly to the young spring wheat crop. When the winter wheat crop is harvested mites and virus remain on volunteer plants or immature plants from the spring wheat crop, and these

FIGURE 15.5 Wheat streak mosaic—leaf symptoms. Photograph courtesy J. T. Slykhius, from *Biological transmission of Disease Agents*, copyright © 1962, Academic Press, New York.

serve as sources of inoculum and vectors for crops sown in the autumn. As Slykhuis (1962) points out, control is thus best achieved by breaking the succession of immature wheat. In southern Alberta winter wheat is sown late after all the spring crops have matured, and all immature wheat nearby is removed a week or so beforehand. Similarly spring wheat is not sown near winter crops which have

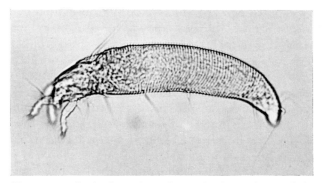

FIGURE 15.6 *Aceria tulipae*. Lateral view of an adult mite, about 250μ long. Photograph courtesy J. T. Slykhuis, from *Biological Transmission of Disease Agents*, copyright © 1962, Academic Press, New York.

harboured the virus and *A. tulipae*. Such a scheme is not practicable in all areas where the disease occurs and here mosaic-tolerant varieties are useful in reducing losses.

Transmitted by Nematodes

It has long been known that some viruses are soil-borne in the sense that they have an 'underground natural method of spread which does not depend simply on contact between tissues of infected and healthy plants' (Harrison, 1964). Since 1958, when Hewitt, Raski and Goheen showed that a virus disease of the grapevine called 'fanleaf' was transmitted by the nematode *Xiphinema index*, it has become clear that several soil-borne viruses are so transmitted (Cadman, 1963). There are two types, one with polyhedral particles is transmitted by nematodes belonging to the genera *Xiphenema* and *Longidorus* (NEPO viruses), the other with rod-shaped (tubular) particles by *Trichodorus* spp. (NETU viruses). Information on these viruses is now accumulating rapidly, so much so that further general statements regarding their behaviour are soon likely to require modification.

Arabis mosaic virus

At present there is probably as much known about arabis mosaic virus as any other so this will serve as an example of the nematode-transmitted group. This is a NEPO virus, two principal strains of which are so far recognized, the type strain transmitted by *Xiphenema diversicaudatum* causes diseases known as strawberry mosaic and strawberry yellow crinkle, raspberry yellow dwarf, rhubarb mosaic and cherry raspberry leaf; the grapevine strain transmitted by *X. index* causes a yellow mosaic in grapevine and the fanleaf disease in which nematode transmission was first demonstrated.

Both adults and larvae of *Xiphenema* can acquire and transmit arabis mosaic virus. Jha and Posnette (1961) found that *X. diversicaudatum* became infective after feeding on diseased plants for a day and that infective nematodes transmitted the virus to healthy plants within 3 days. The indications are that once acquired the virus persists in the nematode for at least 8 months but it is not transmitted through the egg and is apparently lost when the nematode moults (Harrison and Winslow, 1961).

X. diversicaudatum can survive for relatively long periods in soil and in Britain at least, is widely distributed. Most of the population occurs within 76–228 mm of the surface but some nematodes are found at depths of nearly one metre. The nematode also has a wide host range and hedgerow trees are particularly important because some species, e.g. *Sambucus niger*, are also hosts for the virus. Plants with arabis mosaic virus often occur in crops next to hedges or isolated trees suggesting that infective nematodes have spread from these sources. Movement of the nematode vector is unlikely, however, to result in a rapid spread of the disease for in uncultivated soil it appears to be no more than about 0.3 m per year. Distribution of the virus to areas in which the nematode is already present accounts for long distance spread and one sure way is through the movement of infected propagative material from one locality to the next. Another is through the pollen and seed of infected plants (Lister and Murant, 1967; Murant and Lister, 1967). It appears to be a feature of the NEPO viruses that they can be transmitted in this way and this is specially important where the virus has common weed hosts, as does arabis mosaic in Shepherds' Purse (*Capsella bursa-pastoris*) and chickweed (*Stellaria media*).

Care in the movement of propagating material and weed control are important factors, therefore, in limiting arabis mosaic virus. With some crops treatment of the soil with chemicals to kill the nematode may be worthwhile. Harrison and others (1963) obtained good control on strawberries by applying methyl bromide or D-D mixture at a rate of 98·5 kg/100m^2, because this killed over 99% of the nematodes. Kills less than this gave inefficient control so the margin of error with this method is not great.

Transmitted by Fungi
There are indications that certain fungi are vectors of other soil-borne viruses. The experimental evidence is impressive for the viruses of lettuce big-vein and tobacco necrosis (Hewitt and Grogan, 1967), but there is also circumstantial evidence that the transmission of wheat, barley and oat mosaic viruses is fungus-assisted.

Wheat mosaic
This disease was first recorded in Illinois and Indiana in 1919 (Slykhuis, 1967) and in some regions can result in heavy yield losses. Some strains of the virus cause a rosetting, others a yellow mosaic and stunting. Various soil treatments suggest that an organism is involved in transmission, for instance soils known to harbour the virus are rendered non-infective by treating with certain fungicides, by heating to 50°–60°, and by passing through screens with a pore size less than 2μ. Similarly, soil can be made infective by adding a small quantity of virus-containing soil to it but not by adding filtrates of such soil. Two other pieces of evidence are more striking in that they implicate a specific fungus. In Nebraska Estes and Brakke (1966) found a significant correlation between the presence of the fungus, *Polymyxa graminis*, and the transmission of wheat mosaic, and Canova (1966) in Italy infected wheat by transferring zoospores of *Polymyxa graminis* from the roots of diseased to healthy plants. Isolates of the fungus which did not apparently transmit the virus could be made to do so by allowing them first to parasitize the roots of wheat infected with wheat mosaic.

It seems likely that within the next few years not only will vectors be demonstrated for other soil-borne viruses but information will be obtained on the nature of the virus-vector relationships of those already known.

ASTER YELLOWS

Symptoms of the yellows type may also result when leafhoppers feed in turn on diseased and healthy plants, and it has long been considered that these diseases are caused by viruses which are transmitted by the leafhoppers. However, recent evidence suggests that in some diseases the causal agent is not a virus and, for this reason, the group was omitted from the preceding section. The disease known as aster yellows is one in which there are new ideas about the nature of the pathogen. This adds yet another intriguing twist to an already fascinating tale.

In the early 1900's a serious disease developed on the cultivated Chinese aster, *Callistephus chinensis*, in many parts of the U.S.A. Developing leaves became chlorotic and deformed, dormant buds within the axils of these leaves grew and produced thin, yellow branches with internodes longer than normal, and flowers were distorted and of no market value. The disease became known as aster yellows and it was first shown by Kunkel (1926) to be transmitted by the leafhopper *Macrosteles fascifrons*. He found that leafhoppers only became infective some nine or more days after feeding on a diseased plant, but once infective they remained so, apparently for life. The causal agent was not transmitted through the egg but was retained during consecutive moults. Kunkel believed the causal agent was a virus and the experimental evidence was consistent with this view. The virus nature of the disease was not seriously challenged for the next 40 years and subsequent experiments only strengthened this belief.

Further investigation by Severin and his associates (Severin, 1929; Frazier and Severin, 1945) in California, and by Kunkel (1931, 1932), showed that aster yellows 'virus' could infect a wide range of plants and cause diseases of considerable economic importance on celery, carrot, onion, lettuce, endive, potato and many ornamentals. The symptoms varied but involved, to different degrees, yellowing of the leaves, bud and shoot proliferation, and malformation and sterility of the flowers. It also became clear that Severin and Kunkel were dealing with different strains of the pathogen, one that infected celery (Western or Californian strain) and one that did not (Eastern or New York strain). Apart from host range these strains also differed in the length of their incubation periods in the vector and plant, the celery strain having the shorter periods (Maramorosch, 1962).

In his early paper Kunkel (1926) suggested that aster yellows 'virus' might reproduce in the leafhopper and evidence in support of this view was obtained from various investigations (Maramorosch, 1955). Proof was obtained by Maramorosch (1952) by transferring the pathogen mechanically through ten batches of leafhoppers so that ultimately a dilution (10^{-40}) was obtained, which exceeded with certainty the maximum dilution of starting material necessary for a successful inoculation. After a suitable incubation period leafhoppers with this dilution were found to be infective. These experiments were accepted as some of the best evidence for the multiplication of a virus within a vector.

Though information on the disease and on the relationships

between the pathogen and its insect vector accumulated, there was one significant gap: typical virus particles could not be demonstrated convincingly in diseased plants. One reason for this could be that people were not looking at the right tissues, while another was the lack of suitable techniques for examining thin sections of plant tissue with the electron microscope. By the mid-1960's however, suitable techniques were available and in 1967 Doi and his associates published the results of their investigations on this and other diseases spread by leafhoppers. They could not find any uniform particles in diseased plants resembling those described for viruses, but there were bodies in the sieve tubes and occasionally in the cells of the phloem-parenchyma of these plants which were never found in healthy ones. These particles varied in size but were generally of two kinds: a spherical to irregularly ellipsoidal body, 80–800 mμ in diameter, with a two-layer limiting membrane instead of a cell wall, and the other a round body, 100–250 mμ in diameter, filled with ribosome-like granules of about 13 mμ diameter. The morphology and fine structure of these bodies agree with descriptions of cells of the Mycoplasma series, i.e. the Pleuropneumonia-like organisms, and Doi and his co-workers (1967) suggest that these are in fact the causal agents of the disease. Undoubtedly this is one of the most significant discoveries in plant pathology of recent years.

Several methods have been devised for the control of aster yellows, of which one of the more successful has been the screening of plants in frames, e.g. aster and lettuce seedlings, to exclude the vector. Linn (1940) found that the disease in lettuce and endive on Staten Island was most severe in parts of the beds adjacent to the weed borders. These were not only reservoirs for the pathogen but the leafhoppers moved to them when adjacent crops were harvested. Eradicating weeds within 30 m of prospective lettuce and endive beds was worthwhile provided the young transplants had been protected by screens and were sprayed with an insecticide when set out. Wind direction apparently determined vector movement to a large extent, but leafhoppers did not move in significant numbers much farther than 60 m in 4 weeks.

However, leafhoppers may not always be so restricted in their movements; given the right conditions they may travel or be carried by wind perhaps several miles, and so in stages reach areas where they do not overwinter. Linn thought that such dispersal might be important in relation to aster yellows on Staten Island, and it is certainly so with other diseases in which leafhoppers are vectors such as beet curly top (Severin, 1933).

REFERENCES

Bawden, F. C. (1964). *Plant Viruses and Virus Diseases*, 361 pp. Ronald Press, New York.

Bawden, F. C. and Pirie, N. W. (1937). The isolation and some properties of liquid crystalline substances from solanaceous plants infected with three strains of tobacco mosaic virus. *Proc. R. Soc.* B **123**, 274–320

Bennett, C. W. (1960). Sugar beet yellows disease in the United States. *Techn. Bull. U.S. Dep. Agric.*, No. 1218, 63 pp.

Bhargava, K. S. (1951). Some properties of four strains of cucumber mosaic virus. *Ann. appl. Biol.*, **38**, 377–88

Blencowe, J. W. and Tinsley, T. W. (1951). The influence of density of plant population on the incidence of yellows in sugar beet crops. *Ann. appl. Biol.*, **38**, 395-401

Broadbent, L. (1962). The epidemiology of tomato mosaic. II. Smoking tobacco as a source of virus. *Ann. appl. Biol.*, **50**, 461–6, (1963). III. Cleaning virus from hands and tools. *Ann. appl. Biol.*, **52**, 225–32; (1965*a*). VIII. Virus infection through tomato roots. *Ann. appl. Biol.*, **55**, 57–66; (1965*b*). XI. Seed transmission of TMV. *Ann. appl. Biol.*, **56**, 177–205

Broadbent, L. and Fletcher, J. T. (1963). The epidemiology of tomato mosaic. IV. Persistence of virus on clothing and glasshouse structures. *Ann. appl. Biol.*, **52**, 233–41; (1966). XII. Sources of TMV in commercial tomato crops under glass. *Ann. appl. Biol.*, **57**, 113–20

Bruehl, G. W. (1961). Barley yellow dwarf, a virus disease of cereals and grasses. *Monogr. Amer. Phytopathol. Soc.*, No. 1, 52 pp.

Cadman, C. H. (1963). Biology of soil-borne viruses. *A. Rev. Phytopathol.*, **1**, 143–72

Canova, A. (1966). Ricerche sulle malattie da virus delle Graminacea III. *Polymyxa graminis* Led. vettore del virus del mosaico del Frumento. *Phytopath. Mediterranea*, **5**, 53–8 [*Rev. appl. Mycol.*, **46**, 662]

Doi, Y., Teranaka, M., Yora, K. and Asuyama, H. (1967). [Mycoplasma—or PLT group-like microorganisms found in the phloem elements of plants infected with mulberry dwarf, potato witches' broom, aster yellows or Paulownia witches' broom.] *Ann. Phytopath. Soc. Japan*, **33**, 259–66. In Japanese, English abstract.

Doolittle, S. P. (1920). The mosaic disease of cucurbits. *Bull. U.S. Dep. Agric.*, No. 879, 69 pp.

Doolittle, S. P. and Walker, M. N. (1926). Control of cucumber mosaic by eradication of wild host plants. *Bull. U.S. Dep. Agric.* No. 1461, 14 pp.

Estes, A. P. and Brakke, M. K. (1966). Correlation of *Polymyxa graminis* with transmission of soil-borne wheat mosaic virus. *Virology*, **28**, 772–4

Faan, H. C. and Johnson, J. (1951), The overwintering of cucumber mosaic virus. *Phytopathology*, **41**, 1001–10

Frazier, N. W. and Severin, H. H. P. (1945). Weed host range of Californian aster yellows. *Hilgardia*, **16**, 621–50

Grant, T. J. (1934). The host range and behaviour of the ordinary tobacco mosaic virus. *Phytopathology*, **24**, 311–36

Harrison, B. D. (1964). The transmission of plant viruses in soil. In *Plant Virology* (Ed. M. K. Corbett and H. D. Sisler), pp. 118–47. University of Florida Press, Gainesville.

Harrison, B. D. and Winslow, R. D. (1961). Laboratory and field studies on the relation of arabis mosaic virus to its nematode vector *Xiphinema diversicaudatum* (Micoletzky). *Ann. appl. Biol.*, **49**, 621–33

Harrison, B. D., Peachey, J. E., and Winslow, R. D. (1963). The use of nematicides to control the spread of arabis mosaic virus by *Xiphinema diversicaudatum* (Micol.). *Ann. appl. Biol.*, **52**, 243–55

Hewitt, W. B. and Grogan, R. G. (1967). Unusual vectors of plant viruses. *A. Rev. Microbiol.*, **21**, 205–24

Hewitt, W. B., Raski, D. J. and Goheen, A. C. (1958). Nematode vector of soil-borne fanleaf virus of grapevines. *Phytopathology*, **48**, 586–95

Holmes, F. O. (1938). Taxonomic relationships of plants susceptible to infection by tobacco mosaic virus. *Phytopathology*, **28**, 58–66

Holmes, F. O. (1946). A comparison of the experimental host ranges of tobacco etch and tobacco mosaic viruses. *Phytopathology*, **35**, 643–59

Hull, R. (1960). *Sugar Beet Diseases*, pp. 10–16. H.M.S.O. London.

Hull, R. (1961). The health of the sugar beet crop in Great Britain. *Jl R. agric. Soc.*, **122**, 101–12

Hull, R. (1968). The spray warning scheme for control of sugar beet yellows in England. Summary of results between 1959–66. *Pl. Path.*, **17**, 1–10

Jensen, J. H. (1937). Studies on representative strains of tobacco mosaic virus. *Phytopathology*, **27**, 69–84

Jha, A. and Posnette, A. F. (1961). Transmission of arabis mosaic virus by the nematode *Xiphenema diversicaudatum* (Micol). *Virology*, **13**, 119–23

Johnson, J. (1937). Factors relating to the control of ordinary tobacco mosaic. *J. agric. Res.*, **54**, 239–73

Kennedy, J. S., Day, M. F. and Eastop, V. F. (1962). *A Conspectus of Aphids as Vectors of Plant Viruses*. 114 pp. Commonwealth Institute of Entomology, London.

Kunkel, L. O. (1926). Studies on aster yellows. *Contr. Boyce Thompson Inst. Pl. Res.*, **1**, 181–240

Kunkel, L. O. (1931). Studies on aster yellows in some new host plants. *Contr. Boyce Thompson Inst. Pl. Res.*, **3**, 85–123

Kunkel, L. O. (1932). Celery yellows of California not identical with the aster yellows of New York. *Contr. Boyce Thompson Inst. Pl. Res.*, **4**, 405–14

Linn, M. B. (1940). The yellows disease of lettuce and endive. *Bull. Cornell agric. Exp. Stn.*, No. 742. 33 pp.

Lister, R. M. and Murant, A. F. (1967). Seed-transmission of nematode borne viruses. *Ann. appl. Biol.*, **59**, 49–62

Lucas, G. B. (1965). *Diseases of Tobacco*, pp. 524–59. Scarecrow Press, New York.

Maramorosch, K. (1952). Direct evidence for the multiplication of aster yellows virus in its insect vector. *Phytopathology*, **42**, 59–64

Maramorosch, K. (1955). Multiplication of plant viruses in insect vectors. *Adv. Virus Res.*, **3**, 221–49

Maramorosch, K. (1962). Differences in incubation periods of aster yellows virus strains. *Phytopathology*, **52**, 925

Maramorosch, K. (1963). Arthropod transmission of plant viruses. *A. Rev. Entomol.*, **8**, 369–414

Murant, A. F. and Lister, R. M. (1967). Seed transmission in the ecology of nematode-borne viruses. *Ann. appl. Biol.*, **59**, 63–76

Orlando, A. and Silberschmidt, K. (1946). [Studies on the natural dissemination of the virus of the 'infectious chlorosis' of Malvaceae (Abutilon virus 1, Baur) and its relation to the insect-vector (*Bemisia tabaci*, (Genn.). (Homoptera-Aleyrodidae).] *Archos Inst. biol., S. Paulo*, **17**, 1–36 (English abstract.)

Oswald, J. W. and Houston, B. R. (1953*a*). The yellow-dwarf virus disease of cereal crops. *Phytopathology*, **43**, 128–36

Oswald, J. W. and Houston, B. R. (1953*b*). Host range and epiphytology of the cereal yellow dwarf disease. *Phytopathology*, **43**, 309–13

Paliwal, Y. C. and Slykhuis, J. T. (1967). Localization of wheat streak mosaic virus in the alimentary canal of its vector *Aceria tulipae* Keifer. *Virology*, **32**, 344–53

Piper, C. S. (1941). Marsh spot of peas: a manganese deficiency disease. *J. agric. Sci., Camb.*, **31**, 448–53

Phytopathological Classics No. 7. (1. Concerning the mosaic disease of tobacco by Adolf Mayer; 2. Concerning the mosaic disease of the tobacco plant by Dmitrii Ivanowski; 3. Concerning a *contagium vivum fluidum* as a cause of the spot disease of tobacco leaves by Martinus W. Beijerinck; 4. On the etiology of infectious variegation by Erwin Baur.), translated by James Johnson. American Phytopathological Society, Cayuga Press, Ithaca, New York.

Plant. W. (1951). The control of 'whiptail' in broccoli and cauliflower. *J. hort. Sci.*, **26**, 109–17

Rochow, W. F. (1959). Transmission of strains of barley yellow dwarf virus by two aphid species. *Phytopathology*, **49**, 744–8

Rochow, W. F. (1961). The barley yellow dwarf virus disease of small grains. *Adv. Agron.*, **13**, 217–48

Rochow, W. F. (1963). Latent periods in the aphid transmission of barley yellow dwarf virus. *Phytopathology*, **53**, 355–6

Rochow, W. F. and Eastop, V. F. (1966). Variation within *Rhopalosiphum padi* and transmission of barley yellow dwarf virus by clones of four aphid species. *Virology*, **30**, 286–96

Russell, G. E. (1958). Sugar beet yellows: a preliminary study of the distribution and interrelationships of viruses and virus strains found in East Anglia, 1955–57. *Ann. appl. Biol.*, **46**, 393–8

Russell, G. E. (1962). Sugar beet mild yellowing virus; a persistent aphid-transmitted virus. *Nature, Lond.*, **195**, 1231

Severin, H. P. (1929). Yellows disease of celery, lettuce and other plants, transmitted by *Cicadula sexnotata* (Fall.). *Hilgardia*, **3**, 543–83

Severin, H. P. (1933). Field observations on the beet leafhopper, *Eutettix tenellus*, in California. *Hilgardia*, **7**, 281–360

Slykhuis, J. T. (1953). Wheat streak mosaic in Alberta and factors related to its spread. *Can. J. agric. Sci.*, **33**, 195–7

Slykhuis, J. T. (1962). Mite transmission of plant viruses. In *Biological Transmission of Disease Agents*, (Ed. K. Maramorosch), pp. 41–61. Academic Press, New York.

Slykhuis, J. T. (1967). Virus diseases of cereals. *Rev. appl. Mycol.*, **46**, 401–29

Smith, H. C. (1963). Control of barley yellow dwarf virus in cereals. *N.Z. Jl agric. Res.*, **6**, 229–44

Smith, K. M. (1957). *A Textbook of Plant Virus Diseases*, 652 pp. J. and A. Churchill, London.

Stanley, W. M. (1936). Chemical studies on the virus of tobacco mosaic. VI. The isolation from diseased Turkish tobacco plants of a crystalline protein possessing the properties of tobacco mosaic virus. *Phytopathology*, **26**, 305–20

Storey, H. H. and Leach, R. (1933). A sulphur deficiency of the tea bush. *Ann. appl. Biol.*, **20**, 23–56

Sylvester, E. S. (1956). Beet yellows virus transmission by the green peach aphid. *J. econ. Ent.*, **49**, 789–800

Walker, J. C. (1957). *Plant Pathology*, pp. 473–500. McGraw-Hill, New York.

Wallace, T. (1961). *The Diagnosis of Mineral Deficiencies in Plants by Visual Symptoms. A Colour Atlas and Guide*, H.M.S.O., London.

Watson, D. J. and Watson, M. A. (1953). Comparative physiological studies on the growth of field crops. III. The effect of infection with beet yellows and beet mosaic viruses on the growth and yield of the sugar beet root crop. *Ann. appl. Biol.*, **40**, 1–37

Watson, M. A. (1940). Studies on the transmission of sugar beet yellows virus by the aphis, *Myzus persicae* (Sulz.). *Proc. R. Soc.* B **128**, 535–52

Watson, M. A. (1967). Epidemiology of aphid-transmitted plant virus diseases. *Outl. Agric.*, **5**, 155–66

Watson, M. A. and Roberts, F. M. (1939). A comparative study of the transmission of Hyoscyamus virus 3, potato virus Y and cucumber virus 1 by the vectors *Myzus persicae* (Sulz.), *M. circumflexus* (Buckton) and *Macrosiphum gei* (Koch) *Proc. R. Soc.*, B. **127**, 543–76

Watson, M. A. and Mulligan, T. E. (1960). Comparison of two barley yellow dwarf viruses in glasshouse and field experiments. *Ann. appl. Biol.*, **48**, 559–74

Wellman, F. L. (1937). Control of southern celery mosaic in Florida by removing weeds that serve as sources of mosaic infection. *Tech. Bull. U.S. Dep. Agric.*, No. 548, 16 pp.

Wiggs, D. N. and Lucas, G. B. (1962). Inactivation of tobacco mosaic virus by volatile chemicals. *Phytopathology*, **52**, 983–5

CHAPTER 16

Postharvest diseases

So far we have dealt with diseases found in the field and the problems associated with them. When crops are harvested there are different disease problems because 1. the seeds, fruits or other storage organs are essentially dormant structures, and their cells are physiologically unlike those of the growing plant and, 2. the bulking of these structures in transit and in storage gives conditions quite different from those in the field. For these reasons the study of postharvest diseases (or market pathology as it is sometimes called) is conveniently treated as a special aspect of plant pathology.

THE RANGE OF DISEASES INVOLVED

The numerous diseases which occur in transit and storage result mainly from the activities of bacteria and fungi or are of non-parasitic origin. Stakman and Harrar (1957) further divide the pathogenic storage diseases into two groups—those of dry, bulk material such as grain, and those of succulent storage organs such as fruit, tubers and rhizomes. This is useful because it emphasizes that the type of plant material affects disease development. It is impossible to describe these diseases adequately in a single chapter but the following examples indicate the range and diversity. Comprehensive accounts of many market diseases are to be found in a series of reports on '*Market Diseases of Fruits and Vegetables*' published by the United States Department of Agriculture (Harvey and Pentzer, 1960; McColloch and others, 1968; M. A. Smith and others, 1966; Ramsey and Smith, 1961; Ramsey and others, 1949, 1959; Rose and others, 1943, 1950, 1951). These are both excellent guides to the identification of postharvest diseases and to the extensive literature.

Bacterial rots

Considerable losses of vegetables such as carrots, potatoes, onions and celery are caused by bacteria that produce a soft rot of the host tissue. They achieve this primarily through the action of enzymes on the pectic substances of the middle lamella and the cellulose of the cell wall, as a result of which the host cells separate and their protoplasts die. At the beginning of this century several people isolated soft-rot bacteria—Jones in 1901 from carrots, Van Hall and also Appel in 1902 from potato, Townsend in 1904 from calla lily, and each described their isolate as a distinct species. Similar bacteria have since been isolated from a wide range of hosts but their taxonomy has become increasingly confused (Hellmers, 1959). It is clear that the isolates can be divided into a number of groups based on pathogenicity and on biochemical and serological reactions, but there is no general agreement on the name and rank of representative members of each group. The present situation is well summarised by Graham (1964). He considers that there is only one species, *Pectobacterium carotovorum*, which can be divided into four varieties—*carotovorum*, *atrosepticum*, *aroideae* and *chrysanthemi*. In the seventh edition of Bergey's Manual (1957) the soft-rot bacteria as classified are *Erwinia carotovora*, *Erwinia atroseptica*, *Erwinia aroideae* and *Erwinia chrysanthemi*, but this should not be taken to imply agreement except on the names: the disposition of isolates varies in the two schemes.

Soft rots develop in stored produce under humid conditions resulting from poor ventilation. Temperature also influences rotting; with potatoes for example, soft rot proceeds more rapidly at high temperatures. Kendrick and others (1959) have shown that the amount of bacterial soft rot for a given potato variety in storage can be predicted from temperature and humidity data. They found a significant, positive correlation between a temperature–humidity index derived from such data and rotting of 'White Rose' potato tubers. Under these adverse conditions potato tubers are often reduced to a soft mass held together only by the outer cork layer which the bacteria are unable to attack (Figure 16.1). Tubers infected only with soft-rot bacteria have a slightly musty smell but usually there are also secondary invaders and the potatoes become putrid. Other factors such as bruises or lesions of other pathogens predispose the tubers to attack (Ruehle, 1940). Tubers infected with *Phytophthora infestans* appear specially to favour growth of the soft-rot bacteria and they rapidly advance beyond the limits of the fungal invasion (Dowson and Rudd-Jones, 1951).

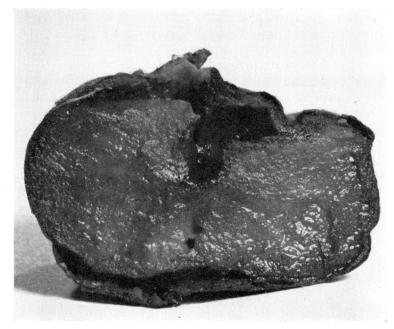

FIGURE 16.1 Soft-rot of potato. The mass of cells is held together only by the skin, and this can be readily detached, as is seen at the base of this tuber. Photograph by A. Ironside.

Other bacteria also cause rots. At high temperatures and high humidity *Bacillus polymxya* reduces potatoes to a yellow sticky mass, with a distinctly fruity odour. Anaerobic clostridia are sometimes associated with the soft-rot bacteria, and the result is a gassy or ropy rot of the tuber, (Rudd-Jones and Dowson, 1950).

Changes induced by fungi

There are many storage diseases specifically caused by fungi. Some fungi attack a wide range of fruits and vegetables. Species of *Rhizopus*, for example, cause considerable damage to peaches, grapes, strawberries, sweet potato, crucifers, cucurbits, tomatoes and egg-plant. They produce a soft rot of the fleshy parts which proceeds rapidly at temperatures over 10°. With fruits there is often a leakage of juices from the affected parts and a pleasant odour of fermentation. Under humid conditions the typical, coarse and stringy mycelium of *Rhizopus* with its black sporangia develops over the diseased tissue.

Stone and pome fruits are particularly prone to brown rot. This first appears as a small, circular, light-brown lesion in which the flesh remains fairly firm. At suitable temperatures (15°–27°) the rot enlarges rapidly and involves much of the fruit in as little as 24 hours. Three fungi are involved: *Sclerotinia fructigena* and *Sclerotinia laxa* in Europe and *Sclerotinia fructicola* in the U.S.A. The presence of these fungi is soon established by the appearance of grey or yellowish, cushion-like masses of conidia (the *Monilinia* stage) on the rotted tissues (Figure 16.2). Infected fruits then gradually shrivel and become mummified (Wormald, 1954).

Bananas in transit are subject to several fungal rots (Wardlaw, 1961). Rotting by *Gloeosporium musarum* is particularly common, and is considered largely responsible for the decline in quality of Jamaican bananas imported into England during recent years. After shipment, black, sunken lesions are found on the fruit, with a surrounding yellow-orange halo separating them from healthy,

FIGURE 16.2 Brown rot of apple caused by *Sclerotinia fructigena*. The conidial cushions are clearly visible on the rotted tissue. Photograph by A. Ironside.

green skin. These lesions increase very rapidly when the bananas are transferred to the ripening room and a watery rot develops in most of the edible pulp.

Two *Penicillium* species cause considerable damage to citrus fruits in transit and in store (Rose and others, 1943). They are *Penicillium italicum* and *Penicillium digitatum*, and the diseases are called blue mould and green mould, respectively, these names referring to the distinctive colour of the spore masses. The rots start as soft, watery spots in the rind about 5–10 mm diameter. Under favourable conditions these increase rapidly and may enlarge to 50 mm in 24–36 hours. Usually lesions caused by *P. italicum* develop more slowly than those of *P. digitatum*. Shortly after infection, the surface of the lesion becomes covered with masses of fungal conidia. The subsequent course of the rot depends on the humidity. In dry conditions affected fruits shrink and become wrinkled rather like apples infected with *Sclerotinia*. If the humidity is high, bacteria often enter the tissue already invaded by *Penicillium* and the fruit is rapidly reduced to a wet and rotten mass.

Potatoes are commonly attacked by *Fusarium caeruleum* which causes a dry rot of the tuber. The first symptom is a darkening of the skin, the affected area appears slightly sunken and later the skin wrinkles. Small, white tufts of mycelial growth develop and also, if the infected tubers are exposed to the light, pink masses of spores. Cavities form within the tuber and become filled with fungal mycelium (Figure 16.3) which has a bluish tinge, this colouration

FIGURE 16.3 Dry rot of potato. An infected tuber cut to show, on the left, the cavities with fungal mycelium and on the right, the wrinkled skin with tufts of fungal growth. Photograph by A. Ironside.

sometimes extending into the surrounding flesh. As the rotting proceeds, the tubers continue to lose water, they become lighter and are finally reduced to a hard, dry mass (Pethybridge and Lafferty, 1917).

Species of *Aspergillus* are considerably involved in the deterioration of stored grains (Christensen and Kaufman, 1965). Under some circumstances they invade the seeds and either kill the embryo, which makes the seed valueless for planting, or with barley of no use for malting, or they discolour the grain which lowers its value for milling. They may also cause biochemical changes which make the grain unpalatable, or produce substances which are toxic to man and animals. Diseases of animals caused by fungal toxins (myco-toxicoses) have been studied intensively in the U.S.S.R. over the past two decades but it is only during the last 7–8 years that they have received much attention elsewhere. One impetus for research was the discovery that the so-called 'X' disease which killed some 10,000 turkey poults in England during 1960 was caused by feeding them groundnut meal infected with *Aspergillus flavus*. It is now known that this fungus produces several toxic materials, collectively known as aflotoxin, and their chemical nature and mode of action are being investigated (Spensley, 1963).

Non-pathogenic diseases

The bulking of large numbers of fruits or storage organs together, appears in itself to favour some diseases in which pathogens are not directly involved. Apples and potato tubers, for example, continue to respire in bulk shipments and if ventilation is poor the level of carbon dioxide may become excessively high in the air surrounding them, and the oxygen content correspondingly lower than normal. In potatoes this leads to a condition known as black heart (Ramsey and others, 1949). The tubers may appear normal externally but when cut, sharply-defined areas of the flesh appear black, usually in the centre of the tuber. Occasionally the tubers appear normal when freshly cut but the tissues then rapidly discolour. Black heart is thought to be caused by a lack of oxygen which kills the tissues and this condition is aggravated by high temperatures (over 32°), and poor ventilation during transit.

A similar condition in apples known as brown heart was common in shipments of apples from Australia to England during the early 1920's. This was also attributed to poor ventilation and particularly to an accumulation of carbon dioxide above a critical level of 13% (Kidd and West, 1923).

The levels of carbon dioxide and oxygen also affect the amount of scald or superficial scald of stored apples (Roberts and others, 1963). In this disease there is a progressive browning of the cells beneath the epidermis which eventually involves the epidermal cells (Bain, 1956; Bain and Mercer, 1963). Large areas of the apple skin appear brown and sunken and the fruit is of little market value (Figure 16.4). Despite considerable research over the past 45 years the cause is still in doubt (Smock, 1961). Research by Brooks and his associates from 1917 onwards suggested that an accumulation of certain volatile substances was responsible, and that these substances were probably esters produced by the respiring apples (Brooks, 1919). This view became widely accepted but has recently been challenged; for instance, it has been shown that additions of volatile substances to stored apples at concentrations expected to occur naturally do not increase scald (Heulin, 1964). Alternative hypotheses are that scald is caused by precursors of the volatile substances, by materials of low volatility, or by toxic substances accumulating beneath the cuticle. Apart from ventilation, the incidence of scald is affected by temperature and humidity during storage. It is generally agreed that high humidity increases scald but there are conflicting reports on the effect of temperature; it was generally thought to increase with temperature rises up to $15 \cdot 5°$ but it appears that with some varieties it may be more serious at temperatures lower than this.

FIGURE 16.4 Apple scald. Diseased apple on the left, healthy one on the right. Photograph courtesy R. M. Smock.

Other non-pathogenic diseases are more closely linked with previous field conditions than those obtaining in the store; bitter pit of apples is one of them. In this disease, brown spots appear in the flesh, near the skin and the vascular system, usually starting at the calyx end of the fruit, and dark, depressed areas form at the fruit surface as these spots extend. The cell walls collapse and an amorphous material accumulates in the pitted area, and there are changes in the pectic materials of cells surrounding the affected zone. Although the disease has been known since 1829, and has been the subject of many extensive investigations, its etiology is still not entirely clear. The current view is that it is related to the calcium/magnesium balance of the tree; the disease can be induced by injecting magnesium salts, and reduced by foliar sprays of calcium compounds (Baxter, 1962).

FACTORS INFLUENCING POSTHARVEST DISEASES

Field conditions

Postharvest diseases are often influenced by the way in which the crop has been grown; for instance, the mineral nutrition of the apple tree affects the incidence of bitter pit in storage. Field conditions may be important in other ways. The amount of brown rot which develops on apples, pears and plums is, to a certain extent, determined by the levels of field inoculum. The species of *Sclerotinia* involved are capable of attacking other parts of the tree such as the fruiting spurs, and conidia produced on them and on fallen, mummified fruit contaminate those that are harvested. Similarly, Meredith (1960*b*) found that there were seasonal differences in the incidence of *Gloeosporium* rot on bananas arriving in England which appeared to be linked with varying levels of field inoculum in the West Indies. For other storage rots there is also convincing evidence that field inoculum is important. *Fusarium caeruleum*, for instance, is frequently present in field soils and in soil adhering to tubers, and this soil subsequently contaminates the seed boxes, sacks, and stores (Small, 1944).

Infections which develop in storage sometimes originate in the field. Latent infection is common with *Gloeosporium musarum* in bananas. Spores germinate on immature fruit in the field, the fungus penetrates and forms a small knot of mycelium in the subcuticular layer, but further extension of the fungus is delayed until the fruit ripens. Then there is an extensive inter- and intracellular development of mycelium, and correspondingly a considerable rotting of the fruit. It is not known why the fungus behaves so differently on immature and ripe fruit but hot extracts of green bananas are strongly inhibitory to *G. musarum* so possibly an antifungal toxin is involved. This and other hypotheses are fully discussed by Simmonds (1963).

The maturity of fruit at harvesting is also important in a slightly different type of *Gloeosporium* rot in which the fungus penetrates through small wounds (Meredith, 1960*a*). Although bananas for shipment are picked when still green, within the trade different grades are recognized from 'thin' for fruit with flattened sides and prominent ridges, to 'full' for fruit which is nearly round in cross-section, with the ridges scarcely evident. These grades correspond to increasing levels of maturity, and generally 'full' grade bananas are more severely affected by this type of rot than the less mature, 'thin' grade. With other diseases the reverse is true; for example, apple scald is more severe on immature fruit.

Some diseases, specially those of non-parasitic origin, are influenced by the weather before harvest. With apple scald there is evidence that hot, dry weather and particularly warm nights, during the last six weeks of the growing season result in much more disease than in corresponding cooler weather (Smock, 1961).

The severity of postharvest diseases also differs with the variety grown. In Australia, bitter pit of apples is specially severe on the variety Granny Smith, and scald is also; in the West Indies bananas of the Gros Michel variety are less susceptible to *Gloeosporium* rot than those of the Lacatan or Robusta varieties. The reasons for these varietal differences are not fully known, but the ability of certain apple varieties to resist infection by brown-rot fungi is partly related to the rapidity with which injured tissue turns brown (Byrde, 1956). The browning reaction involves the oxidation of polyphenols, and their polymerization to tannin-like substances, which affect the activity of the macerating enzymes produced by these fungi (Byrde and others, 1960).

Harvesting and handling

The way in which produce is harvested and handled is critical because many of the pathogens involved in storage diseases enter through wounds. Some wounds are caused by insects in the field, and if these escape notice during sorting they provide ready avenues for fungal and bacterial pathogens. Rotting of citrus fruits by *Penicillium digitatum* and *Penicillium italicum*, for example, is often associated with the punctures made in the skin by the Mediterranean fruit fly (*Ceratitis capitata*), and brown rot of plums by *Sclerotinia laxa* with those made by the plum curculio (*Conotrachelus nenuphar*).

Other wounds result from the harvesting and handling procedures and these often determine the severity of rotting during storage. Investigations of the dry rot of potatoes induced by *F. caeruleum* illustrate this point well (Foister and others, 1952). Tubers destined for 'seed' stock are likely to be injured at harvesting, when graded and transported, and when they are placed in boxes at the store. Experiments showed that infection following harvesting was slight, though this could be attributed to the greater resistance of tubers at lifting as well as to low incidence of damage. 'Seed' potatoes are graded on power-operated reciprocating riddles. Damage during this operation was found to be of major importance with wire screens; only 4% of hand-selected tubers developed dry rot later, compared with 12% for tubers graded once by machine, and 24% for tubers which were riddled twice. Rough handling of the bags after grading doubled the amount of dry rot found after normal handling, but placing the tubers in boxes at the store had little effect on disease incidence.

Conditions during transit and storage

Temperature, humidity, and ventilation largely determine the rate of disease development during transit and storage. Much attention has been paid to these aspects in the U.S.A. where transit of fruits and vegetables by rail over long distances has played an important part in the development of its agriculture. Information on this latter topic has been collected by Redit and Hamer (1961) into a most useful handbook.

Fruits and vegetables continue to respire after harvesting and as a result heat is produced; this is known as vital heat. The amount varies with the particular commodity (Table 16.1); generally the fruits and vegetables which have a high rate of respiration and so generate most heat are those that perish most rapidly. High temperatures further accelerate respiration and ageing, so these fruits must be cooled quickly to remove their field heat. This is done in several ways: by spraying with or immersing in water held close to 0°, by vacuum treatment which induces rapid evaporation of water from the produce, or by placing in precooled rooms or railcars. The produce is then transported in vehicles at near zero temperatures (0–2·2°). Strawberries and green peas come into this category.

TABLE 16.1 Heat of respiration (as B.T.U./ton/day), and recommended transit temperatures for certain fruits and vegetables.

Commodity	Evolution of heat at				Transit temperature
	$0°$	$4·4°$	$15·6°$	$25·6°$	
Strawberries	3265	5180	17960	41830	$0°- 1·7°$
Peaches	1110	1735	8285	20200	$0°- 7·2°$
Apples	900	1625	5075	—	$0°- 4·4°$
Lemons	690	1255	3630	5010	$10°-12·8°$
Peas, green	8260	14620	41880	79210	$0°- 2·2°$
Lettuce	2640	3500	9200	—	$0°- 2·2°$
Cucumber	1690	2550	10460	—	$7·2°-10°$
Tomatoes, mature-green	580	1070	6230	—	$12·8°-18·3°$

Data from Redit and Hamer, 1961, *Agric. Hdbk U.S. Dep. Agric.* No. 195.

Some produce can be transported safely at higher temperatures; for example, the amount of heat generated by cucumbers is fairly low still at $4·4°$ but rises spectacularly at $15·6°$ ($60°F$), so transit temperatures between $7·2°$ and $10°$ ($45°-50°F$) are satisfactory. For other fruits and vegetables, particularly those with low respiration rates, higher temperatures during transit are essential for they are damaged by low temperatures. Thus lemons become pitted and develop internal browning if held at $4·4°$ or lower, and exposure to these temperatures leads to uneven ripening of mature-green tomatoes.

Near freezing temperatures prevent most fungal and bacterial rots though *Sclerotinia sclerotiorum* can continue to rot vegetables slowly under these conditions. The development of some non-parasitic diseases such as bitter pit and scald of apples is also inhibited. The humidity during transit and storage must necessarily be high otherwise the produce dries out and loses prime market quality. Most pathogens also require high humidity so temperature control is critical in suppressing them.

CONTROL

Control of some postharvest diseases starts in the field. Spraying apple trees with $1-1\frac{1}{4}\%$ calcium chloride, three to four times from about a month after petal fall greatly decreases incidence of bitter pit; so do soil applications of calcium nitrate. General field hygiene such as the removal of infected fruiting spurs and mummified apples helps to control brown rot. Enough has been said of the entry through wounds of pathogens inducing rots to emphasize also that careful harvesting and handling of the crop is essential.

Refrigeration in transit and storage, however, is the main way in which postharvest diseases are controlled but other methods must often supplement this to achieve the best results. For example, the relatively high temperatures under which lemons are transported still permit development of *Phytophthora* or brown rot. Lemons are therefore given a hot-water dip in the packing house, and for adequate control an immersion of about 4 minutes at 46°–49° (115°–120°F) is necessary (Klotz and DeWolfe, 1961). Experiments suggest that similar treatments may be valuable in controlling brown (*Monilinia*) rot and *Rhizopus* rot of peaches and nectarines (W. L. Smith, Jr. and others, 1964) and *Gloeosporium* rot of apples (Burchill, 1964).

Most other methods involve some kind of chemical treatment (Eckert, 1967; Eckert and Somer, 1967), and here three conditions determine its usage. Obviously it must be efficient in controlling the disease, it must be economic, and most important, chemical residues must not constitute a health hazard. The aim of many chemical treatments is to reduce inoculum of the pathogen on the produce, and most of these involve dipping the fruits and vegetables in a dilute solution of the chemical, dusting them, or fumigating them with some volatile material. Some of these treatments have the additional benefit of eradicating established infections. Other treatments appear to be effective because they inhibit spore germination.

Several dip treatments have been evolved for the control of the *Penicillium* rots of citrus. One of the older methods was to immerse the fruit in a 6–8% borax (sodium tetraborate, $Na_2B_4O_7.10H_2O$) solution at about 43·3° (110°F) for 4–5 minutes; the fruit was then rinsed. The low solubility of borax was one disadvantage of this treatment and several alternatives were introduced; one was a mixture of 4% borax and 2% boric acid at 43·5°C, since borax is more soluble in the presence of boric acid. Various soluble borates such as sodium pentaborate ($Na_2B_{10}O_{16}.10H_2O$) were also used extensively. The fruit was again rinsed immediately after treatment. Since the mid-1950's sodium-o-phenylphenate has largely replaced borax and borates in dip treatments. The methods differ in detail, with concentrations of sodium-o-phenylphenate ranging from 0·5% to 2% and temperatures from 32° to 43·5°C., but all solutions are kept alkaline (pH 11·5–11·8) to limit the amount of free o-phenyl-phenol which otherwise might harm the fruit. Sometimes 1%

hexamine is added to precipitate free o-phenylphenol, particularly in situations where the pH cannot be rigidly controlled. In the U.S.A., residues of o-phenylphenol and its sodium salts on citrus fruits that have been treated must not exceed 10 p.p.m.

A dip treatment with dichloran (2,6-dichloro-4-nitroaniline) is now used to control *Rhizopus* rot of peach (Cappellini and Stretch, 1962). The fruit is immersed for 1–2 minutes in a suspension containing 1000–2000 p.p.m. active ingredient, and this is effective even when fruits are rinsed following treatment (Dewey and Mac-Clean, 1962). The tolerance level of dichloran on treated peaches is 20 p.p.m. in the U.S.A.

Other dip treatments are still in the experimental stage or have only recently left this stage so their commercial value cannot yet be assessed. Good control of apple scald has been obtained with diphenylamine and with ethoxyquin (1,2-dihydro-6-ethoxy-2,2, 4-trimethyl quinone) but so far only the latter has been cleared by the Food and Drug Administration in the U.S.A. (Smock, 1961). Similarly, Meredith (1960c) obtained some control of *Gloeosporium* rot by treating bananas with sodium salicylanilide but its commercial worth remains to be seen.

Dusts have not been much used in the control of postharvest diseases but dusting potatoes after lifting with tetrachloronitrobenzene (TCNB) is effective against *Fusarium caeruleum* (Brooks and Chesters, 1957). Both seed and ware potatoes can be treated since 4–5 months after applying the chemical negligible amounts remain on the tubers and they do not constitute a health hazard.

Similarly, comparatively few fumigants are used but one notable exception is sulphur dioxide. This is the standard method for controlling *Botrytis* rot of the vinifera grape in California; it relies for its success on the tolerance of this grape to sulphur dioxide, others such as the American or eastern varieties cannot be so treated (Harvey and Pentzer, 1960). The sulphur dioxide is usually released from cylinders and allowed to mix with the air in the storage room; this is aided by a fan. For the first fumigation a 1% concentration of sulphur dioxide is used; if the grapes are to be stored further fumigations are made at seven to ten day intervals with 0·25% sulphur dioxide. For grapes stored only for short periods an alternative method is to mix sodium bisulphite with sawdust in the packing medium. This compound releases sulphur dioxide slowly in contact with moist air.

Another approach to the control of postharvest diseases is to impregnate fruit wrappers, box linings and separator sheets with a chemical, and some materials used in dips are equally if not more effective when applied this way, for example dichloran in the control of *Rhizopus* rot of peaches (Luepschen, 1964). Impregnating wrappers with an odourless mineral oil was the first really successful method evolved for the control of apple scald (Brooks and others, 1923). It was then thought that the oil absorbed the volatile esters which were held to be responsible for this disease. In view of the doubt now cast on the role of these compounds some other explanation may have to be found. Recently, combinations of oil and diphenylamine in the wrappers have been tried with conspicuous success; but again it is not known how diphenylamine controls scald.

Undoubtedly the most significant application of this method is the use of biphenyl (diphenyl) for the *Penicillium* rots of citrus. There is now an extensive literature on this subject which has been ably summarized by Eckert (1967). This account is based on his review. Although biphenyl is not effective against a wide range of fungi it is inhibitory to *Penicillium italicum*, *Penicillium digitatum* and other fungi that rot citrus fruits. Wrappers for these fruits are impregnated with a heated solution of biphenyl in a mixture of paraffin and mineral oil, so that on drying some 40–50 mg are deposited in a wrapper measuring 254 × 243 mm. More recently in the U.S.A. wrapping of individual fruits has been discontinued in favour of two biphenyl-impregnated sheets in each carton, but this is also linked with changes in the packaging methods. The type of container and the degree of ventilation it allows influences the extent of the biphenyl treatment. The action of biphenyl is fungistatic rather than fungicidal for when the wrappers are removed fungal growth recommences. The main disadvantage of the method is that biphenyl imparts an odour to the fruit, and though this is lost by exposing the fruit to fresh air for several days, there has been some reluctance by traders and consumers to accept that all is well. Biphenyl does become absorbed to a certain extent in the fruit, and residues are found mainly in the oil glands. In the U.S.A. these residues must not exceed 100 p.p.m. of the whole fruit. Another disadvantage is that in biphenyl-treated lemons the remains of the calyx and receptacle, the 'button' of the fruit, ages more rapidly and the fruit is then more liable to *Alternaria* rot. Also, from time to time biphenyl-resistant strains of *Penicillium* arise and these reduce the efficacy of the treatment if they contaminate the packing house. In spite of these limitations, however, no other material has yet matched biphenyl in the control of postharvest diseases of citrus.

REFERENCES

Bain, J. M. (1956). A histological study of the development of superficial scald in Granny Smith apples. *J. hort. Sci.*, **31**, 234–8

Bain, J. M. and Mercer, F. V. (1963). The submicroscopic cytology of superficial scald, a physiological disease of apples. *Aust. J. biol. Sci.*, **16**, 442–8

Baxter, P. (1962). Bitter pit of apples. *Outl. Agric.*, **3**, 274–7

Bergey's Manual of Determinative Bacteriology, (1957). 7th Edtn. Bailliere, Tindall and Cox, London.

Brooks, M. and Chesters, C. G. C. (1957). The use of tetrachloronitro-benzene isomers on potatoes. *Ann. appl. Biol.*, **45**, 623–34

Brooks, C. (1919). Nature and control of apple scald. *J. agric. Res.*, **18**, 211–40

Brooks, C., Cooley, J. S. and Fisher, D. F. (1923). Oiled wrappers, oils and waxes in the control of apple scald. *J. agric. Res.*, **26**, 513–36

Burchill, R. T. (1964). Hot water as a possible postharvest control of *Gloeosporium* rots of stored apples. *Pl. Path.*, **13**, 106–7

Byrde, R. J. W. (1956). The varietal resistance of fruits to brown rot. I. Infection experiments with *Sclerotinia fructigena* Aderh. and Ruhl. on certain dessert, culinary and cider varieties of apple. *J. hort. Sci.*, **31**, 188–95

Byrde, R. J. W., Fielding, A. H. and Williams, A. H. (1960). The role of oxidised polyphenols in the varietal resistance of apples to brown rot. In *Phenolics in Plants in Health and Disease*, pp. 59–9. Pergamon Press Oxford.

Cappellini, R. A. and Stretch, A. W. (1962). Control of post harvest decays of peaches. *Pl. Dis. Reptr.*, **46**, 31–3

Christensen, C. N. and Kaufman, H. H. (1965). Deterioration of stored grains by fungi. *A. Rev. Phytopathol.*, **3**, 69–84

Dewey, D. H. and MacLean, D. C. (1962). Postharvest treatment with 2, 6-dichloro-4-nitroaniline for fruit rot control on fresh market peaches. *Q. Bull. Mich. St. Univ. agric. Exp. Stn.*, No. 44, 679–83

Dowson, W. J. and Rudd Jones, D. (1951). Bacterial wet rot of potato tubers following *Phytophthora infestans*. *Ann. appl. Biol.*, **38**, 231–6

Eckert, J. W. (1967). Application and use of postharvest fungicides. In *Fungicides: an advanced treatise* (Ed. D. C. Torgeson), **1**, 287–378. Academic Press, New York.

Eckert, J. W. and Somer, N. F. (1967). Control of diseases of fruits and vegetables by postharvest treatment. *A. Rev. Phytopathol.*, **5**, 391–432

Foister, C. E., Wilson, A. R. and Boyd, A. E. W. (1952). Dry rot disease of the potato. I. Effect of commercial handling methods on the incidence of the disease. *Ann. appl. Biol.*, **39**, 29–37

Graham, D. C. (1964). Taxonomy of the soft-rot coliform bacteria. *A. Rev. Phytopathol.*, **2**, 13–42

Harvey, J. M. and Pentzer, W. T. (1960). Market diseases of grapes and other small fruits. *Agric. Hdbk U.S. Dep. Agric.*, No. 189, 37 pp.

Hellmers, E. (1959). *Pectobacterium carotovorum* var. *atrosepticum* (van Hall) Dowson, the correct name of potato black leg pathogen; a historical and critical review. *Eur. Potato J.*, **2**, 251–71

Heulin, F. E. (1964). Superficial scald, a functional disorder of stored apples. III. Promoters and inhibitors. *J. Sci. Fd Agric.*, **15**, 227–36

Kendrick, J. B. Jr., Wedding, R. T. and Paulus, A. O. (1959). A temperature–relative humidity index for predicting the occurrence of bacterial soft rot of Irish potatoes. *Phytopathology*, **49**, 701–5

Kidd, F. and West, C. (1923). Brown heart—a functional disease of apples and pears. *Spec. Rep. Fd Invest. Bd. D.S.I.R.* No. 12, 54 p.

Klotz, L. J. and De Wolfe, T. A. (1961). Limitations of the hot water immersion treatment for the control of *Phytophthora* brown rot of lemons. *Pl. Dis. Reptr*, **45**, 264–7

Leupschen, N. S. (1964). Effectiveness of 2,6-dichloro-4-nitroaniline-impregnated peach wraps in reducing *Rhizopus* decay losses. *Phytopathology*, **54**, 1219–22

McColloch, L. P., Cook, H. T. and Wright, W. R. (1968). Market Diseases of tomatoes, peppers and eggplants. *Agric. Hdbk U.S. Dep. Agric.*, No. 28, 74 pp.

Meredith, D. S. (1960a). Studies on *Gloeosporium musarum* Cke. and Massee causing storage rots of Jamaican bananas. I. Anthracnose and its chemical control. *Ann. appl. Biol.*, **48**, 279–90; (1960b). II. Some factors influencing anthracnose development. *Ann. appl. Biol.*, **48**, 518–28; (1960c). III. Control with sodium salicylanilide ('Shirlan WS') and nystatin. *Ann. appl. Biol.*, **48**, 824–36

Pethybridge, G. H. and Lafferty, H. A. (1917). Further observations on the cause of the common dry rot of the potato tuber in the British Isles. *Scient. Proc. R. Dubl. Soc.* N.S. **115**, 193–222

Ramsey, G. B., Wiant, J. S. and Smith, M. A. (1949). Market diseases of potatoes. *Misc. Publ. U.S. Dep. Agric.*, No. 98, 60 pp.

Ramsey, G. B., Friedman, B. A. and Smith, M. A. (1959). Market diseases of beets, chichory, endive, escarole, globe artichokes, lettuce, rhubarb, spinach and sweet potatoes. *Agric. Hdbk U.S. Dep. Agric.*, No. 155, 42 pp.

Ramsey, G. B. and Smith, M. A. (1961). Market diseases of cabbage, cauliflower, turnips, cucumbers, melons and related crops. *Agric. Hdbk. U.S. Dept. Agric.*, No. 184, 49 pp.

Redit, W. H. and Hamer, A. A. (1961). Protection of rail shipments of fruits and vegetables. *Agric. Hdbk. U.S. Dep. Agric.*, No. 195, 108 pp.

Roberts, E. A., Hall, E. G., and Scott, K. J. (1963). The effects of carbon dioxide and oxygen concentrations on superficial scald of Granny Smith apples. *Aust. J. agric. Res.*, **14**, 765–77

Rose, D. H., Brooks, C., Bratley, C. O. and Winston, J. R. (1943). Market diseases of fruits and vegetables. Citrus and other subtropical fruits. *Misc. Publ. U.S. Dep. Agric.*, No. 498, 57 pp.

Rose, D. H., Fisher, D. F., Brooks, C. and Bratley, C. O. (1950). Market diseases of fruits and vegetables: peaches, plums, cherries and other stone fruits. *Misc. Publ. U.S. Dep. Agric.*, No. 228, 27 pp.

Rose, D. H., McColloch, L. P. and Fisher, D. F. (1951). Market diseases of fruits and vegetables: apples, pears, quinces. *Misc. Publ. U.S. Dep. Agric.*, No. 168, 72 pp.

Rudd Jones, D. and Dowson, W. J. (1950). On the bacteria responsible for soft rot in stored potatoes, and the reaction of the tuber to invasion by *Bacterium carotovorum* (Jones) Lehmann and Neumann. *Ann. appl. Biol.*, **37**, 563–9

Ruehle, G. D. (1940). Bacterial soft rot of potatoes in southern Florida. *Tech. Bull. Fla agric. Exp. Stn.*, No. 348, 36 pp.

Simmonds, J. H. (1963). Studies in the latent phase of *Colletotrichum* species causing ripe rots of tropical fruits. *Qd. J. agric. Sci.*, **20**, 373–424

Small, T. (1944). Dry rot of potato (*Fusarium caeruleum*) (Lib.). Sacc. Investigations on the sources and time of infection. *Ann appl. Biol.*, **31**, 290–5

Smith, M. A., McColloch, L. P. and Friedman, B. A. (1966). Market diseases of asparagus, onions, beans, peas, carrots, celery and related vegetables. *Agric. Hdbk U.S. Dep. Agric.*, No. 303, 65 pp.

Smith, W. L. Jr., Bassett, R. D., Parsons, C. S. and Anderson, R. E. (1964). Reduction of postharvest decay of peaches and nectarines with heat treatments. *Marketing Res. Rep. U.S. Dep. Agric.*, No. 643, 24 pp.

Smock, R. M. (1961). Methods of scald control on the apple. *Bull. Cornell agric. Exp. Stn.*, No. 970, 55 pp.

Spensley, P. C. (1963). Aflatoxin, the active principle in turkey 'X' disease. *Endeavour*, **22**, 75–9

Stakman, E. C. and Harrar, J. G. (1957). *Principles of Plant Pathology*, 581 pp. Ronald Press, New York.

Wardlaw, C. W. (1961). *Banana Diseases including Plantains and Abaca*, pp. 466–551. Longmans, Green and Co. Ltd., London.

Wormald, H. (1954). The brown rot diseases of fruit trees. *Tech. Bull. Minist. Agric. Fish Fd.* No. 3, 113 pp.

CHAPTER 17

Disease assessment and losses

Quantitative assessments are necessary to judge the relative importance of diseases so that attention can be directed to the most harmful, and to determine the value of control measures against a particular disease or the effect of environment on it. In practice plant disease assessment is often a three stage operation: the amount of disease, i.e. its prevalence × intensity in individual plants, is first determined, this is then translated into crop loss, and finally this loss is interpreted in terms of the crop economy (Chester, 1959). Few pathologists have concerned themselves with the last aspect but a knowledge of the methods of assessing disease and the relationship between these assessments and crop losses is essential in many field and greenhouse investigations.

METHODS OF ASSESSING DISEASE

The basic requirements of any disease assessment are that it should provide a practical degree of accuracy, and the results should be comparable from one worker to another, from one location to another, and from one season to the next.

The simplest method is to count the number and hence obtain a percentage of diseased plants. This is particularly useful where the entire plant is killed as in damping-off and seedlings blights, in diseases such as the cereal smuts where an infected ear represents a direct commercial loss, and in certain virus diseases, e.g. virus yellows of beet (Hull, 1953).

Not all diseases are so simple to assess. More frequently plants are affected to different degrees, especially in blight and leaf-spot diseases, and the task is to arrive at an overall assessment of disease severity.

One of the most useful methods is that devised by McKinney (1923), to assess infection of wheat seedlings by *Helminthosporium sativum*. He placed each seedling in one of five classes, depending on disease severity, and assigned a numerical value to each class: 0·0 (healthy), 0·75, 1·00, 2·00 and 3·00 (very severe attack). He then calculated an infection index, viz.

$$\text{Infection Index} = \frac{\text{Sum of all numerical ratings}}{\text{Total number of plants}} \times \frac{100}{\text{Maximum disease category (3)}}$$

The value of this method was critically examined by Horsfall and Heuberger (1942) for early blight of tomatoes caused by *Alternaria solani*. They based their ratings on the proportion of total leaf area killed by the fungus on an individual plant:

0 = free from infection or nearly so
1 = trace—25% leaf area killed
2 = 26–50% leaf area killed
3 = 51–75% leaf area killed
4 = 76–100% leaf area killed

An infection index was then obtained, viz.

$$\text{Infection index} = \frac{\text{Sum of individual ratings}}{\text{Number of plants assessed}} \times \frac{100}{4}$$

In a fungicide trial with twelve treatments plus control they found that although three independent assessors gave slightly different ratings to individual treatments, their conclusion regarding the relative merits of the treatments were the same. They also compared the method with other obvious, but more laborious ways of assessing damage such as number of fruits with stem end rot, number of leaves killed, weight of fruit and weight of vine, and found there was a correlation with infection index in each instance (Figure 17.1).

McKinney's method is still widely used in some form or other but it has two disadvantages: the grades are rather wide, and it takes no account of the fact that the eye assesses diseased areas on a logarithmic scale. Below 50% coverage the eye judges the area diseased but above this it discriminates on the basis of healthy tissue which remains (Horsfall, 1945). To overcome this, Horsfall and Barratt (1945) devised a logarithmic scale, balanced around the

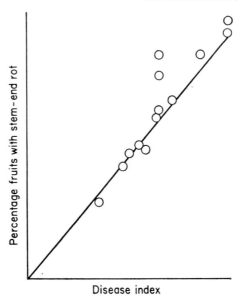

FIGURE 17.1 Relationship between disease index for early blight of tomatoes and number of fruits with stem end rot. After Horsfall and Heuberger (1942), *Phytopathology*, **32**, 226–32.

50% point, and based on a factor of two. For convenience fractions are ignored and the residues are included at either end of the scale—

0–3, 3–6, 6–12, 12–25, 25–50, 50–75, 75–87, 87–94, 94–97, 97–100. These are percentages, e.g. of leaf area diseased, and the grades are alloted 1=nil, 2=0–3%, 3=3%–6% and so to 11=97%–100%, 12=100%. The disease index is obtained by summing the individual grades alloted to individual leaves or plants and then dividing by the number assessed. One disadvantage is that the figure so obtained is a logarithm of the geometric mean of the percentage assessments and, as Large (1966) points out, the use of geometric means in disease assessment is best left to research workers who fully appreciate their mathematical properties.

Many of the descriptive scales for disease assessment in the field, developed under the aegis of the British Mycological Society, correspond closely in their lower ranges to Horsfall and Barratt's, though they diverge from it beyond the 75% level as the key for tomato leaf mould illustrates (Table 17.1). Similar keys have been

TABLE 17.1 Key for the assessment of tomato leaf mould.

per cent	
0·1	Lesions found with difficulty, and on less than one plant in fifty.
1	Lesions on most plants, but only on a few leaves.
5	Lesions on every plant, and on most leaves except the young ones, but only about two to ten spots per leaf.
10	All except the youngest leaves affected, with ten to fifty spots per leaf.
25	All except the youngest leaves affected, but with about three-quarters of the leaf area green, although lowest leaves may be severely attacked.
50	All leaves affected. Most of the middle leaves show only half their area green.
75	All leaves affected. Most of the middle leaves show only one-quarter of the leaf green, giving a grey appearance to the crop as a whole.
90	Very little green visible on middle and lower leaves, but youngest leaves show green.
100	All leaves completely covered with lesions.

From Beaumont, 1954, *Pl. Path.*, **3**, 21–5, by permission of the Controller, H.M.S.O.

devised for potato blight (Anon, 1947), and apple scab (Croxhall and others, 1952*a*) amongst others.

Some people find it easier to assess disease if the levels are depicted diagrammatically, and as early as 1892 Nathan Cobb devised such a standard diagram for assessing leaf rust of wheat in Australia. With a slight modification this scale was adopted by the United States Department of Agriculture in 1917 (see Chester, 1946). Many such standard diagrams have now been evolved. Figure 17.2 shows those for apple scab on leaves and fruits; the cross-hatched areas and spots represent the percentage of total surface area affected. A similar set of diagrams was used in a survey of common scab of potatoes caused by *Streptomyces scabies* (Large and Honey, 1955). In this instance there were four grades indicating the proportion of the tuber surface affected. Usually each diagram is regarded as representing the upper limit of a group, for example with apple scab on fruit any apple from just over 2·5% to 3·5% infected is placed in the 3.5% category (Croxall and others, 1952*b*).

THE ESTIMATION OF CROP LOSSES FROM DISEASE ASSESSMENTS

Disease assessments are of little value to the field pathologist unless they are related to crop losses. Horsfall and Heuberger (1942) were able to do this for early blight of tomato because the range of treatments resulted in different amounts of disease and the regression of infection index on rotted fruit could be determined. As

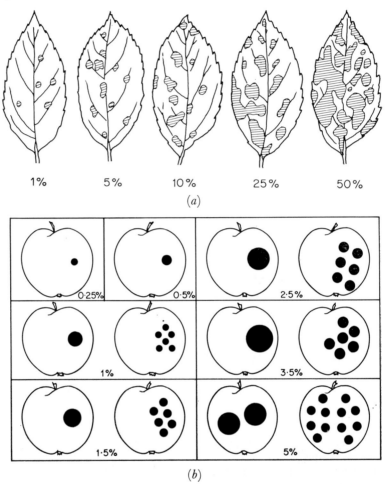

FIGURE 17.2 Standard diagrams for assessment of apple scab on leaves and fruit. (The spots represent the amount of scab on the whole surface area of the fruit, not on the uppermost half only.) From Croxall and others, 1952, *Pl. Path.* **1**, 39 and 89, by permission of the Controller, H.M.S.O.

Chester (1959) points out, regressions of this type are strictly valid only in situations similar to those in which they were obtained. The disease severity–loss relationship may differ with host variety, strain of pathogen, and environment. Nevertheless, because the acceptable range of error for loss estimation is fairly wide, such results can often be more widely applied.

This has been done for virus yellows of beet (Hull, 1953). The actual field assessment was relatively easy. The number of plants with yellows, counted in ten samples of one hundred at equal intervals along the diagonals of the field, was taken as the estimate of disease within the crop and from successive readings a disease progress curve was obtained. It was estimated from artificially infected plants in experimental plots that the effect of the disease is to reduce the sugar yield by 4%–5% for every week that the plants show symptoms until harvested (Watson, Watson and Hull, 1946); thus it was possible, with successive estimates, to translate percentage of plants infected into percentage sugar lost, and by assuming that an average root contains 16% sugar, to loss of root yield. Taking the total sugar beet acreage into account, the annual tonnage lost through virus yellows was then calculated (Table 17.2).

TABLE 17.2 Estimated losses of sugar beet in Great Britain caused by virus yellows.

Year	Loss of root yield in thousands of tons
1946	120
1947	141
1948	347
1949	944
1950	317
1951	90
1952	486

Data from Hull, 1953, *Pl. Path*, **2**, 39–43, by permission of the Controller, H.M.S.O.

The conversion of disease intensity into crop losses is not always as simple as these examples suggest. The work of Large (1952, 1958) and his collaborators on potato blight illustrates the complexities of the problem for a leaf disease that shows marked seasonal and regional fluctuations, and against which spraying is only partially effective. These and other aspects of measuring plant disease have recently been reviewed by Large (1966).

As indicated in Chapter 9 tuber growth ceases when 75% of the foliage is affected by blight. Provided one knows therefore, how a potato variety develops in a given situation, probable losses in yield can be estimated from blight assessment curves as indicated in Figure 17.3. The upper part of the figure was derived from data for sixty crops of Majestic potatoes, grown at different centres throughout England and Wales during 1940–45, and from which fortnightly liftings were made. This gives a measure of the effect

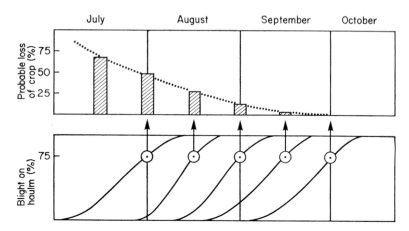

FIGURE 17.3 Estimation of mean probable loss of crop (var. Majestic) from curves for progress of blight on the haulm. From Large, 1952, *Pl. Path.*, **1**, 108–17, by permission of the Controller, H.M.S.O.

of arrested development on the yield of this particular cultivar. The lower part of the figure shows a number of blight assessment curves which indicate some of the seasonal variations for the different regions of England and Wales. By comparing these curves with the cropping behaviour of Majestic it is clear that 75% blight by the end of July is likely to give a 50% loss of crop, and 75% blight by the end of August a loss of 13%.

On this basis, Large (1958) has estimated the losses due to blight, and the advantages to be gained from spraying, for the various potato-growing regions in England and Wales. For this purpose four zones are distinguished by the mean dates on which the 75% blight stage is reached, in seasons favourable for disease development ('blight years'). They are South West, Fen, Southern and Northern zones. Crop losses in these regions over a 10-year period, 1947–1956, were first estimated assuming that no spraying was carried out. By relating these losses to the acreage of potatoes grown in the four regions the overall loss to the country was derived (Table 17.3).

The value of spraying against potato blight lies in delaying the destruction of the foliage and correspondingly the 75% blight stage (Chapter 9). Detailed studies of spraying data indicated that efficient commercial spraying gave on average a 2-week extension in this respect, but against this potential gain must be offset additional losses due to blight not controlled, since no spraying is perfect, wheel damage by spraying machinery, and copper injury on plants sprayed

TABLE 17.3 Estimated defoliation losses due to Potato blight if all maincrops in England and Wales had been left unsprayed over a ten-year period (1947–56).

Zone	Main crop Acreage per cent of Total	Number of Years in Ten in which the 75 per cent Blight stage was reached by				Mean Loss per annum over the Ten years	
		Mid-Aug (28% Loss)	End Aug (13% Loss)	Mid-Sept (4% Loss)	End Sept (No Loss)	to Zone per cent	to Whole Country per cent
South West	8	5	5	0	0	20	1·7
Fens	13	4	2	1	3	14	1·8
Southern	51	0	5	2	3	7	3·7
Northern	28	0	0	5	5	2	0·6
England and Wales							7·8

From Large, 1958, *Pl. Path.*, **7**, 39–48, by permission of the Controller, H.M.S.O.

in dry seasons. On such considerations Large (1958) estimated the mean gain from spraying for the various regions in the 10-year period. This detailed survey showed that spraying was seldom profitable in the Northern zone, that it could be profitable on better crops in 5 years out of 10 in the South, and in 6 out of 10 in the Fens. In the South West it was profitable on main crops in almost every year.

Before summarizing his results and relating them to the country as a whole, Large took three additional factors into account:

1. That, on average, spraying is carried out only on 30% of the crop, so the possible benefits must be correspondingly adjusted.

2. That in addition to losses which result indirectly from death of foliage, some tubers are lost because they are infected in the ground before lifting or they are infected at lifting and rot during storage. (The amount lost appears to be fairly constant irrespective of whether it is a 'blight year' or not.)

3. That in 'blight years' the average yield of potatoes is higher than in other years because the abundant rainfall during July and August favours growth of the potato.

The final analysis is shown in Table 17.4. This illustrates two important points regarding the economy of the crop. There are about 500,000 acres of main crop potatoes in England and Wales so a 0·3% gain from spraying in blight years represents an increase in the national yield of some 150,000 tons. Some individual growers may, of course, increase their yield by more than 0·3 tons per acre, but nationally such an increase might well produce a glut of potatoes, and the grower would gain little financially. As Large points out,

TABLE 17.4 Forecasts of yields of potatoes, losses through blight, and gains derived from spraying over a 10-year period (based on experience in 1947–56).

	Averages for England and Wales Tons per acre		
	Blight years	Other years	All years
Potential yield	9·6	7·7	8·6
Defoliation loss by blight if all crops were left unsprayed	− 1·6	− 0·2	− 0·8
Reduction of this loss by efficient spraying of 30 per cent of the crops	+ 0·3	− 0·1	+ 0·1
Loss from blight in tubers	− 0·3	− 0·3	− 0·3
Actual yield of sound tubers	8·0	7·1	7·6

From Large, 1958, *Pl. Path.*, **7**, 39–48, by permission of the Controller, H.M.S.O.

the value of spraying in blight years depends on the availability of outlets for surplus potatoes and is something that requires a national, rather than a local policy. On the other hand, a loss from spraying of o·1 tons per acre in other years is equally significant because this represents a loss of approximately 50,000 tons when supplies are already poor from lack of rain.

Inevitably, changes in agricultural practices often invalidate some of the premises on which such deductions are based. Hull (1963) has pointed out that converting duration of infection by virus yellows into yield of sugar beet lost, by the methods proposed in 1953, is now inaccurate, because the widespread application of systemic insecticides has altered the distribution pattern of this disease in England, and also different sugar beet varieties are now grown. The substitution of dithiocarbamates and organo-tin compounds for copper in potato blight spraying also makes Large's conclusions less relevant to the present day. Nevertheless, this outstanding survey has not only yielded valuable information on the economics of spraying, but has also laid the foundation for further appraisals of newer materials and methods.

In comparatively few instances have disease losses been so thoroughly and objectively assessed; most estimates are based on opinion or personal judgement. Even so, these do at least have the merit of focussing attention on diseases that are most harmful. The appraisal of plant disease losses is discussed at length by Chester (1950), there are shorter reviews of early work in the U.S.A. by Chester (1955) and in Britain by Large (1955), and various aspects were more recently discussed in symposia organized by the American Phytopathological Society (1964) and by FAO (1967). The publications of Ordish (1952), Watts-Padwick (1956) and Cramer (1967) provide further guides, and valuable information on losses of particular crops in the U.S.A. through specific diseases may be gleaned from the current numbers of the *Plant Disease Reporter* and similarly, in Canada, from the *Canadian Plant Disease Survey*.

REFERENCES

American Phytopathological Society (1964). Symposium on plant disease losses. *Phytopathology*, **54**, 1305–19
Anonymous (1947). The measurement of potato blight. *Trans. Br. mycol. Soc.*, **31**, 140–1
Beaumont, A. (1954). Tomato leaf mould: spraying trials in Lancashire and Yorkshire, 1949–52. *Pl. Path.*, **3**, 21–5
Chester, K. S. (1946). *The Nature and Prevention of the Cereal Rusts as exemplified in the Leaf Rust of Wheat*, pp. 19–23. Chronica Botanica, Waltham, Mass.
Chester, K. S. (1950). Plant disease losses: their appraisal and interpretation. *Pl. Dis. Reptr, Suppl.* No. 193, 191–362
Chester, K. S. (1955). Scientific and economic aspects of plant-disease loss appraisal. *Ann. appl. Biol.*, **42**, 335–43
Chester, K. S. (1959). How sick is the plant? In *Plant Pathology: an advanced treatise* (Ed. J. G. Horsfall and A. E. Dimond), **1**, 99–142. Academic Press, New York.
Cramer, H. H. (1967). Plant protection and world crop production. *Pfanzenschutz-Nachrichten 'Bayer'*, **20**, 1–524
Croxall, H. E., Gwynne, D. C. and Jenkins, J. E. E. (1952a) The rapid assessment of apple scab on leaves *Pl. Path.*, **1**, 39–41
Croxall, H. E., Gwynne, D. C. and Jenkins, J. E. E. (1952b). The rapid assessment of apple scab on fruit. *Pl. Path.* **1**, 89–92
FAO (1967). Papers presented at the FAO symposium on crop losses. Rome, 2–6th October, 1967. 330 pp.
Horsfall, J. G. (1945). Assessing field data. In *Fungicides and their Action*, pp. 38–41. Chronica Botanica, Waltham, Mass.
Horsfall, J. G. and Barratt, R. W. (1945). An improved grading system for measuring plant diseases. *Phytopathology*, **35**, 655
Horsfall, J. G. and Heuberger, J. W. (1942). Measuring magnitude of a defoliation disease of tomatoes. *Phytopathology*, **32**, 226–32
Hull, R. (1953). Assessments of losses in sugar beet due to virus yellows in Great Britain, 1942–52. *Pl. Path.*, **2**, 39–43

Hull, R. (1963). Sugar beet yellows in Great Britain, 1962. *Pl. Path,* **12**, 155–6

Large, E. C. (1952). The interpretation of progress curves for potato blight and other plant diseases. *Pl. Path.,* **1**, 109–17

Large, E. C. (1955). Methods of plant-disease measurement and forecasting in Great Britain. *Ann. appl. Biol.,* **42**, 344–54

Large, E. C. (1958). Losses caused by potato blight in England and Wales. *Pl. Path.,* **7**, 39–48

Large, E. C. (1966). Measuring plant disease. *A. Rev. Phytopathol.,* **4**, 9–28

Large, E. C. and Honey, J. K. (1955). Survey of common scab of potatoes in Great Britain, 1952 and 1953. *Pl. Path.,* **4**, 1–8

McKinney, H. H. (1923). Influence of soil temperature and moisture on infection of wheat seedlings by *Helminthosporium sativum. J. agric. Res.,* **26**, 195–217

Ordish, G. (1952). *Untaken Harvest,* 170 pp. Constable, London.

Watson, M. A., Watson, J. D. and Hull, R. (1946). Factors affecting loss of yield of sugar beet caused by beet yellows virus. *J. agric. Sci., Camb.* **36**, 151–66

Watts-Padwick, G. (1956). Losses caused by plant diseases in the colonies. *Phytopathol. Pap.,* No. 1, 60 pp.

CHAPTER 18

Plant disease control: exclusion

Exclusion comprises methods that prevent the spread of pathogens to areas where they do not already exist. The methods themselves fall into three groups:

1. Plant disease legislation, which prohibits or restricts the introduction of plants or plant parts,

2. Inspection of this material before it is distributed, and where necessary,

3. The elimination of pathogens before planting.

PLANT DISEASE LEGISLATION

Most countries have regulations covering the importation of plant material. Useful summaries are given in the *Digest of Plant Quarantine Regulations* (Ling, 1952) and its supplements, and in the *Plant Protection Bulletin*, published by the Food and Agriculture Organization (FAO) of the United Nations. The regulations for individual territories are basically similar and are in three parts:

1. A general section which, for example, prescribes the form of health certificate to accompany imported material, authorizes inspection of material and its disposal if found unsatisfactory, and provides penalties for violation of the regulations,

2. A list of prohibited imports,

3. A section which details restrictions on the importation of certain material.

311

L

The way in which these regulations are enacted varies with the territory (McCubbin, 1954; Gram, 1960). In the U.S.A., *The Plant Quarantine Act of 1912* with its various amendments, lays down the general law under which specific quarantines are promulgated. In England and Wales, *The Health Act 1967*, now fulfils the same function of authorizing plant disease legislation in general, under which various orders are promulgated such as *The Importation of Plants and Plant Produce (Great Britain) Order 1965*, containing the specific regulations outlined above.

Legislation of this type is aimed primarily at 'non-resident' pathogens. For example, restrictions on the importation of lettuce seed into England and Wales attempt to exclude lettuce mosaic virus, and similar restrictions in respect of tomato and pea seed aim to exclude the bacterial pathogens *Corynebacterium michiganense* and *Pseudomonas pisi* respectively.

Plant disease legislation is concerned with two other aspects. One is the prevention of further spread of pathogens that are established only in some localities. In England and Wales certain diseases of local occurrence are the subject of special orders, e.g. progressive wilt of hops. This disease is caused by a virulent strain of *Verticillium alboatrum* and first appeared about 1930 in Southeastern England. Under the *Progressive Verticillium Wilt of Hops Order 1947*, growers must notify the appropriate Government official of any outbreak and burn all infected stems and leaves. They are also prohibited from selling any planting material from affected farms (Keyworth, 1951). In the U.S.A. Section 8 of the *Plant Quarantine Act* similarly provides for interstate quarantine by the Federal Government.

Other legislation aims to limit the distribution of diseased plants in general within a territory. In England and Wales it is an offence under *The Sale of Diseased Plants Orders of 1927 to 1943* to sell plants substantially affected with certain pests and diseases, e.g. those with club root (*Plasmodiophora brassicae*), American gooseberry mildew (*Sphaerotheca mors-uvae*) and woolly aphid (Moore, 1951).

Certification schemes are often linked with such legislation in that planting material can only be sold if it has been inspected while growing, and certified free from disease and of a certain prescribed standard. Other certification schemes are purely voluntary whereby producers of seed and planting-stock may gain evidence of a certain quality. This is essential if the material is to be exported to other countries.

Plant disease legislation has developed primarily on a national basis, with each country imposing regulations to exclude pathogens with which it is particularly concerned. There is not always a sound biological basis for the measures adopted and they, in turn, provide barriers to international trade (Moore, 1952). Clearly, plant disease legislation is an international problem rather than a national one and with this in mind there was drawn up in 1951 at Rome an International Plant Protection Convention, which at present has fifty signatory nations. Briefly, each contracting Government agrees to make provisions for:

1. An official plant protection organization with the specific tasks of inspecting growing crops and the produce derived from them and issuing phytosanitary certificates.

2. The distribution of information regarding pests and diseases both within the country and to FAO, so that a world reporting service is established,

3. Research and investigation in the field of plant protection, where necessary on a cooperative basis for diseases which need international action.

Within the framework of this International Convention there are six regional groups: The European Plant Protection Organization (EPPO), which was formed prior to the Rome Treaty, the Inter-African Phytosanitary Commission (for Africa south of the Sahara), the Plant Protection Committee for the South East Asia and Pacific Region, Organismo International Regional de Sanidad Agroperciana (Central America and Mexico), and Convenio Interamericano de Proteccion Agricola (South America) and the Near East Plant Protection Commission.

One of the chief functions of these organizations is to consider measures which should be taken against specific pests and diseases such as Colorado beetle (*Leptinotarsa decemlineata*), San Jose scale (*Quadraspidiotus perniciosus*), ring rot of potatoes (*Corynebacterium sepedonicum*), oak wilt (*Ceratocystis fagacearum*). Their publications summarize our present knowledge of these problems and are useful sources of information.

INSPECTION OF PLANT PRODUCE

Plant quarantine regulations require an inspection of plants or plant produce at the point of entry, and this is often preceded by an inspection in the exporting country. There are two basic problems here: one is to recognize diseased material, the other is to determine how much of the consignment must be sampled to obtain a fair appraisal of the disease situation.

The recognition of disease in planting material is not always straightforward since on dormant structures such as bulbs, corms and setts there is seldom the variety or indeed, the same symptoms, that are visible on the diseased plants in the field. Some countries partially overcome this by providing guides for their plant produce inspectors: an example is *Diseases and Pests on Horticultural Material*, published by H.M.S.O. London.

Some pathogens do not induce sufficiently well-marked symptoms on propagative material to allow immediate detection. To safeguard against this, material is often sent to a quarantine station where it is planted and inspected regularly for disease before it, or material propagated from it, is distributed (Kahn and others, 1967; Sheffield, 1968). For example, sugar cane setts entering East Africa are first put into quarantine at the East African Agricultural and Forestry Research Organization (E.A.A.F.R.O.) at Maguga to see if they carry viruses (Sheffield, 1955). Similarly, bud wood of rubber sent from South America to Malaya is put into intermediate quarantine in Florida; it is then sent to Kew where it is repacked before dispatching to Malaya. This is to ensure that the leaf blight caused by the fungus *Dothidella ulei* which is common in South America is not introduced into Malaya (Brookson, 1956).

The sampling methods appropriate to large consignments of imported produce are often determined by the particular disease which is of concern, and require both a statistical (Healy, 1955) and commonsense approach. The standard sampling technique for detecting ring rot (*Corynebacterium sepedonicum*) and brown rot (*Pesudomonas solanacearum*) in a consignment of potatoes will serve to illustrate this (EPPO, 1961). Theoretically, the relation between size of sample (w) to be taken for examination, the proportion of infected tubers that are detectable by visual examination (p) and the probability (P) of failing to detect this number in the sample, is

$$w = \frac{\log P}{\log (1-p)}$$

From this it can be calculated that if 1000 tubers are taken at random from a consignment in which ring rot or brown rot is randomly distributed then one would expect to detect the disease with 95% confidence if not less than 0·3% tubers showed visible or external symptoms. A convenient method is thus to select 20 bags at random, tip the contents out, examine for external symptoms and then from each bag cut 50 tubers near the heel end for signs of vascular infection. The main difficulty is that ideal consignments are rare, and often the disease is not randomly distributed especially if a consignment includes crops from different areas. In these instances much larger samples are necessary to be sure of detecting infection. Further, with ring rot, latent infection of the tubers is common and this cannot readily be detected.

ELIMINATION OF PATHOGENS FROM PLANTING MATERIAL

If planting material is found to be contaminated or infected it does not necessarily mean that it has to be destroyed. There are several ways of eliminating pathogens without serious damage to propagative material, and many are used by growers to keep particular diseases out of their crops, or by distributors to produce disease-free planting stock.

Sorting is the simplest method and is, in effect, an extension of the inspection of plant produce. Tulip bulbs infected with *Botrytis tulipae* are recognized by circular lesions on the outer, fleshy scales in which the black fungal sclerotia are embedded, and these bulbs can then be removed by hand from the sample. Mechanical sorting may also be possible. Diseased seeds, or seeds of parasitic flowering plants such as *Cuscuta* and *Orobanche* spp., are often lighter than healthy seeds of economic plants and can be removed by putting seed samples through a fanning mill (for example see Hopkins, 1956 p. 19). A similar separation is obtained by immersing the seed sample in brine when the lighter, diseased seeds float to the surface.

The number of seed-borne pathogens is considerable (Baker and Smith, 1966; Noble and Richardson, 1968) and a variety of methods has been evolved to detect them. For seed-borne fungi, seed samples are frequently sown on damp filter paper or on an agar medium in Petri dishes. The fungi grow and can then be identified (Malone and Muskett, 1964). Grossly contaminated or infected seed samples are discarded, or suitably treated.

The detection of bacterial seed infection is generally more difficult and often the first problem is to concentrate the infected seed so that suitable diagnostic tests can be carried out. With dwarf bean and *Pseudomonas phaseolicola* it is estimated that if there are more than two infected seeds per kilogramme there is a risk of initiating serious outbreaks of halo blight in the field. One method of detecting this low level of infection in stocks of white-seeded varieties relies on the fluorescence of infected areas in the testa under ultraviolet light. Seeds which fluoresce are surface sterilised and transferred to nutrient broth to encourage bacterial growth. Bean seedlings are then inoculated with aliquots of this enrichment culture and the identity of *Ps. phaseolicola* is confirmed from the symptoms of halo blight (Wharton, 1967).

An extension of this type of sorting is used to get stocks of virus-free potatoes and is called 'tuber-indexing'. A bud or 'eye' is removed from each tuber sample to be tested and a plant grown from it in an insect-proof greenhouse. Tubers associated with plants showing disease symptoms are discarded and seed stocks propagated from the remainder. In the U.S.S.R. a variation of this method is used to detect tuber stocks infected with *Corynebacterium sepedonicum* (bacterial ring rot). Tubers of individual 'seed' potato plants are harvested separately, and at the same time a piece is cut from the lower part of the stem. Sap expressed from the stem tissue is later tested against normal serum (control), and serum specific to *C. sepedonicum* with which it agglutinates if it contains the bacterium. Fortunately, *C. sepedonicum* retains its ability to agglutinate when non-viable so this test can be made with stem tissue that has been stored for long periods. Only tubers from plants giving a negative ring rot reaction are selected. Indexing methods have now been developed for a number of diseases carried in propagative material and are reviewed by Nyland and Milbrath (1962), and by Dimock (1962).

Sorting is an indirect way of eliminating pathogens; other methods involve a specific treatment of the planting material. Some are designed to kill pathogens which are essentially surface-contaminants or those which at most invade only the outer tissues. Two of the earliest methods of this type (disinfestation) are flaming and soaking in brine. In certain mid-European countries it was long a practice to disinfest millet seed contaminated with smut spores of *Sphacelotheca destruens* by throwing it through flames. The use of brine seems to have been discovered by accident. Apparently a cargo of wheat was shipwrecked near Bristol about 1660. Shortly afterwards most of the grain was salvaged and sold to farmers and it was observed that the resulting crops were remarkably free from bunt (*Tilletia caries*), which was elsewhere very destructive.

Over the past century many chemical seed treatments have been devised. Basically these involve either steeping the seed in a solution or suspension of the chemical, or dusting the seed with the chemical, and in some instances adding another material (sticker) to increase adhesion. Copper sulphate, formaldehyde and inorganic mercury compounds such as mercuric chloride were amongst the first materials to be so used (p. 144). More recently, organomercurials such as ethyl mercury compounds and methylmercury dicyandiamide (Panogen), organosulphur compounds, e.g. tetramethylthiuram disulphide (thiram) and quinones, e.g. tetrachloro-p-benzoquinone (chloranil) have found favour. The basic requirement of any chemical seed dressing is that it should kill the pathogens without unduly impairing the germinative capacity of the seed, and preferably it should be of low mammalian toxicity. Unfortunately some of the materials which are most effective against pathogens either have a relatively high mammalian toxicity or are extremely unpleasant to handle. There are accounts of the chemicals used as seed dressings by Sharvelle (1961) and by Martin (1964), and of the problems involved in their use by Purdy (1967). Although the application of these chemicals to seed has been emphasized, many of them are also used on other propagative materials such as bulbs, tubers, and rhizomes where similar problems of surface-inhabiting pathogens exist.

Other methods are designed to eliminate pathogens which have colonized more than the superficial layers of the propagative material (disinfection). They are basically of three types—immersion in hot water (Anon, 1967), exposure to hot air (Baker, 1962), and immersion in chemical solutions or suspensions. Hot water treatments have generally been most successful and are used to eliminate *Ustilago nuda* from wheat and barley seed (p. 143), *Alternaria brassicae* from cabbage seed (p. 191), *Puccinia menthae* from mint runners (p. 129), the nematode *Ditylenchus dipsaci* from Narcissus bulbs (Anon, 1964) and ratoon stunt and other viruses from sugar cane setts (Hughes and Steindl, 1955).

The most important application of hot air treatments is to eliminate viruses from vegetatively propagated material. This was pioneered in the United States by Kunkel (1936) and in Britain by Kassanis (1949, 1954). Plants are kept in 'hot-boxes' usually at 37°–39°, and with a high relative humidity (80% or more) for several weeks depending on the host and virus concerned. Plants withstand the treatment better if they are well rooted, and the tops pruned back slightly a week or so before treatment. It is advisable also to acclimatize them by raising the temperature gradually to 38° over a week, and to provide supplementary lighting on dull days (Hollings, 1962, 1965). It is not necessary for the virus to be completely eliminated. Shoots produced during the heat treatment are often virus-free and small cuttings can be taken from them and rooted. The progeny are tested for viruses by suitable transfers to differential hosts, and serologically. Virus-free plants have also been obtained without heat treatment by tip culture (Holmes, 1955) and by growing excised apical meristems (Kassanis, 1957; Kassanis and Varma, 1967), but some pretreatment with heat before attempting this is often preferred (van Os, 1964). Sometimes an inhibitor of virus multiplication is added to the medium on which the tissue is cultured. For example, Norris (1954) developed a virus-free stock of Green Mountain potatoes by a shoot tissue-culture technique in which he incorporated malachite green in the culture medium.

Treatments of this type are now used commercially to eliminate viruses of sugar cane, strawberries, raspberries, fruit trees and some ornamentals (Broadbent, 1964).

The successful elimination of deep-seated pathogens by soaking seed or other propagative material in a chemical solution or suspension has been demonstrated only in relatively few instances. Tyner (1952) found that soaking barley seed for 48 hours in a 0·2% chloranil (Spergon) solution at 22·2°–25° (72°–77°F), satisfactorily controlled the loose smut fungus *Ustilago nuda*, but long water soaks alone also eliminated the fungus so the control is not entirely due to the fungicide. More recently Maude (1966) successfully used a thiram-soak to eliminate *Septoria apiicola* from celery seed (p. 186), and *Mycosphaerella pinodes* and *Ascochyta pisi* from pea seed (p. 187), and the systemic fungicide vitavax has also been used successfully as a seed dressing on wheat and barley for the control of *Ustilago nuda* (p. 143).

REFERENCES

Anonymous (1964). Bulb and corm production. *Bull. Minist. Agric. Fish Fd., Lond.*, No. 62, 71–7

Anonymous (1967). Hot-water treatment of plant material. *Bull. Minist. Agric. Fish Fd, Lond.*, No. 201, 42 pp.

Baker, K. F. (1962). Thermotherapy of planting material. *Phytopathology*, **52**, 1244–55

Baker, K. F. and Smith, S. H. (1966). Dynamics of seed transmission of plant pathogens. *A. Rev. Phytopathol.*, **4**, 311–34

Broadbent, L. (1964). Control of plant virus diseases. In *Plant Virology* (Ed. M. K. Corbett and H. D. Sisler), pp. 330–64. University of Florida Press, Gainesville.

Brookson, C. W. (1956) Importation and development of new strains of *Hevea brasiliensis* by the Rubber Research Institute of Malaya. *J. Rubb. Res. Inst. Malaya*, **14**, 423–47

Dimock, A. W. (1962). Obtaining pathogen-free stock by cultured cutting techniques. *Phytopathology*, **52**, 1239–41

EPPO (1961). Bacterial diseases of potatoes. Report of the International conference on *Corynebacterium sepedonicum* and *Pseudomonas solanacearum*, Paris, 1960.

Gram, E. (1960). Quarantines. In *Plant Pathology: an advanced treatise* (Ed. J. G. Horsfall and A. E. Dimond), **3**, 313–356. Academic Press, New York.

Healy, M. J. R. (1955). Statistical techniques for inspection sampling. *Trop. Agric., Trin.* **32**, 10–19

Hollings, M. (1962). Heat treatment in the production of virus-free ornamental plants. *N.A.A.S.q.Rev.*, **57**, 31–4

Hollings, M. (1965). Disease control through virus-free stock. *A. Rev. Phytopathol.*, **3**, 367–96

Holmes, F. O. (1955). Elimination of spotted wilt from dahlias by propagation of tip cuttings. *Phytopathogy*, **45**, 224–6

Hopkins, J. C. F. (1956). *Tobacco Diseases with special reference to Africa*, 178 pp. Commonwealth Mycological Institute, Kew.

Hughes, C. G. and Steindl, D. R. L. (1955). Ratoon stunting disease of sugar cane. *Tech. Comm. Bur. Sug. Exp. Stns Qd Div. Path.* 1955, No. 2, 54 pp.

Kahn, R. P. and others, (1967). Incidence of virus detection in vegetatively propagated plant introductions under quarantine in the United States, 1957–1967. *Pl. Dis. Reptr*, **51**, 715–9

Kassanis, B. (1949). Potato tubers freed from leaf-roll virus by heat. *Nature, Lond.*, **164**, 881

Kassanis, B. (1954). Heat therapy of virus-infected plants. *Ann. appl. Biol.*, **41**, 470–4

Kassanis, B. (1957). The use of tissue cultures to produce virus-free clones from infected potato varieties. *Ann. appl. Biol.*, **45**, 422–7

Kassanis, B. and Varma, A. (1967). The production of virus-free clones of some British potato varieties. *Ann. appl. Biol.*, **59**, 447–50

Keyworth. W. G. (1951). The progressive wilt of hops order. *Ann. appl. Biol.*, **38**, 537–8

Kunkel, L. O. (1936). Heat treatments for the cure of yellows and other virus diseases of peach. *Phytopathology*, **26**, 809–30

Ling, L. editor (1952). Digest of plant quarantine regulations. *FAO Development paper (agriculture)*, No. 23, 164 pp. Supplement 1 (1954); Supplement 2 (1956).

Malone, J. P. and Muskett, A. E. (1964). *Seed-borne Fungi*, Handbook on seed health testing, Ser 4(1). International Seed Testing Association.

Martin, H. (1964). *The Scientific Principles of Crop Protection* 5th Edtn., 376 pp. Edward Arnold, London.

Maude, R. B. (1966). Pea seed infection by *Mycosphaerella pinodes* and *Ascochyta pisi* and its control by seed soaks in thiram and captan suspensions. *Ann. appl. Biol.*, **57**, 193–200

McCubbin, W. A. (1954). *The Plant Quarantine Problem*, 255 pp. Ejnar Munksgaard, Copenhagen.

Moore, W. C. (1951). Legislation against plant diseases and pests in England and Wales. *Ann. appl. Biol.*, **38**, 529–31

Moore, W. C. (1952). International trade in plants and the need for healthy planting material. *Rep. Int. hort. Congr.*, No 13.

Norris, D. O. (1954). Development of virus-free stock of Green Mountain potato by treatment with malachite green. *Aust. J. agric. Res.*, **5**, 658–63

Noble, M. and Richardson, M. J. (1968). *Annotated List of Seed-borne Diseases*, 2nd Edtn., 191 pp. Commonwealth Mycological Institute, Kew.

Nyland, G. and Milbrath, J. A. (1962). Obtaining virus-free stock by index techniques. *Phytopathology*, **52**, 1235–9

Os, H. van (1964). Production of virus-free carnations by means of meristem culture. *Neth. J. Plant Path.*, **70**, 18–26

Purdy, L. H. (1967). Application and use of soil and seed-treatment fungicides. In *Fungicides: an advanced treatise* (Ed. D. C. Torgeson), **1**, 195–237. Academic Press, New York.

Sharvelle, E. G. (1961). *The Nature and Uses of Modern Fungicides*, 308 pp. Burgess, Minnneapolis.

Sheffield, F. M. L. (1955). The East African plant quarantine station. *Commonw. phytopath. News*, **1**, 33–5

Sheffield, F. M. L. (1968). Closed quarantine procedures. *Rev. appl. Myc.*, **47**, 1–8

Tyner, L. E. (1953). The control of loose smut of barley and wheat by spergon and by soaking in water at room temperature. *Phytopathology*, **43**, 313–6

Wharton, A. L. (1967). Detection of infection by *Pseudomonas phaseolicola* (Burkh.) Dowson in white-seeded dwarf bean seed stocks. *Ann. appl. Biol.*, **60**, 305–12

CHAPTER 19

Plant disease control: eradication

Sometimes a pathogen becomes established in spite of attempts to exclude it and the problem is then to eradicate it from the area or crop. There are many ways of doing this, but basically the methods involve the direct, physical removal of the pathogen, its elimination by cultural practices, or its destruction, chiefly by chemical means. Some details of particular methods have already been given in previous chapters. The aim here is to review generally this aspect of plant disease control.

Direct Removal of Pathogens

The removal of diseased plants is the simplest form of eradication and is called roguing. It is the traditional method for controlling virus and other diseases in potato seed plots but depends for its success on the early recognition of symptoms. Otherwise infected plants serve as further sources of inoculum and spread of the pathogen continues. In Britain, removing plants with leaf roll or rugose mosaic helps to maintain healthy stocks in the North and West where aphids seldom arrive in a crop before infected plants can be recognized, but not in the South and East where aphids are active much earlier (Doncaster and Gregory, 1948). Roguing is not without its disadvantages, specially with wilt diseases. The removal of potato plants adjacent to those infected with *Verticillium albo-atrum* increased the incidence of *Verticillium* wilt in experiments conducted by McKay (1926). It seems likely in this instance that the inoculum potential of the fungus was increased because it could

321

rapidly colonise pieces of infected root tissue left behind in the soil
and so grow from these to nearby healthy roots.

Removal of adjacent, and apparently healthy, plants is advocated
in some eradication programmes. In a scheme to eradicate banana
mosaic in Honduras eighty plants adjoining the infected one were
eradicated and in addition, the surrounding area was sprayed twice
with nicotine at 20-day intervals. The disease was reduced in a
plantation of some 5,600 hectares from 52 infected banana mats
per 1,000 ha in 1956 to 0·28 mats in 1960 (Adam, 1960).

Eradication programmes on an even larger scale have been under-
taken, most of them in the U.S.A. The total elimination of citrus
canker caused by *Xanthomonas citri* was an outstanding achievement.
This disease was introduced into the Gulf states on orange stock
from Japan in 1910. Initially the symptoms were confused with
those of citrus scab (*Elsinoe fawcetti*) so that little was done for some
four years by which time the disease had become extremely destructive. Between 1914 and 1934 eradication programmes were
organized in Florida, Alabama, Georgia, Louisiana, Mississippi,
South Carolina and Texas. Approximately 250,000 trees were
removed from citrus groves and nearly 3 million from nurseries in
Florida alone. Overall by 1934 nearly 20 million trees were destroyed
in the various state schemes and by this time eradication of canker
in commercial plantings was virtually complete. There remained,
however, numerous wild and escaped trees and abandoned groves
where the disease could still be found, and between 1935 and 1952
schemes were introduced to deal with this situation. Now citrus
canker appears to be completely eliminated (Dopson, 1964). Similar
campaigns were directed against two virus diseases, phony peach
and peach mosaic. Eradication of phony peach started in 1929;
by 1951 the disease had been eliminated from six of seventeen states
in which it was originally present and from a further 175 counties
in eight other states (Persons, 1952). In Colorado, the programme
against peach mosaic has also resulted in a substantial reduction in
disease although complete eradication seems unlikely (List and
others, 1956).

Not all eradication schemes have been so successful. During the
1930's attempts were made to eradicate Dutch elm disease (p. 59)
by destroying infected trees and other sources of the bark beetles.
Although this may have slowed the rate of spread over the United
States new outbreaks are still reported (Holmes, 1962) and large
scale control was abandoned in the early 1940's. The problem now

is essentially a local one and here eradication is still of value in limiting spread (McGubbin, 1954). In Nigeria a massive campaign to eradicate the virus disease of cacao known as swollen shoot was also abandoned in areas of severe infection. Instead, cacao grown outside these areas was inspected regularly and new outbreaks treated immediately (Thresh, 1959).

Within the heteroecious rusts there is the possibility of control by removing the alternate host and attempts to do this with *Puccinia graminis* and *Cronartium ribicola* were briefly described in Chapter 7. In the U.S.A. eradication of the barberry did not check outbreaks of black stem rust in certain years, e.g. in 1935, 1953 and 1954, and in this respect is considered by many to have failed, and to have been useful only in limiting the production of new races of the fungus. In a recent reappraisal van der Plank (1963) considers this judgement too harsh. There is abundant evidence that many outbreaks started around infected barberry bushes and that destroying the bushes did substantially reduce stem rust over a number of years. Indeed, in three successive 5-year periods from the start of eradication, the average annual losses due to stem rust fell from 50 million bushels to 26 million and then to 11 million. The point is that these were years (1917–1934) in which stem rust did relatively little damage, and in the mid-west outbreaks which did occur were associated with infected barberries. It was different in 1935. There was an unusually high rainfall in the southern states, the wheat ripened late and stem rust was severe. As a result large masses of urediospores reached the barberry eradication areas early. Here too, weather conditions favoured rust and it became epiphytotic. In a sense, the success of barberry eradication in the previous years only served to emphasise its failure in a year of massive and widespread urediospore inoculum.

With other diseases, removal of alternative hosts is also a possible way of reducing inoculum, and hence infection of an economic crop; reference has already been made to this in connection with the stylet-borne viruses (p. 264). In Florida eradicating all weeds, especially *Commelina nudiflora* and *Phytolacca rigida*, for a distance of 23m around celery seedbeds and similarly around fields at transplanting, decreased the incidence of southern celery mosaic (Wellman, 1937). Spinach yellows, caused by cucumber mosaic virus, can also be partially controlled by removing wild hosts to a distance of 45.7m around spinach plantings (Doolittle and Walker, 1926). Similarly Simons (1957) found that spread of veinbanding mosaic virus in peppers (*Capsicum frutescens*) was much reduced when plots were

45·7 m away from weed sources of inoculum such as nightshade (*Solanum gracile*).

An alternative host is an obvious complication in large-scale eradication especially where trees are involved. In some resurveys it was found that phony peach disease had reappeared in areas from which it had been eradicated. This was attributed to spread from the wild plum which was not known to be a host of the virus when the eradication campaign began (Persons, 1952).

It is not always necessary to dispose of the entire plant to remove a pathogen. With many orchard crops this can be accomplished by pruning a diseased branch, twig, or fruiting spur and cutting out diseased tissue on a main stem. It is common practice for diseases such as fireblight of pears in the United States (p. 160), and apple and larch canker (chapter 14). Several factors must be taken into account if these methods are to be effective. The operations necessarily entail a certain amount of damage to the tree and since many of the pathogens involved are wound parasites, e.g. *Nectria galligena*, pruning should, if possible, be carried out when inoculum is at a low level. In addition, the wound must be protected by a dressing such as Bordeaux paste or lead paint. At certain times pruning stimulates new shoot growth; this is undesirable if the pathogen readily attacks young tissue as does *Erwinia amylovora*. In this event pruning should be carried out when this effect is at a minimum. Finally, when removing diseased tissue one should always cut back some way into the healthy part because the pathogen may extend into this region without causing obvious symptoms (p. 221) and unless there is healthy cambium at the cut surface, callus tissue will not form and seal off the wound.

Occasionally this principle of eradication is practised on herbaceous crops by removing diseased leaves. This has some value in the control of certain diseases of ornamentals grown in greenhouses, such as leaf spot of chrysanthemum caused by *Septoria chrysanthemella*. In Rhodesia, it used to be standard practice for cultural reasons to remove the lower leaves of field tobacco: this was called 'priming'. The additional advantage of removing inoculum of leaf-spotting fungi has been stressed by Hopkins (1956), and 'priming' is still recommended for the control of some diseases, but attempts to demonstrate the benefits in field experiments have often been unsuccessful. It may well be, as with barberry eradication, that an operation of this type is effective against focal outbreaks but valueless against heavy and widespread inoculum.

Another way in which a pathogen can be directly removed is in the collection and destruction of crop debris. This is particularly important when the crop residue constitutes the chief source of inoculum as with *Alternaria longipes* and tobacco (p. 191). An objection to burning the trash is that potential soil organic matter is lost; deep ploughing of the residues is preferable provided that this is not re-exposed at the next cultivation. In North America considerable attention has been paid to the importance of discarded potatoes (cull piles) as sources of inoculum for *Phytophthora infestans*. There is now good evidence which shows that outbreaks of blight can develop from cull piles and that their destruction prevents the early development of local epidemics. The significance of this eradication in the epidemiology of late blight is discussed by van der Plank (1963).

Elimination by Cultural Practices

Elimination of plant pathogens by cultural methods is practised particularly with root diseases and is discussed in Chapter 3. Crop rotations, for example, eradicate pathogens by depriving them over a number of years of the plants on which they live. Pathogens with a wide host range, or those that form resting structures such as sclerotia, are difficult to deal with in this way, though deep ploughing or 'catch crops' to stimulate germination of sclerotia and resting spores are possible alternatives for the latter. Temporary flooding of land may also serve to eliminate pathogens, for example *Xanthomonas malvacearum* (p. 179). Various aspects of this type of disease control are discussed by Leighty (1938), Newhall (1955) and Stevens (1960).

Destruction of Pathogens

It is possible to eradicate pathogens by destroying them either within the infected host or in the immediate environment. For example, one method of dealing with fireblight cankers is to paint the surface with a caustic solution of zinc chloride (p. 161), and crown gall on almond has been successfully treated by applying sodium-dinitrocresol (Ark, 1941). This compound has also been used on *Gymnosporangium* galls on red cedar. Galls were thoroughly sprayed with a 1% solution when they showed signs of renewed fungal activity. Development of telial columns was completely inhibited

(Strong and Cation, 1940). In these examples the lesions are well defined and the chemical is applied to specific areas. Some chemicals which are more widely used in crop protection also have an essentially eradicative action in that they are effective against existing lesions, e.g. sulphur and dinocap for the powdery mildews, and phenylmercury compounds for apple scab.

Chemicals are sometimes applied to destroy inoculum on or near plants. Two examples are the elimination of *Taphrina deformans* spores on peach by spraying before bud burst (p. 211) and the destruction of *Venturia inaequalis* on fallen apple leaves by DNOC (p. 254). Another striking example is the control of *Peronospora tabacina* in seedbeds with benzol and with *para*-dichlorobenzene (p. 85).

For many diseases soil-borne inoculum is important and some treatment of the soil is often necessary to eradicate it. Its particular value in relation to damping-off and root diseases has been mentioned in Chapters 2 and 3. Most treatments involve heat or the application of chemicals. Of the various heat treatments steaming is the most popular and effective, and many ingenious pieces of equipment have been designed for this purpose (Newhall, 1955; Baker and Roistacher, 1957). Exposure to temperatures above 50° for a few minutes is sufficient to kill most pathogenic fungi. The difficulty is to ensure that this minimum requirement is obtained throughout the soil mass which is being treated. In practice the temperature is held at 80–100° for 30 minutes to achieve this. One of the main problems with soil teated in this way is the rapidity with which it can be colonized if it is inadvertantly recontaminated with a pathogenic fungus (Kreutzer, 1965). There is evidence from more recent investigations that less drastic heat treatment with steam–air mixtures is preferable, since this leaves in the soil a larger pool of saprophytic microorganisms available for recolonization and these limit the development of the pathogen (Olsen and Baker, 1968).

The use of chemicals to kill pathogens in soil began about 1869 when carbon disulphide was applied for the control of *Phylloxera* of the grape vine (Wilhelm, 1966). The number of chemicals now available for treating soils is considerable. Briefly they can be divided into two groups, those that are generally toxic to most animal and plant life and those with more specific toxicity. Kreutzer (1960) divides the first group into three types:

1. *Volatile, water-insoluble compounds*, e.g. methyl bromide and chloropicrin. Both are widely used, specially for treating seedbeds, nursery sites and soil in glasshouses. Methyl bromide penetrates

tissue well and is particularly effective against fungal sclerotia but because of its high volatility is best applied under a gas-tight cover. Chloropicrin is less volatile and water is often applied to the soil surface to act as a seal after treatment.

2. *Unstable compounds*, e.g. sodium N-methyldithiocarbamate (metham) and 3,5-dimethyl-1,3,5,2H-tetrahydrothiadiazine-2-thione ('Mylone'). Both these compounds decompose in soil and, amongst other chemicals, the volatile methyl isothiocyanate is formed. This is believed to be mainly responsible for the toxic action of metham but the evidence is not entirely conclusive. Decomposition of mylone is favoured by high soil moisture, and formaldehyde, hydrogen sulphide and monomethylamine are formed in addition to methyl isothiocyanate so the toxic action is likely to be more complex (Munnecke, 1967).

3. *Volatile, water soluble compounds*, e.g. formaldehyde and allyl alcohol. Of these formaldehyde has been of greatest value though its popularity has now declined. It was, for example, formerly much used in the control of onion smut (p. 145).

The chemicals which are more specific in their action are of two types:

1. *Volatile eradicants*, e.g. ethylene dibromide and carbon disulphide. Ethylene dibromide is of most value as a nematicide; carbon disulphide has been particularly useful in the eradication of *Armillarea mellea* from citrus soils (p. 46).

2. *Non-volatile protectants*. This includes a wide range of fungicides themselves showing great diversity in the range of species against which they are effective. Those with wide spectra of toxicity include tetramethylthiuram disulphide (thiram) and mercurials such as methylmercury dicyandiamide ('Panogen'). At the other end of the scale are materials like pentachloronitrobenzene (PCNB) and *p*-dimethylaminobenzenediazo sodium sulphonate ('Dexon'). These are amongst the most specific fungicides known and are applied specially for the control of damping-off diseases. PCNB is particularly effective against *Rhizoctonia* but not, for example, against *Pythium*. This deficiency is made up by Dexon which is toxic to *Pythium*, *Phytophthora* and *Aphanomyces* but not to most other plant pathogenic fungi.

While some of the materials mentioned are applied on a field scale, costs prohibit the use of others over such large areas. They are of value, however, in the treatment of seedbeds and glasshouse soil where the provision of a water supply and other services make these specially valuable sites which are not lightly discarded for new areas. There are many individual methods for applying chemicals to soil and these are briefly reviewed by Purdy (1967). Fumigants are often applied through devices which probe the soil and then release the chemical, these devices being operated either manually or mechanically. Some chemicals such as PCNB can be mixed and applied with the fertilizer, or spread over the soil and then worked in by tilling or disking. Others are applied as liquids to rows and seed drills, or over the entire soil surface as a drench.

To make the most of these chemicals it is necessary to know the general soil zone in which pathogen and host are likely to make contact, the effects of the chemicals on the soil (and *vice versa*), and the effects on the soil microorganisms. Several factors influence the penetration of soil by chemicals such as the extent to which they are adsorbed on soil particles, the rate at which they are leached by percolating water and, for volatile materials, how quickly they diffuse. Once in the soil they may be broken down chemically or, unlikely though it may appear, degraded by various microorganisms. Indeed for some, ability to decompose quickly is the key to their success, e.g. metham. There has been an increasing interest in these aspects of recent years and the review by Munnecke (1967) is an admirable introduction to the now considerable literature.

REFERENCES

Adam, A. V. (1962). An effective program for the control of banana mosaic. *Pl. Dis. Reptr.*, **46**, 366–70
Ark, P. A. (1941). Chemical eradication of crown gall on almond trees. *Phytopathology*, **31**, 956–7
Baker, K. F. and Roistacher, C. N. (1957). Equipment for heat treatment of soil. In *The U.C. system for producing healthy container-grown plants. Manual Calif. agric. Exp. Stn., Ext. Serv.*, No. 23, 162–96
Doncaster, J. P. and Gregory, P. H. (1948). *The Spread of Virus Diseases in the Potato Crop*. 189 pp. H.M.S.O., London.
Doolittle, S. P. and Walker, M. N. (1926). Control of cucumber mosaic by eradication of wild host plants. *Bull. U.S. Dep. Agric.*, No. 1461, 15 pp.

Dopson, R. N. Jnr. (1964). The eradication of citrus canker. *Pl. Dis. Reptr*, **48**, 30–1

Holmes, F. W. (1962). Recorded Dutch elm disease distribution in North America as of 1961. *Pl. Dis. Reptr*, **46**, 715–8

Hopkins, J. C. F. (1956). *Tobacco Diseases with special reference to Africa*, pp. 37–9. Commonwealth Mycological Institute, Kew.

Kreutzer, W. A. (1960). Soil treatment. In *Plant Pathology: an advanced treatise* (Ed J. G. Horsfall and A. E. Dimond), **3**, 431–76. Academic Press, New York.

Kreutzer, W. A. (1965). The reinfestation of treated soil. In *Ecology of Soil-borne Plant Pathogens* (Ed. K. F. Baker and W. C. Snyder), pp. 495–507. John Murray, London.

List, G. M., Landblom, N. and Sisson, M. A. (1956). A study of records from the Colorado peach mosaic suppression program. *Tech. Bull. Colo. agric. Exp. Stn*, No. 59, 28 pp.

Leighty, C. E. (1938). Crop rotation. *Yb. U.S. Dep. Agric.* 1938, 406–30

McCubbin, W. A. (1954). *The Plant Quarantine Problem*, 255 pp. Ejnar Munksgaard, Copenhagen.

McKay, M. B. (1926). Further studies of potato wilt caused by *Verticillium albo-atrum*. *J. agric. Res.*, **32**, 437–70

Munnecke, D. E. (1967). Fungicides in the soil environment In *Fungicides: an advanced treatise* (Ed. D. C. Torgeson), **1**, 509–59. Academic Press, New York.

Newhall, A. G. (1955). Disinfestation of soil by heat, flooding and fumigation. *Bot. Rev.*, **21**, 189–250

Olsen, C. M. and Baker, K. F. (1968). Selective heat treatment of soil, and its effect on the inhibition of *Rhizoctonia solani* by *Bacillus subtilis*. *Phytopathology*, **58**, 79–87

Persons, T. D. (1952). Phony peach disease—a review of organized control from 1929 to 1951 and the effect of recent developments on future control programs. *Phytopathology*, **42**, 286

Plank, Van der J. E. (1963). *Plant Diseases: epidemics and control*, 349 pp. Academic Press, New York.

Purdy, L. H. (1967). Application and use of soil and seed-treatment fungicides. In *Fungicides: an advanced treatise* (Ed. D. C. Torgeson), **1**, 195–237. Academic Press, New York.

Simons, J. N. (1957). Effects of insecticides and physical barriers on field spread of pepper veinbanding mosaic virus. *Phytopathology*, 47, 139–45

Stevens, R. B. (1960). Cultural pratices in disease control In *Plant Pathology: an advanced treatise* (Ed. J. G. Horsfall and A. E. Dimond), **3** 357–429. Academic Press, New York.

Strong, F. C. and Cation, D. (1940). Control of cedar rust with sodium dinitrocresylate. *Phytopathology*, **30**, 983

Thresh, J. M. (1959). The control of cacao swollen shoot disease in Nigeria. *Trop. Agric., Trin.*, **36**, 35–44

Wellman, F. L. (1937). Control of southern celery mosaic in Florida by removing weeds that serve as sources of mosaic infection. *Tech. Bull. U.S. Dept. Agric.*, No. 548, 16 pp.

Wilhelm, S. (1966). Chemical treatments and inoculum potential of soil. *A. Rev. Phytopathol.*, **4**, 53–78

CHAPTER 20

Plant disease control: protection

Protection in a wide sense involves killing the pathogen before it can invade the host (Horsfall, 1956). In this context, one would include soil treatments and the prebud burst spraying against *Venturia inaequalis* and *Taphrina deformans* which were discussed under eradication. Other authors have restricted the term to the inter-position of some effective barrier between suscept and pathogen (Whatzel and others, 1925) and although this still covers a variety of methods, the emphasis is mainly on the application of chemicals to plants In some instances control can be obtained by this method when infection has already taken place and therefore it is essentially eradication or, as some would prefer, therapy (Horsfall, 1956). Whatever the mode of action there are certain basic problems in applying chemicals to plants and this chapter is mainly about these difficulties.

THE MATERIALS USED

There is today a vast array of chemicals available for crop pro-tection and the characteristics of most of them are listed by Frear (1965). All that can be attempted here is a general statement of the main groups of compounds with particular reference to those pre-viously mentioned in the text. It so happens that most of them are fungicides, and the present account is restricted mainly to those applied to foliage. There are comprehensive accounts of these fungicides and their uses by Sharvelle (1961), Martin (1964), and in the two-volume *Advanced Treatise* edited by Torgeson (1967). Results of field trials with new fungicides are published annually by the American Phytopathological Society.

The various names given to fungicides are often confusing. There are three kinds: the chemical name of the fungicidal compound, a coined name for this compound which is more convenient for general use, (e.g. see Zentmyer, 1955; McClellan, 1966), and the trade names given by manufacturers to formulations containing this chemical. Thus the chemical, zinc ethylenebisdithiocarbamate, has the coined name zineb; the Rohm and Haas Company produce a fungicide containing 85% of this material under the registered trade name 'Dithane Z-78', and so do the Dupont Chemical Company but they call their product 'Parzate'.

Inorganic materials

Many materials first used on crops to control disease were inorganic compounds of copper and sulphur—

1. *Copper compounds:* Bordeaux mixture is certainly the most noteworthy material within this group despite the decline in its use over the past thirty years (McCallan, 1967). It is prepared simply by combining solutions of copper sulphate and calcium hydroxide, but there are many individual recipes for carrying out this operation (Somers, 1959). The two chemicals react in solution to give a gelatinous precipitate the nature and fungicidal action of which are still not entirely clear. The proportions of copper sulphate, lime and water in any particular mixture are usually denoted by a simple formula, e.g. 4:4:50 indicates 4 lb copper sulphate and 4 lb lime to 50 gallons water. The ratio of copper sulphate to lime determines the pH of the mixture and to a certain extent its physical and chemical nature. The older, 'neutral Bordeaux' mixtures had a ratio approximately 1:0·3; the mixtures more commonly used have ratios approaching 1:1 and are alkaline. Several other mixtures have been derived from Bordeaux. Replacing calcium hydroxide by sodium carbonate gives the so-called Burgundy mixture or Soda Bordeaux which was at one time recommended for potato blight control in Ireland. Copper sulphate mixed with ammonium carbonate in the ratio 2:11 is known as Cheshunt compound: this has been used mainly to control damping-off (Martin, 1964). Few fungicides have the tenacity and weathering properties of Bordeaux but it is somewhat tedious to prepare and can damage the foliage of many plants. For these reasons other inorganic copper fungicides have been marketed; they are based mainly on copper oxychloride, cuprous oxide, and basic copper sulphates prepared by reacting copper sulphate with sodium hydroxide.

2. *Sulphur compounds:* Two types of inorganic sulphur are still

used though much less so than in the early days of crop protection: they are elemental sulphur and lime sulphur. There are various commercial processes for obtaining sulphur of different particle size which is suitable for dusting, or with a suitable wetting agent for spraying on plants. Some of the methods are reviewed by Sharvelle (1961). Lime sulphur is obtained by boiling hydrated lime and sulphur together. The main products of the reaction are calcium thiosulphate and calcium polysulphide, and it is the latter compound which confers the fungicidal (and insecticidal) properties. The polysulphide content should be such as to give a specific gravity not less than 1·28 at 60°F.

Organic materials

1. *Dithiocarbamates:* The development of fungicides based on organic sulphur compounds and known as dithiocarbamates (Thorn and Ludwig, 1962) has been one of the outstanding achievements of the past thirty years. They are derived from dithiocarbamic acid and are of two types (Rich, 1960). One series is derived from the interaction of carbon disulphide and simple amines. The most important of these compounds, with their recognized coined names are: zinc dimethyldithiocarbamate (ziram), ferric dimethyldithiocarbamate (ferbam) and tetramethylthiuram disulphide (thiram). Another series stems from the interaction of carbon disulphide and ethylenediamine. Disodium ethylenebisdithiocarbamate (nabam), zinc ethylenebisdithiocarbamate (zineb) and manganese ethylenebisdithiocarbamate (maneb) are commercially the most important of this series, and there is now an impressive list of diseases controlled by these materials (see Sharvelle, 1961).

2. *Quinones:* In the mid-1940's two chlorinated quinones were developed as fungicides. The first was tetrachloro-*p*-benzoquinone, with the coined name of chloranil. This is a water-insoluble chemical, used in the rubber industry, which in light and with moisture is converted to the water-soluble chloranilic acid. Because of this it is of little value as a foliage fungicide but is much used as a seed dressing. A derivative, 2,3-dichloro-1,4-napthoquinone (dichlone) is much less affected by light and can be applied to foliage.

3. *Heterocyclic nitrogen compounds:* In recent years a number of heterocyclic nitrogen compounds have been developed with marked fungicidal and bactericidal activity. The most important is an imidazoline, 2-heptadecyl-2-imidazoline acetate, now called glyodin which has been of value in controlling apple scab and the leaf spot of cherry caused by *Coccomyces hiemalis.*

4. *Trichloromethylthiocarboximides:* One of the outstanding fungicides of recent years is the compound N-trichloromethylmercapto-4-cyclohexene-1, 2-dicarboximide with the coined name, captan. This gives excellent control of many fungus diseases of vegetables, fruits and ornamentals. Folpet is another closely related compound (N-trichloromethythiophthalimide) which has recently been introduced.

5. *Guanidines:* A guanidine, n-dodecylguanidine acetate, was developed as a fungicide during the years 1956–7. It is now known as dodine and appears to be particularly effective in controlling apple scab.

6. *Mercurials:* Organic compounds of mercury were first developed in 1914–15 mainly as seed dressings (p. 144). A number of related compounds have been found to be particularly useful on foliage because they kill fungi when infection is already established. Most of them are phenylmercury derivatives such as phenylmercuric acetate (PMA), phenylmercuric chloride, -nitrate and -salicylate. Other more complex combinations are phenylmercuric triethanol-ammonium lactate and phenylmercury dimethyldithiocarbamate.

7. *Antiobiotics:* From the time that penicillin was produced commercially many metabolic products of microorganisms have been examined for fungicidal and bactericidal activity. Some are remarkably effective against plant pathogens *in vitro* but few are of proved value in the field. There is a good review of their application in plant disease control by Goodman (1959). Two which are in fairly common use were both obtained from culture filtrates of *Streptomyces griseus:* they are streptomycin and cycloheximide. Streptomycin is mainly effective against the bacterial plant pathogens such as *Erwinia amylovora* (p. 161); cycloheximide is of value in the control of *Coccomyces* leaf spot of cherry and cucumber scab as a spray, and in the eradication of *Cronartium ribicola* on pine when painted on the cankers.

8. *Miscellaneous:* One compound which does not fall into the above categories is particularly effective against the powdery mildews. It is 2-(1-methyl-n-heptyl)-4, 6-dinotrophenyl crotonate which is usually called dinocap, or known by the trade name 'Karathane' (Rohm and Haas Co.). Others are systemic fungicides which have recently been developed: Vitavax (U.S. Rubber Co.), 2,3-dihydro-5-carboxanilido-6-methyl-1,4-oxathiin, shows promise as a seed dressing for loose smut control (p. 144); Plantvax, a close derivative manufactured by the same company, has been successfully used as a soil treatment also for controlling loose smut of barley (Reinbergs

and others, 1968); Milstem (Plant Protection Ltd.), 5-butyl-2-ethylamino-4-hydroxy-6-methylpyrimidine, is particularly valuable for controlling cereal powdery mildew (p. 109), and Benlate (E.I. du Pont de Nemours and Co.), methyl-1-(butylcarbamoyl)-2-benzimidazolecarbamate, shows a high degree of activity against a wide range of Ascomycetes and Fungi Imperfecti.

Formulations

The chemicals mentioned above differ considerably in their physical properties and these largely determine the form in which they are prepared or formulated (Somers, 1967). Few are soluble enough to be sold as concentrated aqueous solutions; phenylmercuric acetate is an exception though even this requires certain additives to increase its solubility. Most others are not soluble, or only sparingly so and they are formulated as dusts, water-dispersible powders (often called wettable powders), and emulsions or emulsifiable concentrates. Dusts usually contain less than 10% active ingredient, the remainder is some diluent or carrier, usually a silicate material such as talc, kaolin, bentonite or diatomaceous earth. This and the chemical are mixed by grinding in a mill.

Water-dispersable powders are similarly prepared but usually contain some 25% to 50% active ingredient and the particles are ground finely to something less than 10μ diameter. Usually various other surface active agents are also added such as sulphite lye or methyl celluloses to aid the dispersal of the particles in the suspension, and materials such as polyethylene glycols or sodium lauryl sulphate to ensure good wetting properties.

In an emulsion the pesticide is dissolved in a water-immiscible solvent and a suspension of fine droplets of this is then prepared in water by rapid agitation of the two components. The resulting suspension is stabilized by adding a hydrophilic colloid such as gelatin. Emulsifiable concentrates are prepared by dissolving the pesticide in oil to which is added a high concentration of an emulsifying agent or even a mixture of two such agents like polyethylene glycol and sodium dioctyl sulphosuccinate which facilitates dispersal in water. They are now generally more popular than the stock emulsions.

Toxicity

Many of the materials used in crop protection are unpleasant to handle and toxic to mammals but these obvious hazards are usually clearly stated by the manufacturers and there is often legislation governing the marketing and handling of these materials, e.g. *The Agriculture (Poisonous substances) Act* 1952 for England, Scotland and Wales, and the *Federal Insecticide, Fungicide and Rodenticide Act of* 1947 with its amendments for the U.S.A. There are two other aspects of toxicity which must be considered. One is that some plants react violently to a particular chemical; necrotic areas develop on leaves (scorching) or rough, corky areas appear on fruit (russetting). This phytotoxicity is often a varietal reaction as with apples and sulphur and in this instance is sufficiently well documented to appear in manufacturers' handbooks. In other circumstances it is often a question of trial and error and preliminary tests should always be made when information is lacking. One difficulty is that environmental conditions often modify the degree of toxicity.

The problem of toxic residues is another aspect which has recently received much attention (Carson, 1962). If a chemical is to be successful as a protectant it must persist for some time, and there is then the danger that despite weathering or cessation of spraying before harvesting, enough will remain on the product to constitute a health hazard to the consumer. Special care is needed with organomercurials like phenylmercuric acetate since small quantities are absorbed by plants (Stewart and Ross, 1967). For crops which are sprayed with these compounds there are strict limits on the amount of mercury that will be tolerated in the harvested product. In the U.S.A. there is a nil tolerance; in Britain a level of not more than 0·1 p.p.m. is acceptable on apples (Pickard and Martin, 1961) and tomatoes (Egan and Lidzey, 1960).

Countries differ in their approach to the problem of toxic residues, as the above example suggests. Tolerance levels are strictly controlled in the U.S.A. under the *Food, Drug and Cosmetic Act of* 1938 and the Miller Amendment to this act of 1954 (Public Law 518). The residues currently allowed on produce are to be found in the *Pesticide Handbook—Entoma* (edited by Frear) which is published annually. There is no comparable legislation in Britain, but under the Pesticides Safety Precautions Scheme manufacturers supply data on toxicity to the Ministry of Agriculture and as a result restrictions may be imposed on the use of a particular material (Martin, 1965).

PROBLEMS OF APPLICATION

The choice of material is governed by a number of factors, some of which are essentially problems of application which are now discussed.

Deposition and coverage

The whole point of dusting or spraying a crop is to protect the susceptible tissue with a chemical barrier. The first problem then is to deposit particles of the chemical on the plant in such a way that this tissue is adequately covered. There are forces at the plant surface which tend to repulse particles, for instance, convection currents caused by differences in temperature between leaf surface and the surrounding atmosphere, and these must be overcome by imparting sufficient momentum to the dust or spray particles. Since momentum is mass $\times$ velocity two factors which are important in this respect are the particle size and the speed with which it is propelled from the equipment used. One of the advantages of sprays over dusts is that the chemical is encapsulated in liquid giving a larger droplet which, at relatively low velocities, can attain the momentum required to reach the target area and to overcome the opposing forces at the plant surface. This, however, may be conditioned by the volume of liquid applied. With relatively high volumes, i.e. 0·8–3·3 m³/ha, droplets in the range 0·5–3 mm readily deposit on and cover the plant surface. If for various reasons lower volumes are applied, the droplet size must be decreased to maintain adequate coverage but correspondingly, the droplets must be given greater velocity to reach and deposit on the target (Burchfield, 1960, 1967).

Not all the material applied directly impinges on the target area; with dusts particularly a good deal deposits by gravity. The air around a plant is seldom still but the affects of particle size on this type of deposition can be gauged approximately from Stokes' Law. For example, a particle of diameter 10μ and density $2g/cm^3$ would reach a limiting velocity of 2·3 cm/sec and have a momentum of $1·9 \times 10^{-8}g$ cm/sec. (Burchfield, 1967). This is about the minimum requirement for deposition against the forces operating at the leaf surface. Particles in this range, however, are easily removed by wind and rain, and this is one reason why dusting is generally less satisfactory than spraying.

The nature of the leaf surface is another important factor in deposition and coverage, in particular the amount and type of extracuticular wax regulate the retention and penetration of chemical sprays (Juniper, 1959). Generally plants with smooth, waxy surfaces such as pea, onion and banana are difficult to wet and many spray particles just bounce off. This can be overcome by adding a material to the spray liquid which facilitates its contact with the leaf surface; the term 'spreader' is applied to such a material. In some instances this allows a greater initial deposit of material which is still fairly resistant to rain, as Table 20.1 illustrates, but this is not always so. With plants that are more readily wetted there are disadvantages in using a spreader in high volume applications for the point at which the leaf is completely wetted and the liquid runs off is reached earlier, the volume of liquid retained is smaller and consequently the amount of material deposited is less (Cupples, 1941). The deposit is also more likely to be adversely affected by rain.

TABLE 20.1 Effect of concentration of Triton X-114 on retention of freshly prepared 10 : 10 : 100 Bordeaux to leaves of Gros Michel banana.

Conc. Triton X-114 (p.p.m.)	\% initial Cu retained after inches of rain			
	0·5	2	4	8
0	10	0	0	0
100	86	73	65	61
200	94	83	76	76
300	97	93	79	74

Data from Burchfield and Goenaga (1957), *Contr. Boyce Thompson Inst. Pl. Res.*, **19**, 141–56.

It is often necessary in field trials to assess coverage. Some of the earlier methods are listed by Horsfall (1956). For copper fungicides prints were made by pressing sprayed leaves on filter paper previously soaked with potassium ferricyanide or on treated plaster of Paris. Large and Taylor (1953) similarly made prints of copper deposits by placing sprayed potato leaves between paper moistened with a rubeanic acid solution. A newer method is to incorporate a fluorescent material such as Saturn Yellow in the spray liquid and examine a random sample of sprayed leaves under ultraviolet light (Sharp, 1955; Staniland, 1961). The spray deposit is then clearly visible (Figure 20.1).

Tenacity or persistence of deposits

Maintaining an adequate deposit of a protectant chemical is a major problem. The deposit itself is reduced by weathering and the coverage becomes less complete as the plant grows. Wind and rain are generally the most important environmental factors. Loss of deposit during rain is often rapid; in experiments with cuprous oxide and banana leaves Burchfield and Goenaga (1957) found that the first 6·35 mm of rain removed 43% of the spray deposit. Wind alone takes longer to produce a similar effect: Somers and Thomas (1956) record a 50% loss of cuprous oxide deposits after approxi-

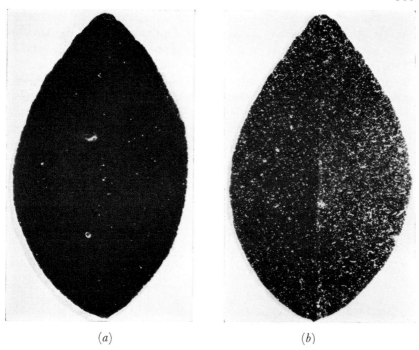

(a)   (b)

FIGURE 20.1 Leaves of lime (*Citrus aurantifolia*) sprayed with phenyl-mercury nitrate plus saturn yellow and viewed under u.v. light. Little fungicide has deposited on the leaf on the left; there is a reasonably good coverage on the right-hand leaf. Photograph courtesy H. R. Mapother, Long Ashton Research Station.

mately 27 days (Figure 20.2). Nevertheless, in the field the plant may be subjected to wind more than rain. There may also be loss of the chemical as vapour, e.g. sulphur deposits during hot weather (Thatcher and Streeter, 1925), or by photochemical decomposition, e.g. chloranil (p. 333).

There have been many attempts to increase the tenacity of various materials. Reduction in particle size is one possibility: for example, Figure 20.3 shows how the tenacity of a sulphur fungicide is increased by this means. Another is the incoporation of a substance, called a sticker; examples are lime, casein, gelatin, linseed oil and polyvinyl acetate (Figure 20.4). In most instances, however, stickers have been found to reduce the toxicity of the spray material. Thus in a trial with several of these compounds, Somers (1956) found that polyvinyl acetate and polyvinyl chloride were the only supplements that did not decrease the toxicity of cupric oxide as measured against *Alternaria tenuis* (Table 20.2). Few compounds can match the tenacity of Bordeaux mixture especially when freshly prepared. Tests indicated that as little as 10% of the deposit was removed by the first 0·5 in of rain and only 30% by 203·2 mm of rain (Burchfield and Goenaga, 1957). This tenacity is associated with the formation of the gelatinous precipitate or hydrogel. The superior performance of some 'tank-mix' dithiocarbamates, for example zineb prepared by adding nabam and zinc sulphate in the tank, compared with the wettable powder (Wilson, 1953; P. Smith, 1966) may also be due to hydrogel formation.

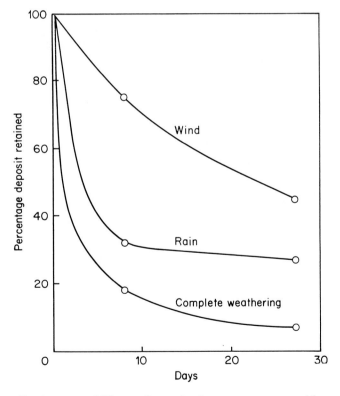

FIGURE 20.2 Effects of weathering on cuprous oxide deposits on bean (*Vicia faba*). Redrawn from Somers and Thomas, 1956, *J. Sci. Fd Agric.*, **7**, 655–67

TABLE 20.2 Effect of supplements on fungitoxicity of cupric oxide, tested against *Alternaria tenuis*.

Supplement	Relative fungitoxicity (CuO = 1·00)
linseed oil	0·47
coumarone resin	0·23
polyvinyl chloride	1·75
polyvinyl acetate	1·28
rubber latex	0·73

Data from Somers (1956), *J. Sci. Fd Agric.* **2**, 160–72.

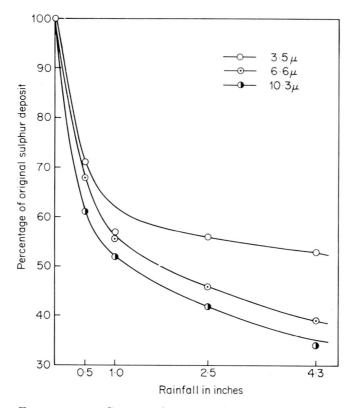

FIGURE 20.3 Comparative retention of a sulphur fungicide of varying particle size on apple leaves in the field. From Hamilton and others, (1943*a*). *Phytopathology*,
33, 533–50

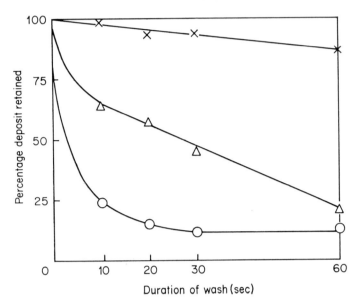

FIGURE 20.4 Tenacity of cupric oxide on cellulose acetate.
o CuO alone, x plus coumarone resin, △ plus 0.5%
gelatin. Redrawn from Somers, 1956, *J. Sci. Fd Agric.*, **2**,
160–72

Redistribution of spray deposits

While rain generally has an adverse effect on spray deposits, initially it may improve control by redistributing material to areas previously unprotected. This may not necessarily involve movement of the deposit itself; toxic copper for example may be released from relatively insoluble fungicides by leaf exudates and other mechanisms, and is then available for redistribution in solution (Hislop, 1966). The extent of the redistribution varies. It may be localized to a leaf surface and this could occur by capillarity along crevices. Information from some field experiments with *Phytophthora infestans* on potato (Bjorling and Sellgren, 1957) and *Hemileia vastatrix* on coffee (Rayner, 1962) suggests that material may also be redistributed from the top surface of a leaf to the lower, or from one leaf to the next (Hamilton and others, 1943*b*). With some materials which are absorbed to a certain extent, such as phenyl mercury compounds, redistribution may also occur by movement within the plant (Stewart and Ross, 1967).

Spraying machinery

The type of equipment used obviously plays a major role in determining deposition and coverage because of its effect on droplet size and momentum and indirectly therefore, also influences the persistence of the spray deposit. There are almost as many pieces of spraying equipment available today as there are chemicals for crop protection, but most depend on forcing the spray liquid through a nozzle so that the stream is sheared into droplets. Despite the apparent diversity in the outward appearance of these machines it is the nozzle type which controls the actual application. The nozzles themselves can be divided into three types depending on the energy source involved. In one group droplets are produced by forcing liquid through the nozzle under hydraulic pressure (hydraulic energy), in the second by air or gas (gaseous energy), and in the third by feeding the liquid onto a rotating wettable surface (centrifugal energy). In the first two groups droplets form by the interaction of air and liquid films, in the third they are spun away from the periphery of the main body of liquid. The energy used to propel the liquid through the nozzle, the orifice size, and the speed with which the liquid moves through the nozzle (throughput) are the main factors influencing droplet size and these are fully discussed by Courshee (1967).

The remainder of any machine consists basically of a tank for holding the liquid, devices to feed the liquid to the nozzle, and mechanisms for producing the energy involved. A useful review is *Equipment for Vector Control* published by the World Health Organisation (1964). Bearing in mind the effects of droplet size and momentum on deposition, the practical considerations in choosing equipment are accessability to the crop, the distance to the target area and the volume of liquid to be applied.

Timing of spray applications

Spraying is often an expensive method of disease control and the number of applications must be kept to a mimum. Timing is therefore important if adequate coverage of the chemical is to be maintained, and this has to be worked out for each pathogen–host combination. The main factors are the habits of the pathogen and growth of susceptible tissue in relation to the environment, and the weathering of spray deposits. In some situations a particular pathogen may so influence the growth of its host that frequent spraying is first necessary before a clear pattern of host growth in a given environment is established. The behaviour of limes (*Citrus aurantifolia*)

M

in Zanzibar is an example (p. 174): only by repeatedly spraying trees to control withertip (*Gloeosporium limetticola*) could a regular pattern of shoot growth and flowering be discerned (Wheeler, 1968).

Coping with the first infections in the growing season is often critical for control by spraying and for some diseases, e.g. potato blight (p. 153) and apple scab (p. 253) and beet yellows (p. 269), there are now methods of forecasting outbreaks with a reasonable degree of accuracy. With vine downy mildew (*Plasmopara viticola*) in France a warning service of this type has resulted in the omission of two sprays in most seasons with a considerable annual saving to growers (Waggoner, 1960).

REFERENCES

American Phytopathological Society. Fungicide–nematode tests 1957, and later publications.

Bjorling, K. and Sellgren, K. A. (1957). Protection and its connection with redistribution of different droplet sizes in sprays against *Phytophthora infestans*. *K. LantbrHogsk. Annlr*, **23**, 291–308

Burchfield, H. P. (1960). Performance of fungicides on plants and in soil—physical, chemical, and biological considerations. In *Plant Pathology: an advanced treatise* (Ed. J. G. Horsfall and A. E. Dimond), **3**, 477–520. Academic Press, New York.

Burchfield, H. P. (1967). Chemical and physical interactions. In *Fungicides: an advanced treatise* (Ed. D. C. Torgeson), **1**, 463–508. Academic Press, New York.

Burchfield, H. P. and Goenaga, A. (1957). Some factors governing the deposition and tenacity of copper fungicide sprays. *Contr. Boyce Thompson Inst. Pl. Res.*, **19**, 141–56

Carson, R. (1962). *Silent Spring*, 368 pp. Houghton, Boston, Mass.

Courshee, R. J. (1967). Application and use of foliar fungicides. In *Fungicides: an advanced treatise* (Ed. D. C. Torgeson), **1**, 239–86. Academic Press, New York.

Cupples, H. L. (1941). Relation between wetting power of a spray and its initial retention by a fruit surface. *J. agric. Res.* **63**, 681–6

Egan, H. and Lidzey, R. G. (1960). Phenylmercury salicylate residues in commercial glasshouse tomato crops. *Pl. Path.*, **9**, 88–91

Frear, D. E. H., Ed. (1965), *Pesticide Index*, 295 pp. College Science, State College Pennsylvania.

Frear, D. E. H., Ed. (1967). *Pesticide Handbook—Entoma* 19th Edtn. College Science, State College Pennsylvania.

Goodman, R. N. (1959). The influence of antibiotics on plants and plant disease control. In *Antibiotics: their chemistry and non-medical uses* (Ed. H. S. Goldberg), pp. 322–448. Van Nostrand, Princeton, N. Jersey.

Hamilton, J. M., Palmiter, D. H. and Mace, G. L. (1943*a*). Particle size of sulphur and copper fungicides in relation to apple scab and cedar-apple rust control *Phytopathology*, **33**, 535–50

Hamilton, J. M., Palmiter, D. H. and Weaver, L. O. (1943*b*). Evaluation of fermate for the control of apple scab and cedar-apple rust fungi. *Phytopathology*, **33**, 5

Hislop, E. C. (1966). The redistribution of fungicides on plants. II. Solution of copper fungicides. *Ann. appl. Biol.*, **57**, 475–89

Horsfall, J. G. (1956). *Principles of Fungicidal Action.*, 279 pp. Chronica Botanica, Waltham, Mass.

Juniper, B. E. (1959). The surfaces of plants. *Endeavour*, **18**, 20–5

Large, E. C., and Taylor, G. G. (1953). The distribution of spray deposits in low-volume potato spraying. *Pl. Path.*, **2**, 93–8

Martin, H. (1964). *The Scientific Principles of Crop Protection*, 376 pp. 5th Edtn. Edward Arnold, London.

Martin, H., Ed. (1965) *Insecticide and Fungicide Handbook.*, 326 pp. Blackwell Scientific Publications, Oxford.

McCallan, S. E. A. (1967). History of fungicides. In *Fungicides: an advanced treatise* (Ed. D. C. Torgeson), **1**, 1–37 Academic Press, New York.

McClellan, W. D. (1966). Common names for pesticides. *Pl. Dis. Reptr*, **50**, 725–9

Pickard, J. A. and Martin, J. T. (1961). Spray application problems: LXIV. The absorption and movement of mercury in plants. *Rep. agric. hort. Res. Stn, Univ. Bristol* 1960, 85–9

Rayner, R. W. (1962). The control of coffee rust in Kenya by fungicides. *Ann. appl. Biol.* **50** 245–61

Reinbergs, E., Edgington, L. V., Metcalfe, D. R. and Bendelow, V. M. (1968). Field control of loose smut in barley with the systemic fungicides vitavax and plantvax. *Can. J. Pl. Sci.*, **48**, 31–35

Rich, S. (1960). Fungicidal chemistry. In *Plant Pathology: an advanced treatise* (Ed. J. G. Horsfall and A. E. Dimond), **2**, 553–601. Academic Press, New York.

Sharp, R. B. (1955). The detection of spray deposits using fluorescent tracers. *Tech. Memo. natn. Inst. agric. Engng*, No 119

Sharvelle, E. G. (1961). *The Nature and Uses of Modern Fungicides*, 308 pp. Burgess, Minneapolis.

Smith, P. M. (1966). The chemical control of chrysanthemum petal blight caused by *Intersonilia perplexans* Derx. *Ann. appl. Biol.*, **58**, 431–46

Somers, E. (1956). Studies of spray deposits. I. Effect of spray supplements on the tenacity of a copper fungicide. *J. Sci. Fd Agric.*, **2**, 160–72

Somers, E. (1959). The preparation of Bordeaux mixture. *J. Sci. Fd Agric.*, **1**, 68–72

Somers, E. (1967). Formulation. In *Fungicides: an advanced treatise* (Ed. D. C. Torgeson), **1**, 153–93. Academic Press, New York.

Somers, E. and Thomas, W. D. E. (1956). Studies of spray deposits. II. The tenacity of copper fungicides on artificial and leaf surfaces. *J. Sci. Fd Agric.*, **7**, 655–67

Staniland, L. N. (1961). Experiences in the use of fluorescent traced sprays as an advisory tool. *N.A.A.S.q. Rev.*, **51**, 132–8

Stewart, D. K. R. and Ross, R. G. (1967). Mercury residues in apples in relation to spray date, variety, and chemical composition of fungicide. *Can. J. Pl. Sci.*, **47**, 169–74

Thatcher, R. W. and Streeter, L. R. (1925). The adherence to foliage of sulphur in fungicidal dusts and sprays. *Tech. Bull. N.Y. St. agric. Exp. Stn.*, No. 116, 18 pp.

Thorn, G. D. and Ludwig, R. A. (1962). *The Dithiocarbamates and Related Compounds*, 298 pp. Elsevier, Amsterdam.

Torgeson, D. C., Ed. (1967). *Fungicides: an advanced treatise*, Vol. 1. Academic Press, New York.

Waggoner, P. E. (1960). Forecasting epidemics. In *Plant Pathology: an advanced treatise* (Ed. J. G. Horsfall and A. E. Dimond), **3**, 291–312. Academic Press, New York.

Wheeler, B. E. J. (1968). Withertip disease of limes (*Citrus aurantifolia*) in Zanzibar. I. Field trials with fungicides. *Ann. appl. Biol.*, **51**, 237–51

Whetzel, H. H., Hesler, L. R., Gregory, C. T. and Rankin, W. M. (1925). *Laboratory Outlines in Plant Pathology*, p.225. W. B. Saunders, Philadelphia.

WHO, (1964). *Equipment for Vector Control*. World Health Organization, Geneva.

Wilson, J. D. (1953). Wettable powder versus tank-mix dithiocarbamates on potatoes and tomatoes in Ohio. *Res. Circ. Ohio agric. Exp. Stn.*, No. 9, 22 pp.

Zentmyer, G. A. (1955). Coined names for fungicides. *Phytopathology*, **45**, 109

CHAPTER 21

Plant disease control: breeding resistant varieties

The basic aim of breeding for disease resistance has been well summarised by Stakman and Christensen (1960): it is 'to produce varieties . . . . that resist disease so well that growers may be relieved of the work of controlling them'. It is indeed the cost and labour involved in applying the control methods outlined in the last three chapters which make resistant varieties comparatively so attractive. Yet the number of diseases which are successfully controlled by this method is still limited; some of the reasons for this are considered in this chapter.

Sources of resistance

It is axiomatic that to start a breeding programme for disease control there must be a source of resistance to a particular pathogen. In the early days this was often obtained by selection from the existing crop population. Seed was taken from plants which survived within severely infected crops, and by continued planting and selection under conditions favouring disease development resistant lines were obtained. In some instances this method alone sufficed to produce acceptable resistant varieties. Orton (1900), for example, obtained lines of Sea Island and Upland cotton in this way that were resistant to wilt, even when grown on soil heavily infested with *Fusarium oxysporum* f. sp. *vasinfectum*. Here the necessary commercial qualities were retained in the selection process. More often resistance to a pathogen is found in varieties or related species which themselves lack some essential feature of the economic crop and the problem is then to combine resistance with good commercial qualities. When resistance to stem rust (*Puccinia graminis*) was first systematically investigated it was found that all the commercial varieties of *Triticum vulgare* (bread wheat) were susceptible. Resistance was found in four related species: *Triticum monococcum* (einkorn), *Triticum diococcum* (emmer), *Triticum turgidum* (poulard) and *Triticum durum* (durum or macaroni) wheats and these were the starting points of the breeding programme. As the work progressed much information was obtained on the ability of varieties to withstand diseases other than stem rust, e.g. crown rust and bunt, and some were used as sources of resistance for these diseases.

With other diseases there are similarly several sources of resistance. Knight and Hutchinson (1950) found that several diploid Asiatic cottons were immune to bacterial blight (*Xanthomonas malvacearum*). They also found marked resistance in *Gossypium hirsutum* var. *punctatum*, and in various Upland cottons from Africa and India which appeared to be derived by hybridization from this species. Others have used the varieties 'Allen' and 'Stoneville 20' as sources of resistance (Innes, 1961). The resistance of one particular species, however, often dominates a breeding programme. Although Mains and Martini (1932) showed that many barley varieties were resistant to powdery mildew (*Erysiphe graminis*), most modern work is with the resistance of the 2-row wild barley, *Hordeum spontaneum* (Bell, 1963). Similarly, in breeding for resistance to potato blight (*Phytophthora infestans*), the wild species *Solanum demissum* has been much used (Black, 1954).

Problems in breeding for resistance

There are problems common to most programmes for breeding disease-resistant varieties (Bell and Lupton, 1960). Many crosses which appear desirable for disease resistance prove valueless because the progeny are sterile and there is no means of acquiring seed. In other instances certain undesirable factors appear linked to the resistance. Some that were encountered in the stem rust of wheat programme are summarized by Stakman and Christensen (1960). They include linkage between rust resistance and the durum type of grain which does not meet the required milling and baking standards, between rust resistance and susceptibility to other common diseases, e.g. bacterial black chaff caused by *Xanthomonas transluscens*, and linkage with an undesirable morphological character, e.g. a weak peduncle.

Sometimes undesirable linkages of this type do not become apparent until a very late stage. The classic example is the linkage between the Victoria genes and susceptibility to *Helminthosporium victoriae* in oats (p. 197). The early programme for breeding disease-resistant oats in the United States was based largely on the varieties Richland, resistant to stem rust (*P. graminis*), and Victoria, resistant to crown rust (*Puccinia coronata*). Hybrids of these varieties eventually failed because they proved particularly susceptible to a species of *Helminthosporium* which had hitherto been undetected and which was than named *H. victoriae*.

The variability of pathogens is, however, the biggest problem. The investigations of Eriksson and Marchal established this variability for the powdery mildews and rusts (pp. 92 and 119). It has now been demonstrated with many other pathogens. It follows that to be successful a variety must be resistant to all prevalent races or strains of any particular organism. Even so its usefulness may be limited. In a sense the very presence of a hitherto-resistant variety encourages the development of a fungal, bacterial or viral strain able to attack it, for should such a strain be initiated by any of the processes which cause these variations, e.g. mutation, hybridization, heterokaryosis (Buxton, 1960), then the appropriate host is available for the selection of this strain. Indeed, the substitution of this particular variety for those which the common strains can attack puts a certain selection pressure on the pathogen.

There are now many, well-documented examples of a resistant variety succumbing to a new race of a pathogen. One of the most spectacular occurred in 1950 with stem rust of wheat. For the previous decade varieties such as Newthatch, Rival, Regent, Renown seemed to have solved the rust problem in North America. These were all derived from a cross between an early variety Marquis and *Triticum diococcum*. In 1950, and again in 1953 and 1954, however, these varieties succumbed to race 15B of *Puccinia graminis tritici*. It was not exactly a new race; it had first been reported in 1939 but was subsequently found only occasionally in areas near infected barberries, and its dramatic and rapid spread over the wheat belt was not envisaged. Some attempts to incorporate resistance for this race into commercial varieties had even been started some years earlier but they were not ready in time (Stakman and Christensen, 1960).

Similar difficulties have been encountered in the breeding of potato varieties resistant to blight (*P. infestans*). This work was pioneered by Salaman in Great Britain and by Müller in Germany (Müller and Black, 1952; Gallegly and Niederhauser, 1959). Salaman obtained several resistant clones in crosses with the wild Mexican species *Solanum demissum* and Müller, the so-called 'W' strains which were also apparently derived from this species. Even before these breeding programmes had started evidence of physiologic specialization in *P. infestans* was obtained by Giddings and Berg (1919). They found that an isolate from potato was pathogenic only to potato but one from tomato could infect both potato and tomato. As the development of varieties based on the *demissum* resistance progressed it became clear that *P. infestans* possessed a greater capacity for variation and more races were described. Most important, some of these races could attack varieties with the factors for resistance derived from *S. demissum*, known as the R-genes. By 1953, sixteen different races were identified in relation to the genes for resistance possessed by these varieties, thus Race 1 was distinguished on its ability to attack hosts with gene R_1, Race 2 similarly because it could infect varieties with gene R_2, Race 1,2 on its ability to infect hosts with both genes R_1 and R_2, and so on for the four R-genes known at that time (Black and others, 1953). Now even more races are distinguished because further genes for resistance have been recognized.

Testing for disease resistance

Apart from the difficulties inherent in the resistant material and in the variability of the pathogen there are problems connected with testing varieties for resistance. It is important that laboratory and greenhouse tests should be standardized, particularly when recording host reactions. Some methods for assessing resistance to potato blight have been summarized by Müller and others (1955) and will serve as an example. Here, either detached leaves or the surfaces of cut tubers are inoculated with a zoospore suspension of *P. infestans* that has been derived preferably from a single zoospore of a defined strain. The suspension is sprayed on the potato material with an atomiser, applied as drops with a capillary pipette or in filter paper disks, 5–6 mm diameter, which have previously been soaked in it. After incubation under defined conditions together with an inoculated, susceptible variety as control the host reactions are recorded. On detached leaves there are four main types of reaction:

1. Small, sharply bordered necrotic spots develop within 18–36 hours, but the fungus ceases to spread within two days and does not sporulate.

2. Small necrotic spots develop within 18–36 hours, and snake-like necrotic lines from the point of primary infection within the next few days. Growth of the fungus in the host then apparently ceases and sporulation, if it occurs at all, is very weak.

3. Necrotic areas develop around the point of inoculation; they are fairly sharply bordered and increase slowly. Sporulation is usually weak but the leaf may be completely destroyed.

4. Necrotic changes appear later than in types 1 and 2. The spots are not sharply defined and they coalesce to give a diffused necrotic area. The host tissues do not collapse until 3–4 days after infection and the fungus sporulates well.

There are, correspondingly, four main types of tuber reaction which vary in the number of cell layers invaded, the amount and rate of necrosis, and in sporulation of the fungus (Figure 21.1). For more precise tests it is possible to subdivide these types, by taking account of the diameter of the necrotic areas.

The degree of subdivision for recording host reaction often varies from worker to worker, for example, five categories were used by Howatt and Hodgson (1954) for potato blight testing in Canada. With bacterial blight of cotton (*X. malvacearum*) scales for leaf re-action vary from three grades to as many as eleven grades, in which there are further subdivisions based on a decimal system, e.g. 0, 0·1, 0·2, 0·3, 1, 1·1, 1·2, 1·3, etc.

One difficulty in work of this type is to decide which test gives the best overall measure of resistance. With some potato varieties

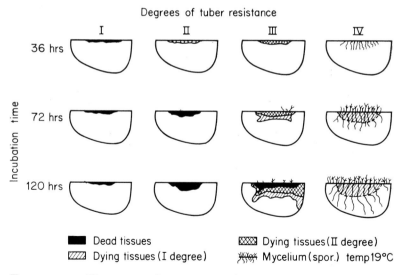

FIGURE 21.1 Diagrammatic representation of the degrees of tuber resistance in potatoes to *Phytophthora infestans*. From Muller and others, 1955, *J. nat. Inst. agric. Bot.*, **7**, 341–54

there is a close correlation between leaf and tuber reaction but this is not always so. Leaves of the variety Pentland Ace, for example, appear resistant to some races of *P. infestans* whereas the tubers are susceptible.

Similar difficulties arise in testing for resistance against *X. malvacearum*. In the Sudan, the reaction of the leaf is taken as a measure of resistance and generally this has proved satisfactory, there being for many varieties a positive correlation between leaf and boll resistance, leaf and stem resistance, and stem and boll resistance (Innes, 1961). But there are exceptions, and some workers advocate a study of resistance at all stages of infection, i.e. seedling, leaf or stem, and boll (p. 177).

The chief difficulty of field tests is to ensure that the varieties are subjected to enough inoculum of the prevalent races of the pathogen. In early investigations of wilt resistance in cotton and flax it was sufficient to plant varieties in soil naturally infested with the two *Fusarium* species concerned. Most field tests are not so simple. For assessing blight resistance Müller and coworkers (1955), recommend inter-planting at least two standard controls of differing maturity classes which are susceptible to all strains of *P. infestans*. These controls provide foci of infection and ensure that the varieties under test are exposed to the fungus for as long as possible. Trials of this type need to be carried out in several localities so that the behaviour of the varieties can be determined in diverse situations. Ideally, varieties should also be tested in disease gardens or elimination plots where many, if not all known races of the pathogen exist, and in areas where the weather is favourable for disease development nearly every year. Certain areas of Mexico, e.g. the Toluca valley, are particularly suitable climatically for testing late-blight resistance of potatoes and in addition, races of *P. infestans* occur there which are not present in other areas, mainly because this is the home of the wild *Solanum* species from which many cultivated varieties of potato are derived (Niederhauser and Mills, 1953; Niederhauser and others, 1954).

Inheritance of disease resistance

Biffen (1905) first demonstrated, with wheat and *Puccinia striiformis*, that disease resistance was inherited in Mendelian fashion. He crossed the variety Michigan Bronze, susceptible to stripe rust, with the resistant variety Rivet and showed that the F_2 progeny segregated 1 resistant: 2 susceptible and the F_3 generation approximately 1 true-breeding resistant line: 1 true-breeding susceptible line:

2 segregating lines. He suggested that in these varieties rust resistance was determined by a single gene pair. Although at the time Biffen's views were not generally accepted, other examples have since been found, e.g. cabbage resistant to *Fusarium* yellows (Walker, 1926). In comparatively few instances, however, is the genic control of resistance so simple; within cultivated plants there is considerable variation in the numbers of genes for resistance to particular diseases and in the way these are inherited.

For diseases in which several races of a pathogen are involved there is evidence that varieties contain specific genes for resistance to specific races. An extensive analysis of host factors for resistance in relation to factors for virulence in the pathogen has been carried out by Flor (1956) for flax and *Melampsora lini*. Through an extensive series of crosses between resistant and susceptible varieties on the one hand and virulent and avirulent races on the other Flor showed that there was a gene for gene relationship between host resistance and pathogenicity. Part of this work involved the separation of the host genes into different flax varieties and, as Johnson (1960) points out, its value in breeding for resistance lies in the possibility of combining these genes in new flax varieties to give maximum protection against rust races.

A more detailed account of the mechanisms governing disease resistance is beyond the scope of this book but Part III of *Plant Pathology: problems and progress*, 1908–1958 (edited by C. S. Holton, 1959) provides a useful introduction to this subject, so does the review by Holmes (1965) with regard to viruses and virus diseases and, to take just one specific example, the inheritance of resistance to *P. graminis tritici* in some wheat varieties is described in a series of papers by Knott and his associates (see Knott 1959, 1960, 1961; Knott and I-Sun-Shen, 1960).

Field resistance

There is an inherent weakness in the type of resistance which has so far been considered, in that basically it relies on a single gene pair; it is monogenic in character. A combination of genes may confer near-immunity to several pathogenic races, but when a new virulent race appears the variety is completely susceptible. The plant breeder has then to search for, and incorporate new genes for resistance into the commercial varieties.

With many crops it has long been noticed that established varieties differ considerably in their reaction to disease in the field. In conditions only moderately favourable for disease development some appear markedly resistant and during epidemics they are destroyed more slowly. This field resistance is polygenic in character. It is less complete and less stable over a range of environment than monogenic resistance but is much less likely to be broken down completely by a new race of a pathogen. Indeed the reaction of a variety with polygenic resistance to many races is often similar. For some diseases varieties with polygenic resistance have been obtained by selection. The yellows-resistant cabbage variety Wisconsin Hollander is an example; this was derived by continued selection of plants which survived in fields heavily infested with *F. oxysporum* f. *conglutinans* (Jones and Gilman, 1915). Other diseases entail a more complex breeding programme but the failure of potato varieties with *demissum* or R-genes has encouraged work on polygenic resistance. In Great Britain the varieties Majestic and Arran Viking possess resistance of this type to *P. infestans*. It appears to be determined by a complex of morphological and physiological characters which limit the rate of infection especially at the start of attack; one reason for this is that the fungus apparently produces fewer spores on these varieties (Lapwood, 1961).

Devising a suitable greenhouse screening test is the initial problem since the phenotypic characters which contribute to field resistance are only partially known. Main and Gallegly (1964) grew plants from single eyes of each clone in a reduced volume of greenhouse soil (fifty plants to each metal container 14 × 20 × 3 inches) and then inoculated them with a race of *P. infestans* effective against the R-genes. They found that under these conditions measurements of disease development by a visual disease index in these greenhouse tests were related to the behaviour of the clones in field trials in Mexico.

So far progress with polygenic resistance is limited but there is now an increasing interest in it and considerable progress can be expected in the next decade. The prospects are well described in a review by Day (1968).

References

Bell, G. D. H. (1963). Cereal breeding. In *Vistas in Botany*, **2**, 62–138. Pergamon Press, London.

Bell, G. D. H. and Lupton, F. G. H. (1960). Disease control by plant breeding. In *Biological Problems arising from the Control of Pests and Diseases* (Ed. R. K. S. Wood), Institute of Biology, London.

Biffen, R. H. (1905). Mendel's laws of inheritance and wheat breeding. *J. agric. Sci., Camb.*, **1**, 4–48

Black, W. (1954). Late blight resistance work in Scotland. *Am. Potato J.* **31**, 91–100

Black, W., Mastenbroek, E., Mills, W. R. and Peterson, L. C. (1953). A proposal for an international nomenclature of races of *Phytophthora infestans* and of genes controlling immunity in *Solanum demissum* derivatives. *Euphytica*, **2**, 173–9

Buxton, E. W. (1960). Heterokaryosis, saltation, and adaptation. In *Plant Pathology: an advanced treatise* (Ed. J. G. Horsfall and A. E. Dimond), **2**, 359–405. Academic Press, New York.

Day, P. R. (1968). Plant disease resistance. *Sci. Prog., Oxf.,* **56**, 357–70

Flor, H. H. (1956). The complementary genetic systems in flax and flax rust. *Adv. Genet.,* **8**, 29–54

Gallegly, M. E. and Niederhauser, J. S. (1959). Genetic controls of host–parasite interactions in the *Phytophthora* late blight disease. In *Plant Pathology: problems and progress,* 1908–1958 (Ed. C. S. Holton and others), pp. 168–82. University of Wisconsin Press.

Giddings, N. J. and Berg, A. (1919). A comparison of the late blight of tomato and potato. A preliminary report. *Phytopathology,* **9**, 209–10

Holmes, F. O. (1965). Genetics of pathogenicity in viruses and of resistance in host plants. *Adv. Virus Res.,* **11**, 139–61

Holton, C. S. Ed. (1959). *Plant Pathology: problems and progress,* 1908–1958, 588 pp. University of Wisconsin Press.

Howatt, J. L. and Hodgson, W. A. (1954). Testing for late blight resistance in the potato in Canada. *Am. Potato J.,* **31**, 129–40

Innes, N. L. (1961). Bacterial blight of cotton. A survey of inoculation techniques, grading scales and sources of resistance. *Emp. Cott. Grow. Rev.,* **38**, 271–7

Johnson, T. (1960). Genetics of pathogenicity. In *Plant Pathology: an advanced treatise* (Ed. J. G. Horsfall and A. E. Dimond), **2**, 407–59. Academic Press, New York.

Jones, L. R. and Gilman, J. C. (1915). The control of cabbage yellows through disease resistance. *Res. Bull. Wis. agric. Exp. Stn.,* No. 38, 70 pp.

Knight, R. L. and Hutchinson, J. B. (1950). The evolution of blackarm resistance in cotton. *J. Genet.,* **50**, 36–58

Knott, D. R. (1959). The inheritance of rust resistance. IV. *Can. J. Pl. Sci.,* **39**, 215–28; (1960) VI. *Can. J. Pl. Sci.,* **41**, 109–23; (1961) IX. *Can. J. Pl. Sci.,* **42**, 415–9

Knott, D. R. and I-Sun-Shen (1960). The inheritance of rust resistance. VII. *Can. J. Pl. Sci.,* **41**, 587–601

Lapwood, D. H. (1961). Potato haulm resistance to *Phytophthora infestans.* I. Field assessment of resistance. *Ann. appl. Biol.,* **49**, 140–51; II. Lesion production and sporulation. *Ann. appl. Biol.,* **49**, 316–50; III. Lesion distribution and leaf destruction. *Ann. appl. Biol.,* **49**, 704–16

Main, C. E. and Gallegly, M. E. (1964). The disease cycle in relation to multigenic resistance of potato to late blight. *Am. Potato J.,* **41**: 387–400

Mains, E. B. and Martini, M. L. (1932). Susceptibility of barley to leaf rust (*Puccinia anomala*) and to powdery mildew (*Erysiphe graminis hordei*). *Tech. Bull. U.S. Dep. Agric.*, No. 295, 33 pp.

Müller, K. O. and Black, W. (1952). Potato breeding for resistance to blight and virus diseases during the last hundred years. *Z. PflZucht.*, **31**, 305–18

Müller, K. O., Cullen, J. C. and Kostrowicka, M. (1955). Testing 'true resistance' of the potato to blight *Phytophthora infestans*. *J. nat. Inst. agric. Bot.*, **7**, 341–54

Niederhauser, J. S. and Mills, W. R. (1953). Resistance of *Solanum* species to *Phytophthora infestans* in Mexico. *Phytopathology*, **43**, 456–7

Niederhauser, J. S., Cervantes, J. and Servin, L. (1954). Late blight in Mexico and its implications. *Phytopathology*, **44**, 406–8

Orton, W. A. (1900). The wilt disease of cotton and its control. *Bull. Div. Veg. Physiol. Path. U.S. Dep. Agric.*, No. 27, 16 pp.

Stakman, E. C. and Christensen, J. J. (1960). The problem of breeding resistant varieties. In *Plant Pathology: an advanced treatise* (Ed. J. G. Horsfall and A. E. Dimond), **3**, 567–624. Academic Press, New York.

Walker, J. C. (1926). Studies upon the inheritance of *Fusarium*- resistance in cabbage. *Phytopathology*, **16**, 87

Index

References to illustrations are given in bold face type.

357